Yale Russian and East European Studies, 5

# MATHEMATICS
# AND COMPUTERS
# IN SOVIET
# ECONOMIC PLANNING

EDITORS AND COORDINATORS

John P. Hardt
Marvin Hoffenberg
Norman Kaplan
Herbert S. Levine

New Haven and London,
Yale University Press, 1967

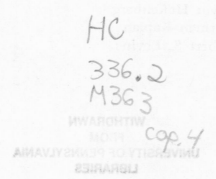

# Contents

# Introduction

The past decade has witnessed an outburst of interest and activity in the Soviet Union in the uses of mathematical methods and electronic computers in Soviet economic planning. A conference supported by grants from the American Council of Learned Societies and the University of Rochester was held at the University of Rochester from May 7 to 9, 1965, for the purpose of describing, analyzing, and evaluating Soviet work and prospects in this area. The present volume contains the papers from that conference. They provide a wide coverage of the area and extensive bibliographies of the pertinent literature. However, since the reader who is unfamiliar with Soviet planning practices may have difficulty seeing the relevance and assessing the importance of many of the matters discussed, it was thought wise to begin this introduction with a brief sketch of some of the important planning practices used by the Soviets, their strengths and weaknesses, the effects on them of the growth and development of the Soviet economy, and some suggested reforms (including "Libermanism").[1]

Although economic control in the Soviet Union was centralized during the early period of Soviet power under the pressures of civil war (1918–21), Soviet centralized planning

1. What follows does not purport to provide a full discussion of the current state of the Soviet economy. Its intention is to highlight those aspects of Soviet planning practice which are of particular relevance for the papers in this volume. For a comprehensive survey of recent economic developments in the Soviet Union, the interested reader is referred to: Joint Economic Committee, *New Directions in the Soviet Economy* (G.P.O., Washington, D.C., 1966). For a fuller discussion, specifically of the methods of Soviet planning, see Bergson, 1964, Levine, 1959, and Levine, 1961, listed in the bibliography on pp. 267–90, below.

as it has come to be known began with the initial five-year plan in 1928. Soviet planning methods were developed in the early 1930s, and since that time the basic features of the system (though not the outer trappings) have remained remarkably unchanged. The introduction of centralized planning was linked to the goal of accelerated growth to catch up, in the shortest possible time, with the more advanced, 'hostile' capitalist nations in the West. The dominant objective—the rapid attainment of the size and structure of an advanced industrial economy—gave the Soviet leaders what they felt to be a clear picture of their key needs. Their priorities were the development of basic industrial commodities (metals, fuels, and chemicals), electric power, and machinery. The task was to increase the stock of productive resources, to direct these resources into the high priority sectors, and thus to alter drastically the structure of the economy.

The Soviets construct a number of types of plans, differing as to time span and the part of the economy covered. Among the economy-wide plans, the five- (and one seven-) year plans are perhaps the best known. But they are not the best understood. The five-year plan, referred to as a "perspective plan," provides a broad-stroke view of the terrain to be traversed, but the relatively limited, highly aggregated data in it do not form the basis of commands to producing units (most of the five-year plans were not completed or published until well after the beginning of the plan period). At best, the five-year plan serves as orientation for the construction of other economic plans.

The method of constructing five-year plans has never been well described. It can be surmised, however, that the key roles are played by the growth and structure goals of the regime, technical information and studies, the Soviet "method of balances" and the calculation capacity of the planning bureaucracy (desk calculators, adding machines, abacuses, and only very recently some computers). Presum-

ably the planners—on the basis of estimates of initial productive capacities, the regime's policy decision as to rates of
investment, and its views on the desired structure of the
economy—begin to construct output targets for major economic sectors. In doing this, they make use of much technical information concerning present and planned levels
of technologies in the different sectors and try to take into
account the effects of the output levels of certain sectors on
other sectors. The plan is supposed to be constructed with
the participation of subordinate functional agencies and
production agencies, but there is evidence that for several if
not most of the plans the work was done almost exclusively
at the center. The process seems to be one of separate sectoral planning, the results of which are tied together,
roughly checking such balances in the overall plan as the
planned uses and sources of materials and primary factors,
national income, money flows, and others.

The primary objective appears to be the construction of
a plan which is realizable. While projecting a set of outputs
in conformity with the desires of the political leaders, it does
not necessarily provide for the maximum satisfaction of
those desires. There is little emphasis on techniques for
scanning alternative processes in search of an optimal plan.
The aim is more the assurance of the feasibility of a satisfactory plan. However, Soviet planners do not have the
knowledge, the techniques, or the time to construct even
such feasible long-term plans. It is still frequently charged
that, as in the old days (under Stalin), many planning
decisions are not based on sound economic calculations, but
are arbitrary, "willful" decisions that lead to unbalanced,
unrealistic plans.

Closely connected to long-term planning and forming a
bridge between it and short-term planning is investment
planning. Of the three types of investment decisions that
have to be made—the share of total investment in national
product, the branch distribution of investment, and the

within-branch project distribution of investment—the first is primarily a policy decision by political leaders. The second is decided in the process of long-term planning, roughly sketched above, in relation to the structure of the advanced industrialized economy the Soviets seek to attain and in the effort to break bottlenecks as they appear over time. For the third—within-branch project making—use is made of a crude interest rate of recoupment period calculation, the effects of which are reduced, however, by the infirmities of Soviet prices as indicators of relative scarcities. Furthermore, these decisions are taken within the confines of individual branches usually without concern for or communication with other related branches. Thus the vaunted advantage of centralized planning, namely, the opportunity to take account of externalities, is not always reaped.

The operational plan in Soviet planning practice is the annual plan (with its quarterly and monthly subdivisions). It is operational in the sense that the numerous and less highly aggregated data in it do form the basis for direct commands to producing units in the economy. The construction of the annual plan is not complicated by the uncertainties involved in long time periods or the complexities of capital planning, but since it is the basis for commands to the economy, the degree of precision required in it is much higher than in the long-term plan.

Again the emphasis is on consistency rather than optimality. The plan is constructed in cooperation with sectoral agencies (ministries) and producing units in a flow–counterflow system. Instructions about output levels and input use flow down the planning hierarchy from the center to the producing units, and information about production technologies and the state of resource availabilities and counterproposals about output levels and input needs flow back up the planning hierarchy. The process of annual plan construction begins with an intensive study of the statistical picture of the state of the economy. With the aid of this information, and in relation to their long-term and short-term policies, the political leaders formulate and communicate their dominant priorities for the forthcoming year to the central planners.

Subsequently Gosplan (the State Planning Committee) constructs a preliminary, consistent set of highly aggregated output targets and input limits (200–300 product designations) and transmits them to the ministries which in turn subdivide them among their subordinate producing enterprises. The enterprises estimate their output possibilities in terms of somewhat more detailed designations and, using input coefficients (norms) established for them at different levels of the hierarchy, calculate their input needs. The plan proceeds back up the hierarchy, is debated, altered, and consolidated at different levels returning finally to Gosplan at the center. At this stage, it is Gosplan's job to work out the internal balance of the plan. For this purpose it records on simple T-accounts (called "material balances") the quantities of planned demands for and sources of supply of each of the centrally allocated materials (varying over time between 750–2,000 product designations) and, through methods to be discussed in a moment, tries to bring the two sides of each material balance into balance. The draft of the plan prepared by Gosplan is sent to the Council of Ministers, where it is frequently hotly debated (of some consequence is the fact that the careers of economic ministers are affected by the plans they get), changed and confirmed as a law binding on all economic units.

The process of plan construction, however, does not end here. The output targets from the confirmed plan, addressed to ministries, are subdivided and passed down to the enterprises which now calculate their input needs at a very detailed level. The detailed input requirements come up the ministerial hierarchies and are sent to central agencies where again material balances are drawn up (currently for 18,000–20,000 product designations, whose quantitative

dimensions, however, are supposed to be just disaggrega-
tions of the data in the state plan). Producing-enterprise to
consuming-enterprise ties are established and formal contracts between them are signed, thus ending the process of
plan construction.

Two elements in this process—the input norms and the
method of material balances—warrant further comment.
The input norms, which establish the production processes
to be employed and thus play a key role in the formulation
of the plan, are constructed primarily on the basis of an
engineering approach. There is no systematic calculation
in this regard of the relative scarcities of inputs. Therefore
the plan cannot be optimal (in the static, Pareto sense of
being on a production possibility frontier).

Furthermore, it is even doubtful whether the plan is ever
reliably consistent. Many of the most important norms are
constructed at the center, far removed from the producing
units. The difficulties involved in such an endeavor are so
extensive, and the Soviet information collection and handling system so hopelessly inadequate, that the norms tend
to be remote from reality. Secondly, the material balances
method is too primitive to be able to cope with the task assigned it. In order to balance a material balance in which
initially planned demands exceed planned supplies (the
usual case), increased production of the deficit commodity
has to be called for and/or decreased use of it. If the input
norms are held fixed, this will require changes in the output
levels of all inputs into this commodity and/or in all products into which it is an input. And this, of course, is merely
the beginning of a long stream of such indirect effects. It is
clear from the literature that the Soviets have not been able
to handle all these indirect effects. Consequently, significant
(though not exclusive) reliance is placed upon avoiding the
indirect effects by tightening or forcing the input norms—
that is, by calling for more output without any increase in
inputs and/or decreasing inputs without decreasing out-

puts. This tightening of norms may at times just reduce the safety margin producers were able to build into their plans, but it may also at times reduce norms excessively and lead to the construction of unrealistic, overly taut plans.

Thus the annual plan is deficient on a number of counts: it is not optimal, it is frequently not even internally consistent and, furthermore, it requires a great amount of time to construct, rarely being completed by the beginning of the plan year. On the other hand, it does maintain the dominant priorities of the political leaders by concentrating output and resources in the growth-producing sectors. And the Soviets do try to compensate for their lack of static efficiency by pressing for improvements in technology in existing facilities and introducing advanced technology in new facilities.

Soviet planning involves not only the centralized construction of plans, but also their centralized implementation. The plan is communicated to producing units in the form of direct commands, a profusion of different targets to be fulfilled and overfulfilled covering such things as volume, composition and disposition of output, use of input materials, differing aspects of labor and capital, and monetary funds. And the fulfillment of these commands is verified by the transmission of performance reports on each of the targets. The data flows involved in this implementation system, added to those needed for plan construction (there is, of course, some overlap) swell the amount of data flowing through Soviet economic information channels to enormous proportions.

The dominant objective of Soviet planning has been rapid, dynamic growth rather than the smooth, harmonious operation of the economy. Consequently, Soviet workers and managers have been subjected to pervasive pressures and incentives to overfulfill performance targets, especially production targets. During the period under discussion in the conference papers, Soviet workers were paid largely on the basis of piece-rates, and management derived a substantial part of its total income from bonuses given primarily for the fulfillment and overfulfillment of volume of output targets. These incentives undoubtedly had some positive effects, from the point of view of the leaders' preferences for rapid growth. They probably led to greater output than would have been forthcoming in the absence of any rewards tied to performance. And in encouraging a successful enterprise in a given branch to surpass its output target, they were able to compensate for a shortfall in the production of an unsuccessful enterprise in that branch and thus contribute to the maintenance of interbranch balance.

However, the incentive system, as is well known, has also had its negative effects on economic growth. These have been well catalogued in Western literature and there should be no need to dwell on them at length. Since managerial reward is a function of performance relative to target, managers strive for low targets and in the process distort the economic information flowing to the planners. The managers limit their overfulfillment because today's performance is the floor for tomorrow's plan. And they have little interest in technological innovations in their processes of production: the rewards are short-lived and the risks never insignificant. As a consequence of the dominance of the volume of output target, managers are concerned solely with their own production problems and not with the needs of those who use their products. Thus innovation in products suffers, as do quality, assortment, delivery schedules, and so forth. Further, the unit of account in which the output target is stated is a source of difficulty. No physical unit can measure the various attributes of a product that comprise its worth: if the output of nails is measured in terms of weight, then large nails are emphasized; if in terms of number of nails, then small nails are emphasized. And the situation is not greatly improved when the output of an enterprise is aggregated in terms of

Soviet prices (as is done in many cases). For, since Soviet
prices are just primarily the sum of direct and indirect
labor costs, with an arbitrary profit margin, and are not
used and adjusted in the equilibration of markets, they are
poor indicators of relative value.

Finally, the implementation system suffers from the ills
of overcentralization. The center gives detailed instructions
to peripheral units without having detailed knowledge of
the units. The set of detailed instructions received by an
enterprise on various aspects of its activity is frequently
not only inappropriate for it, but also internally contradictory (insufficient funds to pay the labor it is commanded
to employ, etc.). And the weight of bureaucratic red tape
retards decisionmaking and adjustments to the unforeseen
developments that take place.

Despite these deficiencies in plan construction and implementation, the performance of the Soviet economy from
the beginning of centralized planning to the mid-1950s was,
by and large, quite satisfactory from the point of view of
the Soviet leaders. The rate of growth of national product
was high and that of industrial output particularly high
(about 5–7 percent per year for the former, and 9–11 percent per year for the latter).[2] Food output lagged, but due
to the collectivization of agriculture the regime was able
to siphon off a large share of output into the rapidly growing urban centers. And what was perhaps most impressive
of all was the speed of the structural change achieved in
the economy. For example, the rate of change of the share
of real investment in real national product appears to have

2. There is a rich literature on the measurement of Soviet economic
growth. See, for example, the data, sources, and references in Abram
Bergson and Simon Kuznets, eds., *Economic Trends in the Soviet Union*
(Cambridge, Harvard University Press, 1963), articles by A. Bergson
and R. Powell; and N. Kaplan and R. Moorsteen, "An Index of Soviet
Industrial Output," *American Economic Review* (June 1960), pp. 295–
318.

been faster in the Soviet Union than in almost any other country for which data are available.[3]

By the mid-1950s this growth and development put mounting strains on the system of centralized planning. The increased size and complexity of the economy, with the multiplication of the interrelationships it produced and the increased sophistication of some of the newest technology, made planning the economy from the center in the old ways increasingly difficult. Furthermore, the original aim of catching up with the West in terms of military power had to all intents and purposes been achieved, and though total Soviet output was less than half that of the United States, the structure of the Soviet economy (with the exception of the proportion of the labor force still in agriculture) was more or less that of an advanced industrialized nation. The focus now shifted away from macro-structural change to improving micro-efficiency. But the strengths of the old centralized planning system were in relation to macro-structural change—its power to mass resources on a few clear priorities. Thus at a time when the weaknesses of the old system were growing in intensity its strengths were becoming less relevant. Reform was in the air and perhaps even more so since the initiator of the old system, Stalin, had passed from the scene. Furthermore, for various reasons in addition to the basic developmental factors discussed above, rates of economic growth decreased after 1958. This deceleration in growth rates lent urgency to the reform movement.

A major theme in this movement has been the need for increased decentralization. In order to improve micro-efficiency, better choices from the alternatives available have to be made. This requires moving more decisionmaking to the periphery where detailed knowledge of alternatives is

3. See the article by Simon Kuznets in Bergson and Kuznets, pp. 353–54.

best. In the work of Liberman (one of the leading proponents of reform), emphasis is placed on reducing the level
of centralization in plan implementation and in improving
the response of producing units to the planning system.
The major tenets of Libermanism call for a decrease in the
number of direct targets assigned to the enterprise—volume
and assortment of output, deliveries, and major input materials—the rest being left to the discretion of the manager.
Libermanism calls for a change in the incentive mechanism, by which managers would be rewarded in relation to
profitability rather than volume of output (note that profit
is to affect the allocation of rewards, but only insignifi-
cantly the allocation of resources). And through a series of
details Liberman tries to take account of many of the specific deficiencies in the implementation system discussed
above. Thus, for the most part, Libermanism is concerned
more with plan implementation than with plan construction.[4]

The mathematical wing of the reform movement, on the
other hand, is heavily concerned with plan construction as

4. Libermanism proper should be differentiated from the reforms
that are being introduced in certain consumer goods industries. The
latter were instituted in response to the Soviet consumer's refusal,
starting in the mid-fifties, to buy everything offered him and the con-
sequent buildup of unsold stocks of goods. They do involve questions
of resource allocation, albeit in a limited way. Under the experiments
being tried, some consumer goods producers are not given an inflexible output plan but are to respond to changes in consumer demand,
as reflected in retail sales, by altering their output mix. The regime
is giving more freedom to consumers to influence the composition of
consumer goods output, but it retains full control over the total volume of consumer production.

Some aspects of Libermanism were introduced in September 1965.
The number of targets centrally assigned to an enterprise was reduced.
A volume of sales target was substituted for the volume of output
target as the dominant reward criterion. And an increased importance
was given to profit.

well as implementation. Open Soviet discussion of mathematical methods and computers in economics began almost abruptly after the Twentieth Party Congress in 1956, at which Khrushchev made his anti-Stalin speech. Activity in the field spread rapidly. Articles, books, and special journals appeared. Committees were set up, conferences held, courses and programs introduced at universities.

The early discussions frequently involved the ideological orthodoxy of the new mathematical methods. In time their acceptance grew, and any lingering doubts were put to rest by the official recognition of their ideological acceptability and their usefulness in the awarding of Lenin Prizes to three leading mathematical economists in the spring of 1965.

Substantively, the Soviet discussions have covered a broad front, from highly abstract questions in pure mathematics to problems in the application of mathematics to economics. Among the latter, attention has been given to such topics as: information systems (data collection, transmission, processing, storage, and utilization) and the use of input-output and linear and non-linear programming for the construction and operation of internally consistent and optimal short-term and long-term plans, for investment planning, and for materials supply planning. And attention has been given to the various levels of economic activity: economy-wide, branch, region, enterprise, and shop.

The conference held at the University of Rochester in May 1965 brought together economists who specialize in the study of the Soviet economy and economists who specialize in the study and use of mathematical methods in economics. It was hoped that by exposing the Soviet work in mathematical methods to the joint scrutiny of those with experience in Soviet economic matters and those with experience in mathematical methods and computer techniques rich insights and realistic evaluations of Soviet accomplishments and prospects in this field could be gained. This hope was fulfilled.[5]

The papers cover the relation of Soviet work on mathematical methods and computer techniques to the problems of Soviet economic planning briefly outlined in this introduction, and they concentrate on those topics where the Soviets themselves have done the most and where the potential impact on Soviet planning approaches seems greatest. The first paper, by Richard Judy, is concerned with the problem of information flows and the possible impact on them of computerization. It also speaks of the availability and quality of Soviet computers. The second paper, by Vladimir Treml, considers the role of input-output in Soviet planning, primarily short-term planning. It surveys the work done by the Soviets and examines their attempts to make input-output a part of actual Soviet planning practice. The third and fourth papers, by Benjamin Ward and John Montias, discuss Soviet work on optimizing techniques, mostly linear programming. The absence of an optimizing approach, it will be recalled, is a glaring feature of Soviet planning methods. Benjamin Ward deals mainly with static programming techniques, considers the use that may be made of them, and examines some proposed models. John Montias covers multiperiod optimizing methods and analyzes in detail several of the more interesting models developed by Soviet mathematical economists.

It was originally feared that the pace of Soviet work on mathematical methods would quickly outdate the conference papers. But that fear has so far been unfounded. To be sure, Soviet work has continued at a vigorous pace, but the basic observations and conclusions in the papers still stand. The unified computer system described by Richard

5. The papers and discussants' comments included in this volume were those formally presented at the conference. It has not been possible, of course, to include the very fruitful informal discussions that took place.

Judy is still in the discussion stage (although the task of setting one up has now been assigned to a specific agency: the Ministry of the Radio Industry).[6] The input-output front has been relatively quiet. The planning input-output study for 1970, mentioned by Vladimir Treml, was apparently not an overwhelming success.[7] New optimizing models have appeared and much discussion of the objective function (or the criterion of optimality) has continued, but what Benjamin Ward says about the limited application and applicability of static optimizing techniques and what John Montias says about the unsatisfactory state of the multi-period theoretical work tends still to be true.[8]

The general tone of the papers in this volume is quite negative. This is due in part to the questions the authors were asked to explore: what work have the Soviets done on mathematical methods, what has been the role of these methods in actual Soviet planning, and what are the problems they face? The authors all conclude that the work has been primarily derivative and not outstanding, the actual role slight, and the problems significant. But perhaps we all expected too much. The period since these matters were first broached is still quite short. As one Soviet practitioner recently contended, everyone accepts the fact that it takes up to eight years to design and produce a new airplane. Then why be impatient with the introduction of mathematical methods in economics? "Is the control of the national economy any less complex than the flying of an airplane?"[9]

Moreover, this negative evaluation of the work done so

6. *Izvestiia,* Apr. 26, 1966.

7. See, for example, the negative remarks of Kosygin in *Planovoe khoziaistvo,* 1965:4, p. 7.

8. On the latter, see especially the report of the conference held in Novosibirsk in March 1966 on "Problems in the Use of Mathematical-Economic Methods in Long-Term National Economic Planning," in *Voprosy ekonomiki,* 1966:6, pp. 158–60.

9. N. Fedorenko in *Literaturnaia gazeta,* Mar. 29, 1966.

far should not be understood to mean that the total impact of mathematical methods on Soviet economics has been slight. It has not. For the mathematical revolution has had a profound effect on the idiom of Soviet economic discussions. Before it occurred, Soviet economic "theory" consisted of a collection of "economic laws" which were in reality statements of the problems to be solved, pious objectives, or covers for conscious political policies. Stalin was in fact able to say that the science of economic planning was the province of policymakers, not economists.[10]

The mathematical revolution has focused attention on the logical structure of economic decisionmaking, the relationship between desired ends and limited means. It has illuminated the relationship of economic information to this logical structure. It has made clear the need to state objectives unambiguously and has helped in opening up the discussion of these objectives themselves. And although it has been used in support of centralization, it has more frequently of late been used in support of decentralization, to show the role that meaningful prices and profit criteria could play in achieving established objectives, even if those objectives are established centrally. In this regard, cybernetics, which has become a new faith in the Soviet Union, may turn out to be the ideological prop the Soviets need to permit them to accept the use of market mechanisms. It may allow them to view the meanderings and fluctuations of markets not as signs of anarchy (as Marx saw them), but as responses to feedback mechanisms ever returning a straying economy to a desired path set for it by the leaders of the state.

The coordinators of the Rochester Conference (who are also the editors of this volume), Messrs. Hardt, Hoffenberg, Kaplan, and Levine, wish to thank the authors of papers, the discussants, and all the participants in the con-

10. J. Stalin, *Economic Problems of Socialism in the USSR* (New York, International Publishers, 1952), p. 63.

ference for the excellence of their efforts. We especially wish to thank John Montias and Michio Hatanaka for their graciousness in stepping into a breach at the eleventh hour. We wish to express our indebtedness to the American Council of Learned Societies and to Gordon Turner for the Council's financial support, to the University of Rochester for its financial support and warm hospitality, to the Research Analysis Corporation for its efficient clerical assistance, and to the Yale University Press and its Managing Editor, Marian Ash, for their cooperation and understanding.

HERBERT S. LEVINE

*Philadelphia*
*February 1967*

*Note:* Since the papers in this volume pertain to Soviet planning practices primarily in the period of the first half of the 1960s, reference is sometimes made to now defunct regional organs of economic administration. From 1957 to September 1965, Soviet economic administration was organized along geographic lines with an important role played by regional economic councils (*sovnarkhozy*). Prior to this period, however, and also subsequent to it, economic administration was and is now again organized along branch of production or ministerial lines.

# 1. Information, Control, and Soviet Economic Management

*Richard W. Judy*

Recent years have seen the development of new tools that promise to revolutionize the practice of economic management. Research into the nature of decisionmaking, elaboration of the art of model building, and the perfection of the technology of information handling have laid the foundations for a new science of management. As it matures and displaces traditional intuitive managerial practices, this science will respect no national boundaries. Many economic and military entities of the West have moved the new managerial technology rapidly from drawing boards and blackboards into board rooms and command centers. For a variety of reasons, however, the potential of management science is practically untapped in the Soviet Union.[1]

## MANAGEMENT AND INFORMATION

To illustrate certain basic ideas about management, decisionmaking, and information, and to provide a common set of concepts and terms, it is useful to develop an abstract model of a simple management system. This model pictures a "manager" who faces an external "system" and who seeks to manipulate that system for his own purposes.[2] On the basis of this model, various managerial activities are dis-

1. For a discussion of some of these reasons, see Leontief, 1960.
2. The idealized manager need not be one individual. "He" may be a plurality of people or a machine or a "man-machine system." The external system may be anything subjected to manipulation for a purpose.

cussed and the role of information in those activities is analyzed.

## A Model of a Management System

Consider a system Z whose status at each of many discrete points in time is described by the values of a set $S^t$ of n state variables. Over time, the status of Z traces a locus of points in state-time space G of dimension $n + 1$.

The set $S^t$ may be partitioned into two exhaustive and mutually exclusive subsets $I^t$ and $O^t$. The set $I^t$ consists of state variables whose values are determined exogenously to the system Z; they are called "inputs." The set $O^t$ consists of state variables whose values are determined endogenously to the system Z; they are called "outputs."

At any point in time, we suppose that the values of the set $O^t$ are a function of $S^{t-1}$, i.e. of the system's state at the immediately preceding point in time. Symbolically, there exists a function $Q^t$ such that $Q^t(S^{t-1}, O^t) = O$. Note that this function may change over time.

We postulate the existence of a manager possessing the following:

a. An objective set $s^t$ which is a subset of $S^t$. Over time the values of the elements of $s^t$ determine a locus of points in the objective-time space g of dimension $m + 1$ where $m \leq n$.

b. An objective function by which any locus of points in g may be transformed into a scalar measure of performance P, i.e. $P = P(s^1, s^2, \ldots)$.

c. A set of control variables $c^t$ which is a subset of $I^t$. The elements of $c^t$ are those elements of $I^t$ over which the manager presumes himself to have some control, i.e. to be free to set values within some boundaries. The complement of $c^t$ in $I^t$ is denoted $U^t$ and represents the noncontrolled exogenous variables. The manager may perceive the existence of only a proper subset $u^t$ of $U^t$.

d. A model $q^t$ which represents the manager's approximation of the function $Q^t$. The model $q^t$ is of the form $q^t(c^{t-1}, u^{t-1}, o^t) = O$, where $s^t = c^t \cup o^t$.

The manager seeks to maximize P by choosing plans. A plan is the assignment of a specific set of values to the control variables, i.e. to the elements of the set $c^t$. At each point in time, the manager formulates a plan which he hopes will maximize P over all future time periods.

With the aid of Figure 1 we may elaborate the interaction between manager and controlled system as postulated above. If we break into the operation at time $t - 1$, we see at point 1 that status information is feeding into the model. There it is combined with forecasts of the uncontrolled variables entering from point 2. On the basis of these two pieces of information, the model elaborates alternatives and evaluates them according to the performance measure P; this process is shown by the exchange at point 3. Eventually a plan is chosen and this is shown at point 4 where a set of values of the control variables are ordered to the actuator. The actuator at point 5 interprets the commands and causes approximately the desired plan to be implemented. Points 6, 7, and 8 show the controlled (approximately) variables, the noncontrolled variables, and the output variables joining to constitute the state set $S^{t-1}$. The state set enters the functional relation $Q^t$ as shown at point 9 and is transformed by the functional properties of the system into the outputs for time t as shown by point 10. Point 11 shows the output variables returning for the next cycle. Point 12 shows information flowing via the feedback link to the model at point 1.

Several points deserve emphasis. The first is that the manager chooses his plans according to some scheme, i.e. according to how he *thinks* the system Z will react to his choice of values for the decision variables. But how the manager expects Z to react to a set of values chosen for $c^t$ depends upon inferences drawn from his "understanding" of how Z works, i.e. from his model $q^t$. Unfortunately, $q^t$

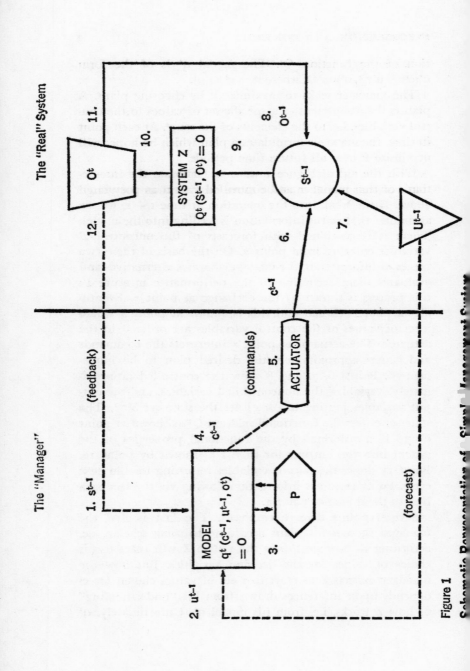

Figure 1

Schematic Representation of a Signal Management System

is merely an abstract representation of $Q^t$; it is not the "real" functional relationship; it is only some better or worse approximation to the "real" relationship symbolized by $Q^t$. The quality of this approximation is a crucial element in determining the quality of the decisions rendered by the management system. If a model is a poor one, i.e. if it poorly predicts how the real system will react to given sets of input and state variables, any decisions made on the basis of that model must be more inferior than they might otherwise be.[3]

While on the subject of models, let it be noted that a model need not be a formal, mathematical representation of the controlled system. The subjective intuition of an experienced manager is no less a model in the present sense than a group of symbols formally arranged on paper. Either can provide predictions of varying quality. When the real system is very large and contains many interrelated subsystems (as does, for example, an economic system) it is very difficult to hold an adequate representation in the human brain. Furthermore, if there are many control variables which can range over large intervals, the number of possible plans quickly reaches combinatorial proportions. What is needed in this case is an *algorithm* to cut through the maze of possibilities to the optimal alternative. A model may be a very adequate representation of a given system in that it correctly predicts the system's response to a set of inputs, but if there is no known algorithm by which the model may be solved for an optimal plan, the model itself is of restricted use. It follows that the adequacy of models and algorithms must be of serious concern to designers of management systems. This is surely as valid for the designer of an economic management system as it is for the designer of, say, an inertial guidance system.

A second point to be emphasized is that the set of control

3. This point is not invalidated by the fact that people are sometimes right for the wrong reason and vice versa.

variables is only a subset of the entire set of input variables $I^t$. In other words, the actual state of the system Z is only partly under the control of the manager. The output of a given period depends upon the system's state in preceding periods, upon the values of the control variables, and upon the values assumed by the uncontrolled variables. The latter are beyond the influence of the manager, but their values are obviously not a matter of indifference to him. The optimal plan depends upon what happens to the uncontrolled variables.

The third point, which follows directly from the first two, is that the manager cannot work in an informational vacuum. At a minimum, it would seem, the manager needs to know the state of the system before he can choose values for the control variables. Otherwise, managing is analogous to driving a car when blind and deaf. But knowledge of the past, however excellent, is rarely sufficient; it is analogous to driving a car with one's gaze glued to the rearview mirror. Information plays a vital role in all decisionmaking processes. Before considering the kinds of information required by management, I attempt a classification of managerial activities based on the model of the management system set out above.

## Types of Managerial Activity

Table 1 features a classification of managerial activities. The highest stage of managerial activity is labeled "Management System Design." This embraces three types of activities: *objective formulation, model building,* and *information system design.* The second stage of managerial activity is "Planning" and includes the functions of *intelligence, design,* and *choice.*[4] The third major category of managerial activity is termed "Operations," and includes the *implementation* of the plan and *control* over its fulfillment. Implementation in a centrally managed system consists of

4. I am here indebted to Herbert Simon. See Simon, 1960, Chap. 1.

Table 1

## TYPES OF MANAGERIAL ACTIVITIES

### A. *Management System Design*

| | |
|---|---|
| I. Objective Formulation | 1. Selection of the objective set $s^t$. |
| | 2. Formulation of the objective function P. |
| II. Model building | 1. Selection of the model's form. |
| | 2. Estimation of the model's parameters. |
| | 3. Development of a computational algorithm. |
| | 4. Selection of control variables. |
| III. Information System Design | 1. Design of a system for data collection, transmission, storage, processing, and information dissemination. |

### B. *Planning*

| | |
|---|---|
| I. Intelligence | 1. Determination of present state of the system. |
| | 2. Prediction of future values of uncontrolled variables. |
| | 3. Evaluation of the adequacy of the management system. |
| II. Design | 1. Elaboration of alternative plans. |
| | 2. Evaluation of available alternatives in view of the objective function and of possible values of the uncontrolled variables. |
| III. Choice | 1. Selection from among the alternative plans. |

### C. *Operations*

| | |
|---|---|
| I. Implementation | 1. Transmission of implementing instructions (commands) to actuators. |
| | 2. Establishment of success criteria. |
| II. Control | 1. Comparison of actual state of system with planned state· |
| | 2. Undertaking corrections where necessary. |

transferring planning directives downward to implementors and actuators who execute the plan. Implementational control consists of detecting deviations from the plan and making necessary corrections; control at this level is merely a lower-level loop of the same type of activity as in planning, viz. intelligence, design, and choice.

The management model of this part was a very simple one; it consisted of only one stratum and it pictured one manager controlling an integrated physical system. When the controlled system is very large and complex, the usual method of arranging a centralized management system is to employ hierarchy. Conceptually, there is no limit to the number of control loops within control loops; at each level a certain range of control decisions determined to be within the competence of that level is handled, while matters exceeding the competence of a given level are passed up the management hierarchy.

## Managerial Activity and Information

It is difficult to say anything meaningful about the general information requirements of objective formulation. Such activity at the highest level of economic management is a matter of politics and ideology. At subordinate levels in a hierarchical management system, the objectives should be the success criteria formulated at superior levels and handed down. This topic demands analysis that is beyond the scope of this paper to provide.

Model building has great informational requirements. If the model is informal and intuitive, the entire professional experience of a manager may be regarded as the accumulation of information for the purpose of model building. If the model is of the formal variety, the information collection processes are also of a more formal nature. Selection of the model's form, i.e. whether it is to be a system of linear equations, a system of difference equations, etc., is ordinarily a compromise between what the model builder thinks will adequately represent the system and the limits imposed by his conceptual and computational tools. Typically, it is based on observations of the physical system's behavior in a variety of circumstances and an iterative modification of the model's form. Estimation of the model's parameters is also based on observations of the system's performance in response to different sets of inputs. In the simple linear models frequently used in the management of centrally controlled systems, parameter estimation often takes the form of collecting "usage factors" (in the U.S. Department of Defense), "input coefficients" (in Leontief models), or "norms" (Soviet material supply planning). One of the central problems in management information systems is arranging for those parameters to be maintained and kept up to date. Selection of control variables demands information on the identity of input variables and on their susceptibility to direct control.

Intelligence activity, by its very nature, is an information collecting and processing function. To determine the present or recent status of the controlled system demands a reporting system that will feed this status information back to the manager. Prediction of future values of uncontrolled variables may involve significant data collection and analysis. Finally, intelligence activity involves the scrutiny of the environment beyond the controlled system to determine whether further management system design is in order.

Design and choice activities are essentially algorithmic— or should be in a well-designed management system. Given status and forecast information, a well-specified and estimated model, and an unambiguous objective function, the algorithm should be able to develop an optimal plan without additional information.

At the implementation level, it is important that plan directives be communicated to those responsible for fulfilling them; this command information should be clear and unambiguous. In management systems where humans are the actuators, it is important to accompany the commands with appropriate success indicators. Humans are not docile automata that obey commands without question; it follows that an incentive system should be created that rewards the

human actuators in accordance with how well they fulfill
their functions. For control, it is necessary to have information on the current state of the system and shorter-term
forecasts of uncontrolled variables so that discrepancies
between planned and actual states can be promptly identified and corrections initiated in a timely manner.

Each type of managerial activity, then, has its information requirements. The purpose of management information system design should be to build a system that will
provide each level with the information necessary to its activity. With this introduction to management and information, we turn to an examination of the Soviet system of
economic management and the information flows that serve
it.

## THE EXISTING SOVIET ECONOMIC INFORMATION SYSTEM

Viewed as a single system to be managed, the Soviet
economy's most striking feature is its gigantic size and
complexity. In 1962 there were 46,587 independent industrial enterprises, 66,000 communications enterprises, over
11,000 construction and design enterprises, about 50,000 agricultural enterprises, 603,400 retail establishments, 163,100
places of public eating, 174,697 warehouses and storage
points, and uncounted transportation and finance facilities.[5]
The system is laced by a lattice of interdependencies; its
functional relationships are changing under the impact of
technological development; it is subject to an array of uncertainties of natural, human, technological, and political
variety.[6]

A second striking feature of the Soviet economy is the
crudity of the management system by which it is controlled.
The present system of economic management in the U.S.S.R.

5. Prom., 1964, p. 82; *Nar. khoz.*, 1962, pp. 225, 440, 442, 534, 540.
6. Aganbegian, 1964a, p. 65.

was essentially developed ad hoc thirty-five years ago. The economy has grown in size and complexity, but the economic management system is still the one designed to force industrialization in a few key sectors during the period of "primitive socialist accumulation." However appropriate the system may have been to the tasks of the 1930s, it is anachronistic in the '60s. That this antediluvian system fetters further economic development is increasingly apparent.

In terms of the management model presented in the first part of this paper, the physical system Z to be managed is the entire collection of people, machines, and other productive facilities of the Soviet economy. Oversimplifying, we may say that this system is to be manipulated to achieve the aims of the political leadership of the Communist Party. The management system consists of the people, facilities, and information flows in ministries, planning commissions, economic councils (sovnarkhozes), enterprises, and other organizations of economic administration. Generally speaking, this system is hierarchically structured on a combination of territorial and sectoral (e.g. industry, type of industry, agriculture, transportation, trade, etc.) principles. Leaving institutional description aside, we may examine how the various managerial activities mentioned above are accomplished.

### Management Activities in the Soviet Economy

Ideally, objectives are formulated by the top political leadership. In fact, objective formulation at the top levels of Soviet power appears to be a very untidy and ambiguous process. Elements of the objective set are not usually specified with clarity, and the objective function (some economists would call this the social welfare function) exists only as an informal compromise of the preferences of influential leaders. There is nothing remotely resembling the objective function P which was postulated in the management model to be capable of reducing a time pattern of the objective set to a scalar measure of performance.[7]

Model building at all levels of the Soviet economic management system takes the form mainly of an informal gathering of job experience by planners, administrators, and other managers. Coupled with this is a selection process which, when it works, identifies and promotes the successful managers who have, among other things, demonstrated the superiority of their "models" over those of their fellows.

Recall that the term "model" as used here means an abstract representation of reality, an approximation of the "real" functional relations of the system. Its purpose is to permit the manager to evaluate the consequences of alternative sets of values for the control variables and corresponding sets of values of the uncontrolled variables. A desirable companion of a model is an algorithm which makes possible the rapid elimination of nonoptimal plans.

The "model" used in Soviet economic management is disorderly and variegated in the extreme. In large measure, it consists of knowledge born of experience in the minds of seasoned Soviet managers. Intelligent humans can accumulate a great deal of knowledge of even a very complex system if they are embedded in it for years. This subjective "intuition" or "judgment" of which professional managers are wont to speak accounts for the greater share of managerial models in all large management systems.[8] In very large and complex systems, however, the scope of the model needed to provide a reasonably satisfactory representation

7. The Soviet economic management system is certainly not unique in this respect. The problem of objective formulation plagues economists and operations researchers in Western business and military management systems.

8. A major task of management science is to replace (or augment) intuition and judgment with better (hopefully optimal) decision rules based on formal models. See Simon, 1960, pp. 14–20, and Forrester, 1961, Chap. 1.

of the managed system is beyond the information storage and retrieval capacity of one human mind or even a few score of them. The consequence, observable in the management of large business and military organizations of the West as in the Soviet Union, is that the "model" is fragmented into submodels based on territorial, ministerial, sectoral, service, functional, or other criteria. Each of these submodels concerns a piece of the managed system which, in reality, is laced to its sister pieces by many bonds of interdependence. But the managers of these subsystems are unable (because their submodels are partial, i.e. analogous to a subset of a set of equations whose simultaneous solution is required for a solution, or their information about "spillovers" into other subsystems is inadequate) to take account of the interdependencies or are unwilling (because the proximate objective functions at subordinate levels are in conflict with each other and the objective function of the total system) to do so.[9] Because the Soviet economic management "model" is so fragmented into submodels that are subjective in nature, not even the Russians fully understand the operation of their economic management system; at any rate, they are unable to communicate that understanding if they have it.

Certain aspects of the Soviet economic management model are relatively systematic. I have in mind particularly the "method of balances" so revered in the Soviet economic literature. This "method" is a primitive linear representation of the input-output technology of the economic system. Although it is far from being an integrated, formal model, the method of balances does seek to represent quan-

9. These familiar maladies are known to Western management scientists as "suboptimization problems." See Hitch and McKean, 1960, pp. 161–69; and McKean, 1958, Chap. 2. Western specialists on the Soviet economy recognize them as problems of "success indicators." See Nove, 1958. Economists have long known them as "external economies and diseconomies." See Ellis and Fellner, 1943.

titatively some of the functional relationships of the managed system.[10]

Essentially, the material balances postulate a linear model of the following form:

$$(1) \qquad X_i = \sum_{j=1}^{n} a_{ij} X_j + Y_i \qquad i = 1, 2, \ldots, n$$

where,

$X_i$ = gross output of the $i^{th}$ good,
$a_{ij}$ = the amount of the $i^{th}$ good required to produce one unit of the $j^{th}$ good,
$Y_i$ = net output of the $i^{th}$ good.

The method of balances was hardly designed; rather, it just grew. It is similar to budget preparation procedures in many large organizations. If one visualizes the system of equations implied by formula (1), the method of balances works by assigning each row of the system to a responsible planning body, e.g. sectoral departments in Gosplan. Obviously the word "algorithm" could not be used to describe the process by which a system of such balances is rendered mutually consistent.

Briefly stated, the control variables in the Soviet economic management system are "what," "how," "where," "when," "by whom" and "to whom" of all primary and intermediate goods and services of the system. Needless to say, many constraints bound the ranges within which these values may be set.

Until recently, information system design has hardly existed per se in the Soviet economy. Lately, however, with a flowering of interest in "economic cybernetics," there has been a good deal of explicit attention given to this problem. Discussion of these recent efforts constitutes a major topic of this paper and is deferred until the third part.

As it is far beyond the scope of this study to provide a

10. See Montias, 1959, and Levine, 1961, Part II.

detailed description of the Soviet planning process, I will attempt briefly to analyze it in terms of the activities of intelligence, design, and choice. Intelligence activity has the task of providing status information and prediction of future values of the uncontrolled variables; since this is an informational activity par excellence, it will be treated in some detail in later sections of this paper. With the available "model," status information, and forecasts of uncontrolled variables, the planning system grinds out a plan which, at the all-union level, includes sections on production in industry, various sectors of industry, construction, agriculture, transportation, etc., sections on capital investment projects, geological exploration, scientific research, labor, education, trade, culture, health, etc. At the subordinate levels, these sections are specified in greater detail. In addition to the state economic plan, there are plans regarding material-technical supply, foreign trade, budgets, finance, and credit.[11]

Until quite recently, the concept of optimization was foreign to Soviet economic thought; it is still foreign to most of Soviet planning practice. At best, the existing Soviet planning system develops only feasible economic plans; it makes no claim to develop optimal ones.[12] But as the economy grows larger and more complex, even the development of a feasible (in Soviet jargon—balanced) plan is beyond the power of the system. A prominent Soviet economist phrases the situation in the following words:

> Therefore it becomes harder year after year to balance the economy, to construct its plan, and to manage it. Because of the growing interconnections of its sectors, the flow of information in the economy expands ap-

11. Some important things have been neglected in this list, but the point that the plan is comprehensive is beyond dispute. See Bor, 1964b, p. 410.

12. Except, of course, for propaganda purposes. See Levine, 1959, and Levine, 1961, Chap. 9.

proximately as the square (and sometimes as the cube) of the expansion in the volume of production . . . and requires that ever more people be drawn into the sphere of planning and management. According to calculations made by V. M. Glushkov, Director of the Institute of Cybernetics of the Academy of Sciences of the Ukrainian SSR, the preservation of the existing system of economic planning and management until 1980 will require the employment of the entire adult population of the nation in these activities. And since that is impossible, it is necessary to limit the surging information about the national economy.

But the basic difficulty is not only nor even mainly this. It chiefly consists in the fact that under the existing system of planning and management based on manual accounting and the assimilation of only limited information by the human planner, it is difficult not only to find an optimal decision . . . , *it is physically impossible to fully balance the plan.*[13]

In the source just quoted, Aganbegian continues in a Robbinsonian vein to point out that the construction of a feasible plan for several tens of thousands of products (approximately the dimension of the state plan at the all-union level) would require billions of calculations to solve simultaneously the required set of equations, a hundredth of which task Gosplan's entire staff could not do at desk calculators. Much less could they compute an optimal plan; even on relatively simple planning tasks, Aganbegian claims that the planners fall short of the optimum by 10–20 percent.[14] We may conclude that, although we do not understand well the activities of design and choice in Soviet

13. Aganbegian, 1964a, p. 66. Emphasis supplied.
14. Aganbegian, 1964a, p. 66.

economic planning, the process is certainly not algorithmic; neither is it efficient.[15]

The operations activities of Soviet economic management consist of implementation and control. Plan directives are passed down the management hierarchy to the basic units (i.e. enterprises, etc.). Because of the limitations on the models and information processing abilities of superior levels, the plans arrive at the implementing levels incompletely specified. This leaves a certain range of values for control variables to the enterprise management. This fact and the circumstance that enterprise success criteria are poorly formed leads to serious suboptimization problems. The purpose of control is to ensure that plans are being implemented as designed, to spot errors, and to respond to the occurrence of unexpected events, i.e. to unforecasted values assumed by uncontrolled variables. In Soviet economic management, control is exercised mainly at the enterprise and *sovnarkhoz* levels. One of the purposes of *sovnarkhozes* is to ensure that plans are properly executed by subordinate enterprises. The ministries, state committees, the state bank (Gosbank), the state control commission, the party, and other organs share in this control function. We shall see later that the efficiency of the control activity leaves much to be desired.

## Types of Managerial Information in the Soviet Economy

In accordance with the management model in the first part of this paper and the preceding discussion of management activities in the Soviet economy, we may distinguish five types of information necessary to service the management system: information for goals setting, information for model building, information on system status, plan directives, and feedback information for control.

15. For recent experiments with formal models in Soviet planning, see Chapters 3 and 4.

Little is known about the kinds of information required by the Soviet leadership for their objective formulation. Explicit formulation of objectives has yet to occur at the top levels of the Soviet power structure. Until recently the problem was not even recognized; lately, however, the mathematicians and economists who are elaborating formal optimizing models of the Soviet economy have urgently pressed for full, explicit, and unambiguous statements of top-level objectives.[16]

To the extent that the "model" used in Soviet economic management consists of the collective intuition and judgment of thousands of managers, it is difficult to say anything about the information requirements of building this model. Presumably what is required here is an inquiry into the process of training and selection of managers in the U.S.S.R. Such an inquiry would take us far afield; I propose to limit the discussion to the informational requirements of the more systematic parts of the Soviet management model. The requirements here are data on the technological coefficients of the managed system. This includes, for a linear model, input-output coefficients for all products and processes in the system. These coefficients exist in great number at the firm level. To the extent that planning is centralized, these data must be reflected in the models used at higher levels.

Status information concerns the productive capacities of all facilities, stocks of productive resources, and flow rates of productive services in the system. The uncontrolled variables whose values require prediction include research and development activities, natural factors such as climatic conditions, catastrophes, political conditions, and the personal tastes and whims of humans in the system. The lower the level of the management hierarchy, the greater the proportion of uncontrolled variables; for example, at the enterprise level, the degree of fulfillment of a contractual obliga-

16. See e.g., Nemchinov, 1962a, p. 44; Pugachev, 1964, pp. 95–96.

tion by another enterprise is an uncontrolled variable even though at a higher level such a thing may be controllable. Evaluation of the adequacy of the management system presumes the feedback of information from actual system performance and the comparison of that information with planned performance. Did the system perform as the model predicted when given the values of controlled and uncontrolled variables that prevailed? Were scarcity relations in fact those predicted by the model? Answers to questions such as these facilitate the evaluation of the management system.

Implementing instructions in the Soviet economy take the form of plan directives to firms and other basic enterprises. These directives specify the quantity and quality of output, the organizations to whom finished product is to be delivered, the time of delivery, the limits of certain inputs that the enterprise is authorized to use, targets for cost reduction, instructions for capital investment, allocations of investment resources, and so forth. These directives are of varying degrees of specificity. In high priority industrial sectors, they tend to be detailed and specific; in sectors of lesser priority, they are often vague and ill specified.

Success criteria are established by superior echelons for the enterprises. Bonuses and promotions are made according to these criteria in order to give enterprise managers an incentive to comply with the plan directives. A common criterion is the degree of fulfillment of the gross output plan, but there may be others, e.g. degree of fulfillment of cost reduction plan, innovation of new processes, etc.

Operational control of plan fulfillment relies on short-run reporting of output and other productive activity. For this information to be effective in identifying difficulties in time for corrective action to be taken, the reporting must be swift and discriminating. If it is too slow, the opportunity for correction will have been lost. If it is insufficiently discriminating, the important information which signals an anomaly will have been lost in a sea of irrelevancies.

In concluding this section, we may mention four attributes of management information, viz. completeness, accuracy, relevancy, and timeliness. Each one of these attributes goes to determine the value of information to any management activity at a given time and place. The values placed on these attributes depend, quite obviously, upon the specific circumstances. A management information system is adequate to the extent that it supplies information with these attributes to the various managerial activities. But an information system must be judged also on the basis of its efficiency. The production of information involves the collection, transmission, storage, processing, and dissemination of data; each of these things has its cost.

### Systems of Economic Information in the U.S.S.R.

Data entering an information system for the first time may be distinguished from information produced or reproduced within the system. The former is called *primary information* and the latter *secondary information*. An example of primary information is a basic technological input coefficient at the enterprise or plant level, e.g. actual inputs of coke and iron ore per ton of pig iron produced by a given blast furnace. Examples of secondary information are aggregated direct and full (direct and indirect) input-output coefficients.

Figure 2 shows in greatly simplified outline the structure of the main economic information systems now existing in the Soviet Union. Primary information enters all systems at the enterprise or subenterprise level. Above the enterprise, information flows upward through the following four more or less autonomous systems:

1. *The administration and production planning system*
   Enterprise—Sovnarkhoz—Republic Gosplan—State Economic Council and Gosplan

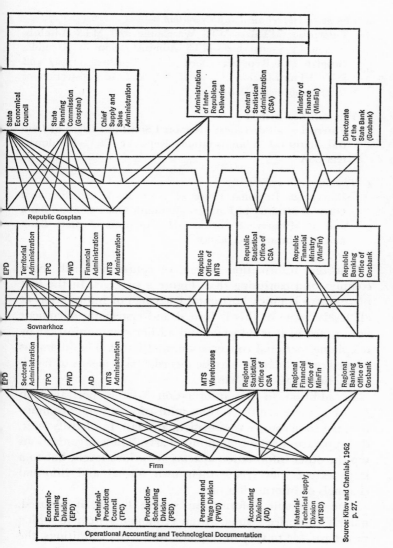

**Figure 2**    **Information Structures in the Soviet Economy**

Source: Kitov and Cherniak, 1962 p. 27.

2. *The material-technical supply system*
   Enterprise (MTSD)—MTS Warehouse and MTS Adminis-
   tration in Sovnarkhoz—MTS Administration in Republic
   Gosplan and Republic Office of MTS—Chief Supply and
   Sales Administration (*Glavsnabsbyt*) and Administration of
   Inter-Republican Deliveries

3. *The statistical system*
   Enterprise (all divisions)—Regional Statistical Office of Central Statistical Administration—Republic CSA—Headquarters CSA

4. *The financial system*
   Enterprise—Regional Office of State Bank and Regional
   Office of Ministry of Finance—Republic Office of State Bank
   and of Ministry of Finance—Headquarters of State Bank
   and of Ministry of Finance

The real information system, of course, is much more
complex and confusing than Figure 2 suggests. In the first
place, there is much horizontal exchange of information at
all levels; some of this is formal and systematic document
flow, much of it is informal and ad hoc communication by
telephone, personal conversation, and letter. The infamous
"expediter" (*tolkach*) may be regarded as a means of facilitating information exchange.

In addition to the information systems portrayed in
Figure 2, there are the various ministries and state committees, the state control commission, and last, but hardly least,
the apparatus of the Communist Party. These organizations
tap the other information systems at various levels, but to a
large extent they create their own formal and informal
channels of information flow.

One economic information system has been omitted,
namely the price system. In an economic system in which
prices are free to vary in response to scarcity conditions, the
price system is a most important system of information exchange. In the Soviet economy, the price system is prevented

from playing this crucial role by arbitrary methods of price formation and by the fact that planning decisions do not take prices as a prime informational input.[17]

At the bottom of all the information pyramids shown in Figure 2 is the individual enterprise: industrial, construction, trade, agricultural, etc.[18] The quantity of information collected, stored, processed, and transmitted here is frequently enormous. Some impression of the volume of data handled within Soviet industrial enterprises may be gained from Table 2. The figures in this table are based on Soviet studies of machine-building enterprises and are reported to be representative.[19]

Corresponding to the specialized nature of its managerial function, each of the major hierarchies shown in Figure 2 has constructed its own information system upon the enterprise.

*The administrative-production planning system* extracts a great quantity of information from the enterprise. A major instrument of this transfer is the *tekhpromfinplan* (technical-industrial-financial plan). The volume of information demanded by some *sovnarkhozes* in these *tekhpromfinplans* amounts to 13,000 data items.[20] In machine-building enterprises, the typical *tekhpromfinplan* may have 30,000–40,000 data items.[21]

Such a quantity of information obviously requires a great

17. The price system is perhaps the most thoroughly studied of all Soviet economic information systems. To avoid covering familiar ground the topic is not discussed here.

18. Strictly speaking, the scheme of Figure 2 is accurate only for information flows within industry, construction, and state trade. But the impression of parallel information systems extracting data from the basic enterprise remains valid elsewhere in the Soviet economy.

19. This "representative machine-building enterprise" has an annual gross output of 24 million rubles and has 6,000 employees on its payroll; 1,130 of these employees are of the white-collar variety. Kovalev, 1964a, pp. 349–50.

20. Kitov and Cherniak, 1962, p. 28.

21. Cherniak, 1963, p. 52.

## Table 2

## INFORMATION PROCESSING IN A SOVIET
## INDUSTRIAL ENTERPRISE

| | | Volume of information | |
|---|---|---|---|
| Type of information | Character of data | Quantity of pages, cards, indexes, etc. (thousand) | Quantity of characters of data (thousand) |
| Production planning and technical documentation Of which: | | | |
| Production job assignments | Primary | 120 | 90,000 |
| Job completion documents | Primary | 120 | 90,000 |
| Accounting | Primary | 30 | 22,500 |
| Coefficient documentation Of which: | | | |
| Detailed specification of coefficients | Primary | 26.5 | 265 |
| Summary coefficients of material inputs | Secondary | 95 | 950 |
| Labor input coefficients | Primary | 15,000 | 90,000 |
| Material-technical supply Of which: | | | |
| Planning | Primary | 89 | 500 |
| Accounting and reporting | Primary | 13 | 65 |
| Operational | Primary | 7,500 | 37,500 |
| Operating and plan execution Of which: | | | |
| Receiving and shipping | Primary | 76 | 380 |
| Scheduling and operating | Secondary | 11,360 | 56,800 |
| Planning-economic | Secondary | 52 | 260 |
| Payroll | Secondary | 56 | 280 |
| Other | Primary | 1,000 | 5,000 |

Source: Kovalev, 1964a, p. 250. Based on data for a "representative machine-building enterprise." See footnote 19, above.

deal of preparation. In the Moscow Ballbearing Works No. 1, for example, the preparation of a single version of its *tekhpromfinplan* requires about 600,000 computational operations. This enterprise calculates one or two variants of its annual *tekhpromfinplan* in the course of plan preparation. During the course of plan implementation, an average of two more recalculations are required to introduce necessary corrections, and a separate calculation is made for each quarterly division of the plan. In total, about six million computational operations are required. This work occupies 42 full-time employees working with conventional computing equipment; their annual salaries amount to about 40,000 rubles.[22] Kovalev estimates that the annual quantity of information flowing from a "representative" machine-making enterprise to its *sovnarkhoz* amounts to 44 million characters of information; 22 million of these are planning data and 13 million are reporting data.[23] About 12–15 percent of all data gathered at the enterprise level is passed up to the *sovnarkhoz*.[24]

This large volume of data passing upward from the enterprise to the *sovnarkhoz* is processed mainly by manual means or with the aid of the simplest computational aids. Studies have shown that 80–90 percent of the time of Soviet managerial personnel is spent on computational or simple logical operations connected with the processing of these data.[25] Several consequences follow from this situation.

The first consequence is that enterprise and *sovnarkhoz* managers are so occupied with routine data processing activity that they have little time and energy remaining for the kind of analysis and decisionmaking that good management requires.

22. Popov, 1963, p. 142.
23. Kovalev, 1964a, p. 351.
24. Ibid.
25. Kozlova et al., 1964, p. 419.

The second consequence is that the quality of the information for managerial use is very low. Despite the great mass of primary data collected, much of the relevant information is lost or rendered useless before it reaches the men who could use it. Obsolete, erroneous, or crudely aggregated information introduces errors into "models" and creates incorrect impressions of the state of the system. These, in turn, foster nonoptimal plans or, worse yet, plans that are not even feasible because they are not internally consistent.[26] For control purposes information arrives late, immersed in irrelevant "noise," or not at all; in any case, corrective action cannot be taken soon enough. Belkin compares the operational activity of Soviet economic management to an unguided ballistic missile; it is fired off in the right general direction by the plan, but after leaving the launching pad, it is on its own. The implication is that the economy is out of control and would profit by the installation of the economic counterpart of a guidance system.[27]

The information channels between *sovnarkhoz* and republic gosplans and thence to Gosplan U.S.S.R. share many of the attributes of the enterprise-*sovnarkhoz* channels. Data are processed manually at high cost, and managers suffer a lack of timely, accurate, and relevant information. Attempts to introduce more sophisticated models at the republic and all-union levels have foundered on the information shortage. The builders of the 1959 Soviet Input-Output Model considered the data collected through the regular channels to be useless and felt obliged to carry out an expensive sampling study to estimate the parameters of their model. One Soviet economist explained matters as follows: "The chief difficulty impeding the construction of regional interindustry balances is the imperfection of the existing system

26. Ibid., pp. 60–61.
27. Belkin, 1961a, p. 191.

of economic information and the inadequate accuracy of the data." [28]

*The material-technical supply system* occupies an enormous number of people, many of them highly qualified. Despite this, the system is the whipping boy of Soviet economic critics—and with good reason. Improper supply and irrational inventories have long plagued the Soviet economy.

Much of the material-technical supply planning is model building activity. Another important part is intelligence activity. The former takes the form of collecting input-output coefficients (norms in Soviet parlance). Table 2 suggests the volume of the enterprises' data processing task in this area. The intelligence gathering concerns materials inventories on hand and due in from production, imports, etc.

At the *sovnarkhoz* level, the volume of data is magnified by the flows from all subordinate enterprises. A recent study undertaken for the Moscow City *sovnarkhoz* showed that more than 100,000 punched cards were required to contain the input coefficients for one aggregative category of rolled steel.[29]

According to Soviet authorities, this enormous volume of coefficient data must be scrutinized and approved by management. The most important coefficients must be approved by the Council of Ministers; before the 1957 reorganization, there were about 2,500 of these "most important norms." [30] Another large quantity of coefficients must be reviewed and approved by Gosplan U.S.S.R., the republic gosplans, and the republic councils of ministers. The *sovnarkhozes* must review and approve summary coefficients for their subordinate enterprises, and the enterprise directors are supposed

28. Liebkind, 1963, p. 16. See also Shatalin, 1964, p. 155; *Vestnik AN SSSR*, No. 2 (1963), pp. 128–29, and Kovalev, 1964a, p. 300.

29. Popov, 1963, p. 176.

30. Koldomasov, 1961, p. 55.

to do the same annually and often quarterly for the coefficients used within their organizations.[31]

The purpose of all this reviewing and approving is apparent: to try to keep the coefficients of the planning "model" abreast of changes in the technology of the managed system. The body of coefficient data constitutes a file that must be updated and purged as required. Despite all the effort, there is much evidence to indicate that the quality of coefficients is not high. Labor and materials input coefficients are totally lacking on many components, assemblies, and finished products; this is notably true in newly produced products and models. Technical documents from design organizations frequently contain little or no coefficient information.[32] Updating of the coefficient file appears to be very haphazard. Either changes are not made promptly —and often not at all—or, at other times, changes are made for no apparent reason. Failure to update the coefficients properly introduces error into models at all levels of the hierarchy from the detailed models at the enterprise level to the more aggregative models at the *sovnarkhoz*, republic, and all-union levels.[33]

Another consequence of the primitive information system in material-technical supply is that stock records contain paltry information necessary for efficient inventory management. Information about item substitutability and interchangeability is acutely lacking because of poor cataloging.[34] Lack of information on unit prices, order costs, storage costs, shipping costs, lead times and variations therein, supplier performance, and the usage quantities and variations therein impair the efficiency of inventory operations by prohibiting the calculation of optimum order quantities and safety levels by means of inventory models. The conse-

31. Ibid., p. 56.
32. Kozlova et al., 1964, p. 31.
33. Ibid., p. 31.
34. Ibid., p. 32.

quences of all these information deficiencies are shortages of some supply items and excesses of others, interruptions in production, nonoptimal lot size in production, high-cost expedite orders, costly retinues of expediters, and other unnecessary costs.[35]

The process of formulating the annual plan of material-technical supply is too involved to be explained here.[36] Briefly, it is a complex budget-making operation involving the passage of much information up the hierarchy (twice) and down again (three times). The process begins in March or April and is supposed to be finished by December.[37]

The limitations of the material-technical supply system's model, algorithm, and informational processing capacity make it a major problem of Soviet economic management. Many people labor in an expensive system to produce non-feasible plans and inefficient inventory management. As inconsistencies are discovered during plan implementation, it becomes necessary to change the plan. So great is the instability and so frequent the changes of the plan that by the end of the planned period, the plan is a document of only historical curiosity.[38]

*The Soviet system of accounting and statistical collection* presents a picture similar to that of planning and material-technical supply.[39] In 1962, this system employed about three million persons.[40] Some 200 different forms of

35. Ibid., pp. 31–39; Dudorin, 1961, pp. 159–63; and Belkin, 1961a, pp. 196–201.

36. See Levine, 1959, and Levine, 1961.

37. Koldomasov, 1961, pp. 29–38, and Dudorin, 1961, pp. 27–40.

38. During a recent quarter, one sectoral administration of the Moscow City *sovnarkhoz* changed its plan 80 times; in five months there were 150 changes. A Moscow shoe factory had its plan changed 30 times in one year. The Likhachev automobile plant finds its quarterly plans changed an average of 9–10 times. Kozlova et al., 1964, p. 59.

39. See the following excellent studies of Soviet accounting and statistics: Campbell, 1958a; Campbell, 1958b; Campbell, 1961; Grossman, 1955; and Grossman, 1960.

40. Kitov and Cherniak, 1962, p. 26.

monthly, quarterly, and annual reporting are required from industrial, construction, and agricultural enterprises. Processing of the monthly industrial reports requires 10–12 million computational operations. Most of this processing is done manually or with primitive means of mechanization.[41] Because of the inability of the system to cope with the quantity of information funneled into it, much relevant information is lost or mixed with "noise" in aggregation.[42] For purposes of control, the information often becomes available to decisionmakers either not at all or too late to permit timely corrective action.[43]

*The financial and banking system* of the Soviet Union is a far-flung network of information processing. Gosbank employs over 80,000 people and processes an average of 3.3 million documents daily for 3.5 million accounts. In 1962 there were an additional 71,000 savings banks.[44] The principal means of mechanized data processing in Gosbank and the Ministry of Finance are the abacus, adding machine, and accounting machine. Very few punched card installations exist in the financial system, and computers seem not to be used at all.[45] Of the incompatibility between the archaic data processing system and the growing volume of work, Belkin writes the following:

> Given the existing growth rates of document flow, a situation will arise in the very near future in which the processing of this information within acceptable time limits will become impossible without qualitative changes in the mechanization of this work. Expanding

41. Shchedrin, 1962, pp. 184–86.
42. Belkin, 1961a, pp. 189–90.
43. Maslov, 1964, p. 11.
44. Grundfest and Isakov, 1963, p. 364; Belkin, 1961a, p. 201.
45. No mention is made of the use of computers in the account of financial data processing given by Grundfest and Isakov, 1963, pp. 346–411. There may have been changes since this book went to press in January 1963.

the number of offices and staff will be of no significant help.[46]

This is the familiar pattern of slow and expensive data processing and a dearth of useful managerial information.

From this survey of existing Soviet economic information systems, it seems obvious that a major information crisis faces Soviet economic management. Each of several parallel information systems imposes its own burden of reporting upon the enterprises. This requires repeated input of much primary data into each system, a costly redundancy. There is little standardization and collaboration among the parallel systems.[47] Voluminous files are kept separately in each system in spite of great commonality of the data items contained in them. Proper file maintenance is difficult because of poor file organization, inadequately designed inflow of updating information, and manual methods of processing. For the same reasons, information in the files can be retrieved for management use only with difficulty and after prolonged delay. Pertinent information is frequently not available to decisionmakers even though managerial personnel spend most of their time in routine data processing activities. Lack of information and the delays in its availability diminish the system's ability to respond to change. In short, information is incomplete, insufficiently accurate, largely irrelevant, and slow. Furthermore, it is expensive. This means that models are built by intuitive guesswork, status information is inadequate and inaccurate, forecasting is nonexistent or unreliable, plan directives are inconsistent and ambiguous, and control is slack.[48] Like the talking

46. Belkin, 1961a, p. 201.

47. The simple fact that different organizations have different part and stock numbers for identical items precludes data exchange. Kozlova et al., 1964, p. 29.

48. With primitive data processing techniques a high error rate is unavoidable, but there is, in addition, systematic distortion. Data being put into the systems by humans who know their performance will be

donkey, the wonder is not that the system works badly but that it works at all.[49]

All of the ills just mentioned have persuaded Soviet authorities that major improvements in the system of economic information are necessary if the centralized system of economic management is to be preserved. Academician N. P. Fedorenko stated in a recent report to the Presidium of the Soviet Academy of Sciences:

> The existing system of economic information, its methods of collecting, transmitting, and processing, can barely attain even a balanced plan for an aggregate group of products. The basis of that system is data collected by the Central Statistical Agency and by means of an enormous number of telephone conversations and meetings held in organs of planning and management. Of these data, collected with a great delay, no more than 10 percent are used for purposes of planning and management. The country essentially lacks a more or less unified, scientifically based coefficient base. An enormous amount of planning-managerial information is largely subjective in character. Relying on such a system of information, the organs of planning and management often cannot formulate scientifically based plans even when using computers and modern scientific methods; and the economic organs cannot guarantee their implementation.[50]

## SOVIET ECONOMIC CYBERNETICS

As in the West, Soviet interest in closed loop control systems was evident first in engineering and the physical sci-

judged by those data will certainly contain distortions. Man is not an automatic sensor that will unhesitatingly report information that shows it in bad light.

49. To be fair, I must admit that during several years' work with large U.S. military logistics systems, I was filled with the same wonder —albeit of a lesser order of magnitude.

50. Fedorenko, 1964b, p. 6.

ences. Slowly, interest has spread from electrical engineering and computer science to biology, linguistics, psychology, artificial intelligence, and economics. For reasons unclear to me, Soviet scientists have been more greatly enamoured of the romantic grandeur of cybernetics than have their American counterparts. In this country, a man will admit to having an interest in feedback control systems or servomechanisms, but few care to call themselves cyberneticists. In Russia, on the other hand, the grand sweep of cybernetics seems to appeal to some national propensity for total systems.[51] For whatever reason, cybernetics has become very fashionable in the Soviet Union, and many now are trying their hands at it.

Norbert Wiener coined the word "cybernetics" from the Greek *kybernetes* which means ship's steersman. Wiener called cybernetics the science of communications and control.[52] Soviet definitions are in accord with this spirit. A. I. Kitov, for example, defines cybernetics as "the science of optimal management and the design of managerial systems." [53] N. I. Kovalev emphasizes that cybernetics concerns the common aspects of management in machine, biological, social, or other large systems. It focuses on how the status of the managed system is communicated to the manager, how this information is perceived, processed, and transformed

51. One possible reason for the reluctance of Westerners to embrace cybernetics was the suspicion that, like speaking prose, it was what they were doing all the time without knowing it. Soviet economists, on the other hand, have not been doing it all the time; perhaps this accounts for its popularity. Soviet ideologues suspect that cybernetics and dialectical materialism are incompatible; this suspicion has impeded the development of cybernetics. See Graham, 1964.

52. Wiener, 1948.

53. Kitov, 1961a, p. 9. Soviet cybernetics literature makes much use of the Russian word *upravlenie*. This word has no unique English equivalent and is variously translated as "management," "control," "government," "direction," or "administration." In the cybernetics literature, it is usually clear from the context that the most appropriate English rendition is "management" or "control."

into instructions and commands to the actuators, how the commands are implemented and their execution controlled. It also concerns the learning and self-improving capacity of management systems.[54]

If cybernetics is the science of optimal management and the design of managerial systems, economic cybernetics is the application of the general principles of cybernetics to economic systems. The most enthusiastic of Soviet cyberneticists see the national economy as just another large system for which an optimal management system is to be designed. Thus Kitov writes: "The national economy as a whole may be regarded as a complex cybernetic system incorporating an enormous collection of interconnected contours of control with various levels of subordination."[55] Cherniak stresses the importance of information systems in his conception of economic cybernetics: "Economic cybernetics analyses and designs systems for processing, transmitting, storing, and methods of encoding economic information . . . it is concerned with developing methods of information processing, and also various mechanisms for that processing."[56]

Suggestions that a cybernetic approach to the design of management systems for the Soviet economy might be fruitful began to appear in the late '50s and early '60s. They first came from scientists who had worked with control systems in electronics and other areas of military, engineering, and physical science.[57] These first few articles by noneconomists in noneconomic journals coincided with a great reawakening in Soviet economics. Under the tutelage of Nemchinov, Novozhilov, Kantorovich (a mathematician), and others, Soviet economics was becoming reacquainted with the

54. Kovalev, 1964a, pp. 292–93.
55. Kitov, 1961b, p. 207.
56. Cherniak, 1961, p. 124.
57. See Bruk, 1957b; Bruk, 1960; Liapunov and Kitov, 1961; Berg, Kitov, and Liapunov, 1961.

potentials of mathematical methods and models in economics. Attention was first concentrated on specific techniques such as input-output and linear programming. An early major effort was the construction of the 1959 Input-Output Model. The appalling deficiencies of the Soviet economic information system became apparent at that time. After 1960, there seemed to be a growing awareness that sophisticated models would be of limited use if they could not be supported by more adequate information. From here it was a short step to explicit recognition of the need for integrating models with a vastly improved economic information system. Such recognition began to appear in the economics literature in 1961.[58] These early articles were mainly exploratory and suggestive, but in the period 1962–64 the literature became slowly more specific about what the outlines of nationwide economic cybernetic information might be.

For the past several years, a large number of scientific research institutes and centers have been working on problems of using computers and formal models in economic management.[59] The work of all these groups is coordinated by the Chief Administration on Introduction of Computer Technology into the National Economy of the State Committee on Coordinating Scientific Research Work of the U.S.S.R.

58. See Belkin, 1961a; Kitov, 1961a; Nemchinov, 1961a; Kovalev, 1961a; Kovalev, 1961b.

59. Among the most prominent are: the Computing Center of Gosplan U.S.S.R. (Kovalev's group); the Scientific Research Center for Designing Computer Centers and Systems of Information of the Central Statistical Administration; the Scientific Research Laboratory of Economics and Organization of Production of the Moscow City *sovnarkhoz* in the Moscow Engineering Economics Institute *imeni* S. Ordzhonkidze; the Institute of Cybernetics of the Academy of Sciences of the Ukrainian S.S.R. (Glushkov's group); and the Central Economics-Mathematics Institute of the Academy of Sciences of the U.S.S.R. (Fedorenko's group—formerly Nemchinov's Laboratory of Economic-Mathematical Models and other groups). See Glushkov and Fedorenko, 1964, p. 88; and *Vestnik AN SSSR,* 1963:10, p. 9.

The main thrust of this Administration's work has been toward the creation of a state system of computer centers. Late in 1963, a special commission of this Administration reported that such a system was a necessity. The system's purpose would be to:

> perform computations related to formulating an optimal national economic plan (current and long-range), and simultaneously to perform recomputations of state prices on an expanded list of items, to perform computations related to operational control of the national economy, its sectors, production combines, and enterprises, providing timely information on all deviations from the plan to responsible organs along with recommendations for their correction, to fulfill banking and financial computations according to programs of Gosbank and the Ministry of Finance, to process all accounting and statistical information according to programs of the Central Statistical Administration, and to perform scientific, engineering, and design computations.[60]

By mid-1964, the Institute of Cybernetics of the Academy of Sciences of the Ukrainian S.S.R. and the Central Economics-Mathematics Institute of the Academy of Sciences of the U.S.S.R. had each produced a proposed design for a nationwide network of interconnected computer centers. The following is a synthesis of these two proposals.[61]

### The Proposed Nationwide Economic Data Processing System

The structure of the proposed system is hierarchical as shown in Figure 3. At the bottom of the ladder are the en-

60. Glushkov and Fedorenko, 1964, p. 89.

61. The difference in the two proposals is reported to lie less in their structures for the information system than in their algorithms for solving the problem of optimal planning. See Cherniak, 1963; Kitov and Cherniak, 1962; Glushkov and Fedorenko, 1964; Kovalev, 1964a; and Pugachev, 1964.

Figure 3    **Proposed Nationwide Economic Information System**

| Central computer center, U.S.S.R. | | | | | | | | |
|---|---|---|---|---|---|---|---|---|
| | Gosplan U.S.S.R. | State Economic Council | Administration of Inter-Republican Deliveries | Central Statistical Administration U.S.S.R. | Ministry of Finance U.S.S.R. | Directorate of the State Bank U.S.S.R. (Gosbank) | | |

Channels of communication with other regional computer centers

**Regional computer center**

| Regional Management | | | | | | | | | |
|---|---|---|---|---|---|---|---|---|---|
| EPD | Sectoral Administration | TPC | PWD | Financial Administration | MTS Administration | MTS Warehouses | Regional Statistical Office | Regional Financial Office | Regional Office of Gosbank |

**Local data center**

**Enterprise Level**

| Primary Data | Enterprise Management | | | | | |
|---|---|---|---|---|---|---|
| Primary data from technological documents, operational accounting, source data collectors, and other primary input recorders | Economic-Planning Division (EPD) | Technical-Production Council (TPC) | Production-Scheduling Division (PSD) | Personnel and Wage Division (PWD) | Accounting Division (AD) | Material-Technical Supply Division (MSTD) |

terprises and other basic economic entities. Data enter the information system from various primary documents and source data recorders at the enterprise or subenterprise level; it is here that all model building and status information originates. These primary data flow directly or via telephone-grade communication channels from remote input stations into local data centers. Large enterprises have their own data centers; smaller entities feed their data into a local data center operating on a service bureau basis. Data processed by the local data centers provide information by reports, displays, and answered inquiries to enterprise management. Presumably the local data centers would be operating on a time-sharing basis with rapid access to very large addressable bulk storage.

Above the local data centers are a group of 30–50 regional computer centers. These are connected vertically with the local data centers via telephone-grade communication channels. Horizontally, the regional data centers are connected with each other by television-grade channels. These installations consist of at least one large computer serviced by several medium and smaller computers and other peripheral equipment. The center is to be capable of performing 1–1.5 million operations per second. The regional computers connected together and with the central computer center in Moscow are to be capable of operating simultaneously as a single huge computing system. The regional centers also serve the information needs of regional management.

The central computer center U.S.S.R. controls the regional computer centers when they are operating in simultaneous computing mode. In addition, it provides the central organs of management and political power with the information required to do their job.

By completely redesigning the information system of individual enterprises, Soviet economic cyberneticists expect to reduce the number of documents processed at the enterprise level by a factor of 20 or 30.[62] Input of primary data is to be made only once per data item; once entered, it will find its way into its proper place in the enterprise's matrix *tekh-promfinplan* which will be maintained as a file on a machine-processable medium. A large quantity of information will flow from the local data centers to the regional computer centers; this will consist of model-building information such as input-output coefficients, status information such as capacity limits and resource availabilities, forecasting information, and feedback information on the performance of lower-level enterprises. An idea of the quantity of this information flow can be gained from an appreciation of the fact that it requires 100–150 bits (binary digits) of information to encode a single input-output coefficient. The total amount of this information would thus amount to hundreds of billions of bits.[63] It is intended that these data be collected on a regional basis and then sorted by sector and transmitted to a regional computer that would "specialize" in the file maintenance and planning computation for a specific group of sectors. Each regional computer center, in other words, would serve as informational headquarters for one group of sectors. The amount of data transmission to accomplish this task is estimated to amount to $10^{11}$ bits. If each regional center is connected to each other regional center and to the central computer center U.S.S.R. by one television-grade channel, such a transmission is estimated to require about 30 hours.[64]

The general magnitude of an accompanying model of national economic planning has been estimated by Pugachev. If the model is formulated as a quadratic programming problem, Pugachev puts its dimensions at 5 million constraints and 50 million unknowns.[65] This, he admits, is

62. Cherniak, 1963, p. 52.
63. Pugachev, 1964a, p. 103.
64. Ibid., p. 103.
65. Ibid., p. 97.

too big for any known algorithm on any existing computer to solve in an acceptable period of time. He estimates that a computer capable of one million operations per second would take a month to solve a system one-billionth as large.[66] Clearly the problem will have to be compressed.[67]

It is too early to make a meaningful evaluation of the Soviet scheme for a nationwide computer network. Planning and design work is still in its early stages. The project apparently enjoys top-level political support in the Communist Party and government,[68] and it seems to be receiving large allocations of brainpower.[69] A sine qua non for the sort of system envisioned by Soviet cyberneticists is a highly developed computer science, and to a survey of that we now turn.

## SOVIET COMPUTER SCIENCE

Development of digital computing machines in the U.S.S.R. has always lagged behind their development in the United States. This lag has been apparent across the entire front of computer science, but it is especially pronounced in those areas whose development is important to the kind of

66. Ibid., pp. 97, 101.

67. Too few details of the proposed algorithm are known to permit an evaluation. See Pugachev, 1963a, and Pugachev, 1964a. See Boiarskii and Dzhaparidze, 1965, for thinly veiled opposition of the Central Statistical Administration's Scientific Research Institute to the approach and algorithm of the Central Economics-Mathematics Institute of the Academy of Sciences (where Pugachev works).

68. At least it did under Khrushchev. The attitude of the new leadership on this question has not been made public. As a sign of the times, consider that Glushkov, Fedorenko, Kantorovich, and Linnik were all recently made full academicians. They are all cyberneticists. There were no other economists promoted to full academician in 1964. *Vestnik AN SSSR*, 1964:8, p. 9. See also Fedorenko, 1964a, p. 66.

69. The Soviet mathematician S. N. Mergelian recently likened the present concentration of mathematical talent on economic management problems to a similar concentration several years ago on problems of physics. *Vestnik AN SSSR*, 1964:10, p. 11.

large-scale data processing implied by the planned nation-wide computer network.

As in the United States, the first computers in the Soviet Union were designed and developed by and for mathematicians, physical scientists, and engineers. But unlike the situation in the United States where the lead in computer development was taken early by firms with great experience and commercial interest in business data processing, computers in the Soviet Union long remained a preserve of engineers and physical scientists. This one-sided development during the first decade of the computer age has had important implications for the present state of Soviet computer science.

### Computer "Hardware" in the U.S.S.R.[70]

The archetypal piece of computation in numerical analysis frequently involves intensive work upon a relatively small amount of numeric input data; scientific and engineering computation is often of a similar nature. For this reason, computers intended specifically for scientific computing require highly developed arithmetical and logical units, but have need for limited storage and input-output facilities. Business data processing, on the other hand, usually involves large file maintenance operations with great quantities of data read into and written out of the storage of the computer. These data are typically alphanumeric and of variable length. This calls for computers with well-developed input-output capability, the ability to represent alphanumeric characters efficiently, individual character addressability, commodious internal storage, and great quantities of bulk storage.

With few exceptions, Soviet computers are narrowly scientific machines. They have small internal storage, limited input-output ability, modest magnetic tape storage, fixed

70. See Appendix for details on specific Soviet computers.

word length, and inappreciable addressable bulk storage.[71]
Recently the Soviets have announced several new or modified computers for "business" data processing.[72] These are
the Ural-4, the ERA, and the ATE-80. The most powerful
of these is the Ural-4, and it is considerably less powerful
than, say, the IBM-1410.

Soviet computers are slow and unreliable.[73] The Ural-4,
for example, is capable of about 10,000 operations per
second. This compares unfavorably with the speeds of 1–1.5
million operations per second said to be necessary for the
large computers in the proposed regional computer centers.[74]
Both the Ural-4 and the ERA are vacuum tube computers
and subject to the high failure rates of such machines.

Plans called for the design and production of a series of
new Soviet computers by 1961. By 1962 many of these plans
were reportedly still "only on paper." [75] Indeed, if the new
Soviet computers announced prior to this writing are indicative, there is good reason to believe that the gap between Soviet and American digital computer technology is
increasing rapidly.

### Computer "Software" in the U.S.S.R.

In computer jargon, "software" is anything that is not
"hardware." More specifically, it is usually taken to mean
the entire package of programming languages, executive
and generator routines, library subroutines, and "canned"
programs, i.e. programs available to the user either from the
manufacturer or from other users. Of these, the most im-

71. See Kovalev, 1964, p. 97; Dymarskii et al., 1963, pp. 263–446;
Fedorenko, 1964b, p. 8; Ware et al., 1960; and *Datamation* (November
1963), pp. 24–38.

72. The generic term for large file processing has become "business
data processing." I continue to use it here even though there is no
"business" in the Soviet economy. See Appendix for details.

73. Fedorenko, 1964b, p. 8.

74. Rapoport, 1964, p. 26.

75. Panfilov et al., 1962.

portant type of software is undoubtedly the selection of programming languages available to the user. Languages can range from the extremely "machine-oriented" variety in octal or decimal codes through the symbolic "assembly languages" which use mnemonic symbols in place of the numeric machine codes, to the higher-order "automatic programming languages" such as ALGOL, FORTRAN, and COBOL.[76] The so-called "automatic" programming languages are not really automatic, but they are problem- or procedure-oriented and their symbols resemble those of ordinary mathematical (ALGOL, FORTRAN) or commercial (COBOL) use. The object programs (i.e. machine language instructions) produced by the compilers of these languages are often less efficient in their use of machine operating time and storage than are programs for identical tasks coded by highly skilled human programmers. Skilled programmers, however, are scarcer than machine time. Furthermore, the higher-order languages are more easily accessible to ordinary mortals, managers, and scientists; the result is that they facilitate the use of computers by more people for more problems than if the machine had to be coded in machine language by manual programmers. In the United States, the use of higher-order languages began in the late 1950s and has flourished in the '60s—sometimes over the determined opposition of machine language programmers. As their popularity has grown, the quality of higher-order languages and their compilers has greatly improved.[77]

In the United States, the various computer manufacturers have realized that a customer will not buy a computer if he cannot use it. This being so, they have done much to make

76. ALGOL stands for ALGOrithmetic Language; FORTRAN stands for FORmula TRANslation; COBOL stands for Common Business Oriented Languages.

77. A compiler is a translating program that translates from the source language into the machine code.

it easier for him to use it. In the 1960s, this has meant great emphasis on software and systems help. Lacking this competitive prod, Soviet computer scientists have allowed software development to lag; the result is that they are farther behind the United States in programming languages and other software than they are in hardware. Research has been under way for some years in various institutes, but Soviet progress has been very modest in the development of sophisticated programming languages, monitor and executive systems, time-sharing systems, user-group sharing, etc.[78] Programming languages seem not to have developed much beyond the symbolic assembly level; for some years there have been suggestions in the Soviet literature that a Russian language version of ALGOL would become a standard language for Soviet computers. ALGOL and ALGOL-dialect compilers exist for a number of Soviet machines, but the language has apparently not achieved widespread usage. There are no standard algebraic or commercial programming languages comparable to FORTRAN or COBOL. Soviet software development seems to have reached its height of development in relocatable subroutines. Soviet programming textbooks stress octal machine language programming with the use of these subroutines when they exist.[79] This serious lag in software development cannot but hinder the application of computers to economic problems and to the creation of a nationwide computer system. This is a fact that has been recognized for years by some Soviet computer scientists.[80] For lack of progress, however, "the imbalance between manual programming and faster and faster computers continues to worsen." [81]

78. For some rather dated accounts of Soviet software development, see Kitov and Krinitskii, 1961, Part X, and Ershov, 1961.

79. See Krinitskii et al., 1963; Kitov and Krinitskii, 1961, and Dymarskii et al., 1963.

80. Bruk, 1960, p. 45.

81. Professor Isakov in *Ekonomicheskaia gazeta* (May 25, 1963).

In addition to problems of hardware and software, Soviet computer science has problems of people. There is a great shortage of computer operators and skilled programmers. Training programs have been inadequate and plans for producing programmers and operators have been badly underfulfilled.[82]

It is clear that Soviet computer science faces serious obstacles. These must be cleared away before anything so ambitious as the proposed nationwide computer network becomes remotely possible.

## SOVIET COMPUTER SCIENCE AND THE FUTURE

I have sought to analyze the state of economic information in the Soviet Union from the point of view of a theory of management. The existing system of economic information was found deficient in many important respects; for managerial uses, the information it provides is insufficient, inaccurate, irrelevant and slow. The system itself, while providing some useful information, is very expensive in terms of its direct cost and in terms of the opportunity cost of time spent by managerial personnel on routine data processing activities. The important managerial activities of model building, planning, and controlling are severely hampered by informational inadequacies.

Soviet cyberneticists and economists recognize that information is a fetter to further development of their economy. In a grand effort to salvage the system of central economic management, rationalization of that system through cybernetics has been proposed. An important ingredient of the cybernetic solution is the creation of a vast network of interconnected computer centers. The present state of Soviet computer science was found to be far below the level required to support such an ambitious scheme.

Does it follow that the proposed system of computer

82. See A. Kronrod in *Pravda* (Nov. 25, 1964); Panfilov et al., 1962, and *Ekonomicheskaia gazeta* (May 25, 1963), pp. 33–37.

centers is not feasible? Can a cybernetic system of economic management not be built? Can computers give no assistance to the Soviet economy, beleaguered as it is by an onslaught of paperwork?

Soviet computer science at its present state cannot support the system envisaged. But it would be premature to conclude from this that the job cannot be done. Existing American computers of the most recent vintage could probably meet the specifications of the large regional computers mentioned earlier. Machines such as the Philco 2000, the Control Data 3800, and other recently announced computers could probably do the job. Either of these machines is capable of more than one million basic operations per second; both have enormous internal storage capacity (up to 2 million 56-bit words for the Philco 2000), and correspondingly large addressable bulk storage on magnetic drums and discs.[83] The IBM Corporation has recently contracted to produce a rapid-access mass storage device capable of holding 500 billion bits of data. The Hungarians claim to have built a mass storage device that will hold up to $1,260 \times 10^{27}$ alphanumeric characters.[84] The pace of technological advance in computer technology is so rapid that today's science fiction is tomorrow's off-the-shelf hardware. It is difficult, therefore, to conclude that hardware will be an insuperable obstacle to fulfillment of the cyberneticists' dreams.

If the plans seem ultimately feasible from the point of view of computer hardware, the situation is more doubtful on the software front. A systems design and programming task of unprecedented size looms before the cyberneticists' scheme. The only comparable analogues to this effort in the West are the "Big-L" military command and control systems of the United States. The more complicated of these systems (e.g. 435 L) have taken years of calendar time and thousands

83. *Datamation* (January 1965), p. 51.
84. *Datamation* (February 1965), pp. 17, 65.

of man years to design and program—even with a background of experience with SAGE (Semi-Automatic Ground Environment) and other large systems. Soviet computer scientists lack appreciable experience with large system design efforts and can look forward to repeating many of the mistakes of the American Big-L system designers.

It should be borne in mind that Soviet economic managers at all levels lack experience with any but the simplest kinds of mechanized data processing equipment. Soviet mathematicians and computer scientists, on the other hand, lack experience in handling economic and business problems. Soviet economists, for the most part, are no help. The upshot of this, as one might expect, is that the installation of the most pedestrian computer applications (e.g. payroll, financial accounting, etc.) in Soviet industrial enterprises has been attended by confusion, mistakes, and inefficiency.[85] This being so, it is difficult to suppress a certain skepticism that a great leap forward into the brave new world of economic cybernetics will occur.

All of this does not mean that the digital computer cannot help the Soviet economy out of its informational difficulty. I should expect that the greatest contribution could be made at the enterprise level where a large number of less grandiose but potentially fruitful applications await the computer and formal models. It is with persuasive logic that Aganbegian argues that efforts should be concentrated on local tasks first with gradual integration and synthesis coming later.[86]

The gradualist approach is opposed by powerful interests. These interests perceive that the Soviet economy is starving

85. In fairness, I must admit that the same adjectives could describe the early experiences with computers in business data processing on this continent despite (or perhaps because of) a generation's experience with mechanized punched card accounting systems. But see Denisov and Popov, 1963; Popov, 1963, pp. 110–15; *Ekonomicheskaia gazeta* (May 25, 1963), pp. 33–37.

86. Aganbegian, 1964, p. 68.

for managerial information and simultaneously choking on an abundance of irrelevant data. They see the system of centralized planning in grave danger, danger that takes the form of a dilemma: retain the system of centralized economic management and suffer a continued decline in rates of growth and other criteria of performance, or decentralize economic decisionmaking as the Yugoslavs and Czechs have done in the hope of improving allocative efficiency. The cyberneticists seek to break this dilemma by rationalizing centralized economic management. The reluctance of the cyberneticists to accept the decentralization alternative is expressed by Fedorenko in a recent *Pravda* article: "While using economic levers and market mechanisms widely and skillfully, we must never forget that centralized, unified national economic planning is one of the greatest achievements of the socialist system." [87]

87. *Pravda* (Jan. 17, 1965).

## Robert Campbell

Richard Judy provides an excellent introduction to the problems of mathematics and computers in Soviet economic planning. He accurately describes the problem as a general systems problem, thus giving us scope to consider more than particular mathematical techniques and enabling us to see the issue of mathematical techniques as only one aspect of a general problem. His description of the Soviet planning and information system compresses into a short space a good conception of the character of the information system and the weaknesses that limit the effectiveness and rationality of Soviet economic decisionmaking and control. Some might consider his negative evaluation of the usefulness-to-cost-ratio of this system overdrawn, but I share his feeling. His discussion of Soviet research and development work on economic cybernetics is probably as concrete and precise as available information permits. The entire enterprise still has an air of unreality, however, and it would be useful to have more information on the number of people working in these institutes, the amount of computer time they have, and the magnitude of their budgets. The review of Soviet computer technology is illuminating, though the real issue is the capabilities of future Soviet computers; their present backwardness may only reflect low priorities.

A major question is whether economic cybernetics will work. Judy speaks of the frightening magnitude of national economic model-building schemes and the technical impossibility of doing any such job with present Soviet computer technology. But he has not discussed the two related issues: first, whether economy-wide models will work, given enough computer capacity; and second, whether it is possible to approach such a scheme by starting with small, established routine problems rather than by starting on a grand scale.

His conceptualization of the management system, in fact,. is too simple to accommodate either perception or discussion of some of the most characteristic and persistent problems of Soviet economic administration. His description of the management system is based on certain postulates and assumptions: that it is possible to distinguish exogenous and endogenous variables and to specify an objective function in terms of them, that the process involves a single cycle, and so on. But most of the characteristic problems of the administered economy arise just because these assumptions are not satisfied in reality. To develop that point I have tried to ask myself what some of the essential features and problems of the administrative economy seem to be— as revealed by the experience of the Russians—and how the addition of more data processing capacity and formal optimizing models would help, or what problems they might cause.

In describing the Soviet management system and the associated information system as it now exists, or as it might develop in a system of economic cybernetics, Judy concentrates on the problem of current balancing, amended with such optimizing techniques as could be developed on the basis of the same kind of information. That is, he treats planning as essentially current balancing plus a little optimizing of the input mix and output mix within input-output sectors. In this, of course, he is following the lead of the Soviet economists, who tend to formulate the national economic planning model in these same terms. Neither Judy nor the Russians say much about the periodicity of this process. There is a presumption in recent Soviet talk that current balancing will be more nearly continuous in the new system than at present, but it will obviously need some similar short-term time horizon.

If I were setting out to give an empirical description of Soviet planning, it would seem essential to note the existence of some other spheres of decisionmaking about resource allocation quite distinct from the annual balancing spasm. Two in particular are the sphere of design decision-making, or project making, and the sphere of *khozraschet,* or enterprise level, decisionmaking. Each of these spheres plays an important role in determining the actual allocation of resources in the Soviet economy, but each is palpably distinct from the annual balancing process in terms of periodicity and time horizon, the level of the administrative structure involved, and the criteria and mechanisms for making decisions. Judy's partition of the management problem into three kinds of activities—management system design, planning, and operation—involves only a few of these distinctions. Many of the lapses from rationality in the Soviet economy can be attributed to failure to coordinate the decisions taken in these various spheres. I do not see much perception or appreciation of this problem in Soviet discussions of the use of mathematical techniques. Two examples involving the relationship of project making to annual balancing will illustrate.

First, project makers are much concerned with calculations and decisions about capital intensity. Implicit in any rational approach to this issue, and in their actual decisions, is some idea about the period of gestation. But whatever their assumptions, they are surely upset in reality by the fact that, under the expediencies and errors of the current allocation system, the period of gestation is seriously lengthened in general, and differentially, for different projects. The huge stock of unfinished construction and uninstalled equipment in relation to investment must violate any subtle considerations of gestation period as these entered into the original calculations about capital intensity.

Second, project makers designing power equipment make choices between diesel and gasoline engines on the basis of relevant grounds (i.e. cost of operation complicated by a capital intensity problem). As these decisions are implemented in current production, a stock of tractors, say, is built up in which there is a certain division between gasoline and diesel engines. The balancers then face a problem of producing engine fuel in the implied proportions. In fact they have found it impossible to do so, and the refiners turn out a surplus of gasoline and too little diesel fuel. More subtly, the efforts the balancers have made to adjust the fuel mix to that required by the proportions in the engine stock have betrayed the original calculations of the decisionmakers. In fact they have altered diesel fuel standards to enable more of it to be produced, but the resulting deterioration in fuel quality has made repair and operating costs for diesel equipment higher than the project makers had estimated. The gain the project makers thought they were going to apply to recoupment of the incremental investment in diesel engines is thus eaten up by extra current outlays.

How would the new cybernetic system take care of these problems? In general the answer is that shadow prices will be the communication link between the spheres. Confrontation of the relative value for diesel fuel and gasoline which emerges from the calculations of the engine designers with the relative cost which emerges from the refiners' output maximizing calculations will suggest appropriate quantity reactions. In the other case the urge of lower-level people to get facilities finished to satisfy their perfected success indicators, and the kind of shadow price for capital that emerges from these calculations, will offer a corrective to whatever interest rate the project makers are using in their own calculations. In a fully integrated and internally consistent model that combines dynamic and current planning, discrepancy in the relevant prices in the two spheres will not exist, but it is difficult to believe in the existence of such models. And efforts to rationalize either of these spheres of decisionmaking separately will not get at the basic problem.

I am concerned that more is not said about these problems by the Russians. When this is such a glaring problem in the actual system, ought they not to give a little more explicit attention to how the new information system is going to cope with it?

An important feature of the existing management system in the Soviet economy is a certain ambiguity and imprecision in treatment of information and statement of goals. Some have thought it paradoxical that the input-output approach should appeal to the Soviet central planners. It is in many ways a poor representation of how Soviet balancing actually works. Input-output takes norms as given, and balances supply and demand by variations of gross outputs within capacity limits. The real system is about equally likely to take gross outputs as given, and to force an equilibrium (on paper at least) by changing norms.

Discussions of the project-making process usually reveal great ambiguities as to which variables project makers consider constraints, which they consider choice variables, and which they consider elements of the objective function. I once read a number of accounts by project makers explaining how they approached economic decisions for producing a gas field. The basic issues are how many years to take to extract the contents of a reservoir and how to distribute the total output over time. Alternatives involve variations in capital expenditure totals and in time patterns. The gas can be extracted in a shorter time if one is willing to drill more wells and to introduce field compressors earlier. The project makers seemed to be saying in some of their discussions that the capital investment total was given and that their problem was to optimize the time profile of output. In other cases they treated delivery levels as a datum and were concerned to minimize capital investment. In some places they seemed to worry less about the total amount of capital required than about the amount needed in the near term, considering the current tightness of the capital allocations.

Finally, there is often considerable uncertainty as to what the parameters of the success-measurement function (which becomes the objective function of the lower-level administration) actually are.

Such ambiguities are likely to make the rationalizer impatient—the reaction of an economist who considers himself an expert on what is required to be rational and efficient is that this is a hell of a way to run a railroad! Our instinct is to say that goals and constraints must be made clear and explicit, responsibilities must be meticulously defined. Much of the confusion in the Soviet system comes about because these requirements are not met. One of the appeals of economic cybernetics is that the introduction of explicit models will demand clarification of these ambiguities.

On the other hand, the ambiguities are probably not completely dysfunctional. If input norms are out of date, then it may be sensible to treat them with some skepticism in the balancing process and let them bear some of the burden of adjustment. Ambiguity in the statement of problems for project makers is a kind of insurance device—higher-level decisionmakers do not want to commit themselves until they know what the implications are. They do not tell the gas industry project makers that they will have just this amount of capital, and so make capital a precise and strict constraint, because they are uncertain at that stage of the acceptability of the associated output stream. Gundar Frank argued that goal ambiguity has been shown to have a functional rationale in other contexts, and suggested that in the Soviet economy goal ambiguity in success measurement is necessary to preserve flexibility and responsiveness of lower levels to higher. In a real organization, inertia and habit are always competing against conscious decisionmaking as the guide to behavior, and it is no doubt worthwhile, in a world of change and uncertainty, to sacrifice some rationality in favor of instruments to combat routine and inertia. Speaking in terms of the management model outlined in Judy's study, one aspect of the problem of management is to get decisionmakers to consider alternatives. In the design phase which he describes, it is as real and important a problem to scan an adequate range of alternatives at each juncture as it is to evaluate them. One well-established procedure for choosing between alternatives is to reject whatever is new. To keep people alert to novel alternatives there must be some ambiguity in the evaluation of their performance.

My question is, what takes the place of these imprecisions if one goes over to formal optimizing models and computer approaches? In principle the answer is clear. Computerized administration will be a multistage and multisphere process, necessitating iterations between the various stages and spheres. The computer and improved information channels will speed up calculations for whatever conditions are specified, and will make feasible the substitution of the possibility of successive approximation for ambiguity. If the cyberneticists see this point clearly, there is no need for worry.

A persistent obscurity in the theory and practice of economic administration is the kind of behavioral assumptions to make. This is true in the present system and will remain a problem in a more formally modeled system. The goal of top leadership is to control the behavior of lower-level decisionmakers; but they can only do this imperfectly, and often end up accepting this behavior and contenting themselves with modeling rather than controlling it. The dilemma is easily seeen in terms of the kind of national economic balancing and optimizing model we are talking about here. Many of the parameters in this kind of model, such as the input coefficients, their improvement from period to period, inventory norms, and so on, are not purely technical coefficients, but also embody a large element of behavior on the part of managers.

As Judy points out, administrators are not automata: they have some decisionmaking power and some voice in the generation of information. Since one of their important private goals is to minimize strain, to avoid pressure, and so on, their behavior is unsatisfactory from the viewpoint of leadership. But unless the leaders can eliminate this behavioral element in fitting the model, they must acquiesce in it. Will economic cybernetics change this? It is hard to see how. Certainly it will help to have more information—such as disaggregated detail on what input norms really are—but there will always be uncertainty as to the treatment of discrepancies between plan and actual. If the supply of coal does not equal the demand, or if wage payments rise more rapidly than the plan, there is the choice of correcting the model or firing the managers. This is a well-recognized problem, of course, and I want only to add that I am disturbed to see very little discussion of it by the Russian cyberneticists.

As I try to think about the problem in terms of Judy's conceptualization of the management system, many perplexities arise. His model needs to be elaborated in a much more convoluted way before it can give us insights on this problem. In a multilevel system there has to be a new distinction made about the variables of the system—i.e. the introduction of command variables. There are going to be orders given and constraints set for lower-level decisionmakers. Are these endogenous or exogenous variables in his scheme? In the command system as it exists today, planners try to control the behavior of the economy by specifying, for instance, the number of units of a certain truck to be produced. But I take it that this would be an endogenous rather than an exogenous variable in Judy's system. Hence it cannot be a control variable. Perhaps the answer is that he would not term this a control variable—rather the control variables are the allocations of steel, manpower, and other inputs to the truck plant.

The above discussion suggests another problem, that of redundancy in the Soviet system of commands. Plans specify both inputs and outputs, and targets relating the two— a labor force figure, an output figure, and a labor productivity figure. There is not only a cost budget but also a cost reduction target. This raises in my mind a more general question concerning Judy's postulate about the description of the state of an economy by a set of variables. Perhaps there must be some redundancy in any such description, but redundancy would make impossible the kind of partitions postulated. If the assignment of labor to the steel industry is an exogenous variable, and the output of steel is an endogenous variable, what kind of variable is the output of steel per worker? If the answer is that it is unnecessary to include in the set the output of steel per worker, what is there about reality that has convinced Soviet system designers that they must do so in describing the steel industry for intelligence and evaluation purposes?

Judy has made the provocative statement that what corresponds in the Soviet economy to the "model" in his general concept of management is embodied in the minds and experience of Soviet planners and executives, and that the training and selection of management personnel is a form of model building. Improving the model thus means talking about the education, training, and selection of managers. There is great potential for improvement here. For many decisionmakers, especially those higher-level planners who make strategic decisions and project-making decisions, this would seem to be a matter of instruction in economic analysis. Thus one of the main contributions of mathematical methods to rationalizing Soviet planning may turn out to be its contribution to the downfall of Marxian simplemindedness, and the inculcation of elementary but powerful economic notions such as margin, opportunity cost, imputation, choice between alternatives, etc. Economic theory would seem to be of little use to those at lower levels. The interactions in these lower-level systems are more likely to involve engineering and personnel considerations than economic ones. Maybe a traditional business administration course would be the best thing for them.

But the model (at any level) always contains not only the system of production relations but also an objective function, and we ought to consider how that part of the manager's model could be improved. One approach would be to partialize the overall objective function and internalize it in the manager so that he can refer to it. In other words, improving the model means indoctrinating the manager with the goals of the planners. But it is very difficult to internalize the goals of the regime in these decisionmakers in such a way as to offer any guidance in the choices with which they are actually faced. Even if we persuade them to believe in rapid growth, and have complete confidence in their willingness to settle any issue in the interest of furthering growth, it is likely to be extremely difficult to provide them with rules making possible an evaluation of alternatives in terms of the general objective function. This is the basic dilemma we keep coming back to—if there is to be any choice at lower levels, then lower-level decisionmakers must have an objective function. That they have any choices to make results from the fact that model builders or system designers have no knowledge of any algorithm to interpret the local-choice situation in light of the overall objective function.

In conclusion, the theoretical approach to the question whether economic cybernetics can salvage the command system is probably not very helpful. Our arguments on this always end up in paradox and uncertainty. There is no doubt that computers and optimizing models will help (because the fundamental problem is information processing), and the introduction of computers (as in the proposed network of computer centers) will mean a tremendous increase in information-handling capacity. But it also becomes clear that real problems will appear in model building, the discovery of effective algorithms, and in development of the software complement needed to harness the information-handling capacity of the machines to the problem. That is, there will be a new problem to match nearly every existing problem in the administrative system. The economic cybernetic system is going to be some kind of analogue of the present administrative system. The fundamental problems in economic administration are ones of partitioning and aggregation, of obtaining primary information, and of processing and communicating this information as a basis for decisionmaking. In addition to these problems within each sphere of decisionmaking, there is the additional matter of coordinating all the different spheres. It is difficult to expect these problems to be solved as a matter of course in model building when they cannot be found in actual administration.

The real test will be in application. Only as the Russians introduce computers and mathematical methods can we tell whether the improvements in speed and precision with which information is assembled and digested will outweigh the persisting difficulties in knowing how to digest information and draw conclusions from it. In the end it really depends on how one diagnoses the illnesses of the Soviet-type economic systems. If the gap between their actual and potential output is a matter of waste through failure to appreciate the rules of efficient production, then more sophisticated understanding surely ought to help. If it is a matter of waste through lack of coordination between current allocation and longer-range perspectives, then possible improvement through the adoption of mathematical methods would seem to be more problematical. To the extent that the bottleneck to greater output and faster progress is a failure of the system to facilitate and stimulate initiative and innovation on the spot, then further use of mathematical methods and programming would seem to offer little help. The kind of precision and rigidity that they involve would seem to be inimical to fostering change. But it may be that the truly serious wastes in the system flow from the dissipation of resources in gathering useless information tardily, and from the bottlenecks, wasteful substitutions, and idle capacity associated with the slowness and crudities of current misallocation. There is a suggestion in Judy's emphasis that this is the case, and the same implication in the Russian concentration on this as the main problem. Perhaps we should take their word for it.

### Robert Summers

Although a number of issues are raised in Richard Judy's lengthy and complex analysis, I will focus here on a particular set of questions: Is the Soviet Union's proposed system of computers feasible? Can a cybernetic system of economic management be built? Can computers help the Soviet economy?

Let me say at the outset that I think Judy is unduly pessimistic, from the Soviet point of view, about the chances

---

This discussion of Soviet computing prospects draws heavily upon conversations about American computer developments with members of a number of American firms in the computer field, particularly Computer Usage Company, Inc., of New York City and Auerbach Company of Philadelphia. The information gleaned from these conversations was supplemented by bits and pieces obtained from various issues of *Aviation Week, Business Week,* and similar journals reporting on the current business scene. My primary debt in this discussion, however, is to Edward Feigenbaum of Stanford University, who was willing to share with me what he learned about computing in the Soviet Union during his visit there in October 1964. Of course, neither he nor the American computing experts I consulted should be held responsible for my comments.

that the Soviet Union will achieve its cybernetic goal. I may have misunderstood his position, but the essential consideration is what the Soviets' prospects are rather than whether or not we agree.

It is undoubtedly true that American computer technology is much superior to the Soviet Union's—and that in some respects the gap between the two is still widening. But it is worthwhile making these observations about the significance of the gap: we must not make the mistake of thinking of it as analogous to the celebrated—or infamous—missile gap of the late 1950s. In that case, for any given quantity of Soviet missiles, the larger the difference between how many we had and how many they had, the worse for them. One way of putting it is to say that the utility of our missiles to them was negative. However, the external economies resulting from the possibility of their copying our computing equipment makes the utility to them of our advanced designs distinctly positive. They are racing us less than the calendar in preparing for the immense computing burden they envision. In short, for any given level of advancement of Soviet computer technology, the greater the gap between ours and theirs, the *better* for them.

It is instructive to see what can be learned from our experience in the field of computer technology that will help us judge what lies in store for the Soviets as they attempt to implement their plans. First, on the negative side, as far as information networks are concerned, I do not think we can gain much insight into how well the Soviet Union will be able to meet its information-handling requirements from examining our large military information system programs. In developing the SAGE system and the so-called Big-L systems, we encountered formidable problems. At first glance, it might be thought that the Soviet Union will not be able to avoid the problems we met and therefore they still have a very rocky road ahead of them in this area. Without denying the possibility that the road may indeed be rocky, I wish to observe that our systems have all had very demanding real-time standards built into them. The very much simpler real-time demands of the Soviet system make our record only barely relevant to a judgment about their future.

Leaving information networks as a system, let me speak of computer technology under the headings of "software" and "hardware." Software encompasses all of the procedures devised to facilitate the use of the computer, while hardware is the complex of equipment which, when properly directed, processes data (e.g. computing, information handling and retrieval, etc.). The Soviet Union is significantly behind us in both software and hardware. However, this in itself does not deny the possibility that they could have better software and hardware if they had chosen in the recent past to devote resources to a rapid improvement. Their not having a better computer technology does not mean that they could not have a better one.

In the United States software development generally has lagged behind hardware development. (A rationalization of this would be that software items like monitors become important when interruptions in service become expensive.) If the same lag were present in the Soviet Union, their relatively primitive hardware would explain why they delayed developing advanced software. But it is not altogether clear that one should expect such a lag either in the Soviet Union or in the United States. It might be argued that the slower and more inadequate the hardware, the more necessary is a sophisticated software system to squeeze out what little potential computing power is available. The relative strengths of the income and substitution effects lurking in the background here cannot be determined a priori. All one can say is that the fact that the Russians do not have better software cannot be used as evidence that this is due to knowledge or technique limitations.

However, the United States experience with software

design can furnish guidance on the resource cost of developing software systems in the Soviet Union. Estimates of the cost of developing the FORTRAN system vary widely, depending upon what cutoff point is used for the end of development and how costs are allocated between FORTRAN and other programming problems handled during the same period. But the range of uncertainty is not really large in absolute terms. The number of man-years of professional programming that went into the development of FORTRAN has been estimated variously at between 75 and 200; the amount of machine usage was not important. (One can only marvel now that the price tag was so low on the skeleton key that unlocked the mysteries of the large-scale computer, IBM and others as well, for the masses.)

But it is more relevant to know the cost now of developing a FORTRAN system for a new machine at our present state of knowledge. There are a number of companies that specialize in the development of software systems on a contract basis, so in principle a fairly precise estimate of this cost can be obtained. In an informal survey of a number of these firms, I was told that, depending upon the physical characteristics of the machine and the quality of the compiler, the cost of a FORTRAN system might run between one or two and ten or fifteen man-years. (Low-quality systems that are quick-and-dirty can themselves be machine-produced!) Since we are concerned with the Soviets' ability to handle large quantities of data rather than their ability to do scientific computing, perhaps the cost of a FORTRAN system is less to the point than the cost of an information-processing system. Such systems, designed for business use rather than scientific work, are more expensive—between 7.5 and 25 man-years—when purchased at these program-development firms, although one of the first of these, IBM's COMTRAN, originally took 100 man-years to develop.

All in all, I regard the costs I have quoted as quite modest. While the Soviet Union is not likely to be able to contract out its software development work to these firms, the costs quoted are probably within an order of magnitude of the resource cost it will incur when it does the development work itself.[1] (I am not suggesting all costs would be trivial. The programming cost of SAGE was 1,800 man-years, a not inconsequential amount, but the lower real-time requirements of the Soviet system spares them the necessity of facing such an outlay.) And, the Russians are not entirely without software systems now. While they have not done much with monitors, listing programs, and the like, they have developed an automatic programming system called ALPHA which is a sophisticated extension of ALGOL. It has been estimated that the development of ALPHA took about 35 man-years spread over two-and-one-half to three years.

Turning now to the area of hardware, let me illustrate how quickly progress in computer technology takes place by pointing out that as recently as twelve to fifteen years ago (with the exceptions of the important early university computing centers—Harvard, the Massachusetts Institute of Technology, and the University of Pennsylvania), the computing equipment on American campuses was only one

1. Since the conference I have heard the point made that a particular aspect of the incentive system in the Soviet industry may be responsible for retarding Soviet software development or for making it unnecessarily expensive. In the United States, the early software work was done by computer manufacturers with a view to obtaining a competitive advantage by making their computers more readily usable. The external economies inherent in having the software development done centrally and then shared among users makes this an economical arrangement. However, to the extent that the performance of each computer manufacturing establishment in the Soviet Union is appraised solely with reference to its technical efficiency in computer production, the pressure to engage in software research may be slight or even nonexistent. If this is so, the burden of software development will be shifted to equipment users with a resultant loss of the external economies.

step removed from the abacus. The fanciest digital equipment at Stanford fourteen years ago was literally a desk calculator of the Friden-Marchant-Monroe type. Until about seven years ago, there were at Yale only two IBM 602As (small electromechanical machines) hooked together to expand the meager storage capacity of each. But now look at how many computers there are around the country. The rapid development of computers and their widespread use, I submit, was a consequence of demand-pull. When potential users learned what the state-of-the-arts made possible, they called forth the equipment in great quantities. I would expect the same thing to happen in the Soviet Union if and when the cybernetic advocates acquire the priorities. The relative scarcity of large computers, to make my previous point again but in a somewhat different context, is a result of Soviet priorities rather than an inability to produce them.

Judy has presented a wealth of information about Soviet computers, but technology changes so rapidly in this area that it is very difficult to keep up to date. A phantom machine of some sophistication, not actually seen by Westerners (but described in *Datamation,* March 1965), is conjectured to exist on the basis of four Russian articles by men from a single Soviet institute. Very few, if any, of these machines are available, however. The Ural-8, a follow-on machine to the Ural-4 that Judy describes, operates about ten times as fast and may now be in use. He refers to the M-20, a machine no longer produced which is roughly in the class of a small IBM 704. The transistorized successor version of this machine, the M-220, which was scheduled for installation in 1965 at the Soviet Academy, will perform 125,000 to 150,000 operations per second. This is, of course, a quite respectable speed.

While these machines are clearly at least a generation behind those of the United States, the fact that the time span of a generation is not much more than a few years means that speed differentials may not be too important. There was a Soviet government edict that no more vacuum-tube computers would be made after 1964, but the new transistorized computers will not be up to the IBM 7090 class until after 1969. Glushkov, of the Institute of Cybernetics, is quoted as saying, upon hearing that IBM 7090s are going back to the warehouses, "I would like to buy as many as possible."

It should be emphasized that though the Soviets have some fast machines now, the number is quite small.[2] For example, fewer than 100 M-20s have been produced since 1959 when it was introduced. It is worth noting that while IBM produces a dozen 1401s per day, the Soviet Union produces only a little more than one-half that number of Minsk-2s in a month. The differences in capital intensities in production—illustrated by hand-wiring versus wire-wrapping—helps to account for the difference in output rates. Less easy to explain for a country with such remarkable achievements in the advanced technology of space travel is its great difficulty in engineering good input-output equipment, particularly high-speed tape units.

Some perspective on the ability of the Soviet Union to cope with its prospective computational burden can be conveyed by providing another quotation from Glushkov. Judy has given us Pugachev's estimate of the enormity of the computational burden if the cybernetic model is to be handled with the quadratic programming technique. Without question, carrying out the required computations would be impossible. However, Glushkov has estimated that the number of arithmetic operations per year needed to carry out all computations required by the cybernetic network would (only) be in the neighborhood of $10^{16}$. At first this figure

2. It should be remembered that in judging the Soviet Union's potential, primary attention should be given to the performance of its best equipment rather than to the performance of its average equipment.

looks impossibly high, and this first impression seems to be confirmed by the fact that $10^{16}$ computations per year is equal to the sum of the computations that *all* the computers now in the United States (about 25,000, ignoring all machines below the IBM 1620 class) are presently capable of! However, computer technology is advancing so rapidly that the speeds of the newest American machines (for example, the CDC 6600, which under favorable circumstances will perform three million operations per second or $10^{14}$ operations per year) are so great that approximately 100 of these machines could perform the task set out by Glushkov. Perhaps it is not too much to say that at a resource cost of something in the neighborhood of .2 percent of their gross national product (the CDC 6600 sells, in round numbers, for something over $5 million), the Soviet Union could certainly obtain such a battery of machines over a number of years.

In this discussion, I have restricted my attention to the likelihood that computer technology may be the bottleneck that will prevent the Soviet Union from operating a cybernetic system. The following papers discuss other aspects of the Soviet planning problem, and I believe that it is in these other areas that the crucial difficulties will lie. I do not mean to say that in 1967 or 1968 or 1969 the presently projected Russian hardware and software will be adequate. But I contend that their present relatively poor equipment and procedures are a misleading basis for Western extrapolation. In an imitative world where social priorities can be changed dramatically on short notice, by the early 1970s inadequate data-handling capacity need not hold back detailed planning. Quite clearly, the Russian computer technologists are not twelve feet tall now, but they have not yet reached their full height. The growth potential is there to be realized if and when their masters give them the signal.

# 2. Input-Output Analysis and Soviet Planning

*Vladimir G. Treml*

Revitalization of Soviet economic science continues unabated and the trend toward a more rigorous analysis is
especially evident in the gradual exploration and adoption
of mathematical methods and models. But this trend has
been observed for about ten years now, and we may make
some attempt to pause and take stock. There is no point
in enumerating either the Marxian shibboleths discarded or
drastically modified in recent years, or the systematic redis-
covery of economic concepts and analytical tools long
banned from the Soviet scene. They are well known and
have been frequently discussed. The academic debate in the
Soviet Union, having cleared away some onerous deadwood,
has yet to produce general solutions acceptable to the majority of the economic profession and planning practitioners, and palatable to the Party leadership. So far, the

I wish to thank John P. Hardt and Stanley H. Cohn of the Research
Analysis Corporation as well as Marvin Hoffenberg for continuous
assistance and encouragement received in the preparation of this paper.
Earlier versions were presented at seminars at Harvard University,
St. Anthony's College (Oxford), and the London School of Economics.
I have greatly benefited from criticism and discussions at these seminars and gratefully acknowledge contributions and comments of Wassily W. Leontief, Herbert S. Levine, Michael C. Kaser, and Alfred
Zauberman. Abraham S. Becker of the RAND Corporation kindly
made available his extensive and illuminating notes on Soviet input-
output studies and gave me the benefit of several conferences and
prolonged exchange of letters. A summer grant from Franklin and
Marshall College enabled me to concentrate on my research.

Soviet planning and control institutions have displayed a surprisingly high degree of resilience and, aside from purely administrative reforms, planning and control methods have remained essentially unchanged. In a very general way we could suggest that the first phase of "mathematization" of Soviet economic science is coming to an end, and a new phase will probably open in a setting of much wider institutional scope. In this first phase the mathematically oriented economists have come as far as possible. Basic mathematical tools such as linear programming and input-output analysis have been accepted as theoretically valid and relevant for the Soviet economic system. But the applications of these methods, limited as they have been, have produced no apparent improvements. The proponents of the new techniques place the responsibility for this lack of results on the entire system. Thus, a high-ranking Gosplan functionary writing in *Izvestiia* (November 18, 1964) pointedly compared the futile efforts to mathematize and computorize Soviet planning to an attempt to install a rocket engine in a horsecart.

That reforms are indeed in the air became especially evident after the October 1964 leadership change. The most salient features of the "command economy" or, to use the Soviet term, "willful" (*volevoi*) approach to economic decision-making are being challenged with increasing frequency and intensity.

In this tentative attempt at stock-taking, I propose to examine Soviet explorations of the input-output concept and the efforts, so far unsuccessful, to adapt it to the needs of central planning. It would be instructive to summarize and appraise Soviet empirical work in this area and to discuss the difficulties presently facing Soviet proponents of the new techniques. As a very tentative and speculative conclusion, I would like to submit that application of input-output analysis, even in its most elementary static form, has been frustrated by the hybrid nature of the price system, by deficiencies of economic information, and by certain institutional aspects of planning, to name only a few factors. Until and unless these basic theoretical and administrative issues have been resolved in the U.S.S.R., input-output techniques, otherwise uniquely suited to the needs of a centrally planned economy or to macro-economic control generally, cannot be successfully integrated with planning.

## Empirical Work on Ex-Post Models[1]

In the light of current Soviet enthusiasm for applying mathematical tools to economic analysis and planning, it is easy to forget that only a few years ago any mathematical approach to economic problems bordered on ideological heresy. After Stalin's death the situation began to change. Faced with the increasing complexity of economic interrelations in a growing economy and acutely cognizant of allocative inefficiencies in the system, Soviet Party ideologists were willing, up to a point, to give more freedom to economists and statisticians to explore and experiment with new, mostly Western, analytical tools and economic models. It was hoped that if these methods bore any promise of increasing the efficiency of the Soviet system, and could be purged of "bourgeois methodological sins," they would be gradually integrated with traditional tools of planning and control.

Input-output analysis is but one of the many mathematical techniques which, long neglected by the economic profession and planners, is finding its way into Soviet economics.[2] Until the late 1950s input-output analysis was hardly mentioned in Soviet professional literature and,

1. References and citations in this paper will be restricted to the most typical or fullest Soviet sources. The most useful Western sources on the subject are: Becker, 1963; Cohn, 1962; Kaser, 1962; Levine, 1962a; Serck-Hanssen, 1962; and Zauberman, 1963.

2. Leontief, 1960, pp. 261–72.

when mentioned at all, was dismissed as a futile attempt to introduce some semblance of planning and macro-controls into the chaotic and rapidly disintegrating capitalist economies.

The ideological difficulties facing the proponents of new methods in economic analysis and planning were many.[3] Input-output analysis had been developed and applied in the West, and this fact alone made it unacceptable to the majority of the economic profession and Party controllers. The subterfuge resorted to by the proponents of input-output was to claim, somewhat indirectly, that input-output originated in the U.S.S.R. in the earlier work of Gosplan. The first balance sheet of the Soviet economy for 1923–24, completed by Gosplan in 1926, was offered as the prototype of input-output tables.[4] But while the ostensible establishment of the Gosplan parenthood of input-output saved its Soviet proponents from the Scylla of being accused of adopting bourgeois tools of economic analysis, it exposed them to the Charybdis of other ideological pitfalls.

The fact of the matter is that the 1923–24 Balance of the National Economy did not fare well in the Soviet Union. In a 1929 speech, Stalin contemptuously dismissed

3. For a more detailed discussion of the ideological difficulties see Treml, 1963 and 1964a.

4. The 1923–24 Balance of the National Economy was reprinted in several Soviet papers in the late 1950s. However, in order to substantiate the claim of Soviet origin and to emphasize the formal similarity between the Balance and Leontief's interindustry transaction matrix the former was presented in "a somewhat modernized form" (Nemchinov, 1959, p. 9). Other discussants of the history of development of input-output techniques frankly admit that the 1923–24 Balance was "transformed" into the usual input-output table format in the late 1950s (Aganbegian and Belkin, 1961, p. 52). The "modernization" of the 1923–24 Balance apparently consisted, among other things, in disaggregation of the flows in the second quadrant so that the number of rows and columns became equal, and in transferring all deliveries of capital equipment from the interindustry transaction matrix to the final demand quadrant.

the Gosplan exercise as "not a balance of the national economy but a game with figures," [5] and soon thereafter many statisticians and planners associated with the balance studies disappeared in the Gosplan purge. Stalin's negative attitude was probably the main reason for the almost complete evanescence of the study of overall balancing methods in the Soviet Union. Among other things, the 1923–24 Balance was criticized for its failure to reflect the sociopolitical issues of the day, e.g. to distinguish between private and state output, and for its failure to identify separately the flows of consumer and producer goods. One of the most frequently repeated criticisms was the conceptual kinship of the Balance to the "antimarxian" general equilibrium analysis.[6] But as wider and wider circles of Soviet economists and statisticians began to show interest in input-output analysis, the critical discussion of these issues was quietly dropped.

Actual studies of input-output techniques in the U.S.S.R. began in the mid-1950s. The Economic Research Institute of Gosplan constructed a total of seven pilot input-output flow tables which ranged from a small table showing 12 industrial products measured in physical units to a large table in value terms with 44 sectors. Direct input coefficients were estimated on the basis of Soviet data, but for-

5. Stalin, 1951, p. 326.

6. Vairadian, 1964, pp. 194–95; Riabushkin, 1959, p. 87 and p. 90; Sorokin, 1961, p. 358. The dogmatism of Soviet economics is epitomized in the case of rejection of Walrasian analysis. Once declared reactionary, unscientific, and antimarxian the very term "general equilibrium analysis" has been completely banned from the professional literature. The weight of this taboo is amazing—a prominent Soviet statistician, Volodarskii, recently published a paper discussing input-output analysis under the title "Tempy, proportsii, garmoniia." The use of the word "harmony" in this context in Russian is ludicrous and can be explained only by his reluctance to use the appropriate "equilibrium" (*ravnovesie*). Volodarskii, 1961, p. 5.

eign, e.g. U.S. and Japanese, analog data were also used.[7] The work was conducted in complete secrecy dictated by ideological considerations, since the proponents of the new methods probably felt that the Soviet economic profession was not yet ready to accept input-output techniques. The work in progress was described as merely an attempt to improve the material balances by bringing them together into a combined balance. Processing of data and matrix inversion for the Polish 1957 input-output table carried out by the Institute and other Soviet research groups for the Polish Gosplan were described in the press as mere manipulation of coefficients without reference to input-output analysis.[8]

The veil of secrecy that shrouded earlier studies was lifted in 1960 when M. Eidel'man, a prominent statistician and high-ranking official of the Central Statistical Administration (CSA), announced plans for, and work in progress on, the construction of large-scale operational input-output tables for 1959. Two tables were being prepared simultaneously—one in physical units and one in value terms.

The former was essentially a set of mutually consistent and interlocking material balances showing stocks at the beginning of the period, interindustry use, final demand, exports, and increases in stocks of 157 industrial commodities with flows measured in physical units and, in cases of aggregated sectors, in constant prices. Diagonal cells show total output including production of semifabricates produced and used up within enterprises. The totals shown in the table fall substantially short of the gross output of most products. Thus 20 percent of the output of metallurgy and 40 percent of the output of machinery and chemical

7. Two tables (44x44 and 16x16) were prepared in value terms and five (9x9, 12x12, 15x15, 17x17, and 24x24) in physical units. Aganbegian and Belkin, 1961, p. 53; Leibkind, 1963b, p. 16.

8. Grebtsov and Karpov, 1960, pp. 225–47; Belkin, 1959, p. 143.

products are not shown in the table. Agriculture, construction, and services such as transportation are not shown either. Since practically no other information is available on the table in physical units, we will concentrate our attention on the table in value terms.[9]

The table can be described as a traditional, Leontief-type, static, open input-output flow table showing 83 sectors. The flows are measured in current (1959) purchasers' prices; that is, prices which include transportation and trade margins as well as taxes when applicable. The only nonessential difference between the Soviet table and its Western counterparts lies in the classification of services. Following the Marx-inspired Soviet definition of national income, all services (with the exception of freight transportation, communications serving production, and various trade and distribution activities) are shown as claimants on final demand in the first quadrant of the table.[10] The flow table shows production, distribution, and value-added of the entire product and is balanced with Soviet national income and product accounts, with no "unallocated" entries or statistical discrepancies. Since all flows are measured in

---

9. The literature discussing and evaluating the two 1959 flow tables is voluminous, although there are noticeable gaps and inconsistencies and the coverage is uneven. There is no single comprehensive and definitive study. The most useful papers are Eidel'man, 1960, pp. 55–60, 1961a, pp. 9–29, and 1961b, pp. 61–74; Berri, Klotsvog, and Shatalin, 1962a, pp. 51–62; and Kovalev, 1963. Several recently published books also deal with earlier Soviet input-output studies, such as Aganbegian, 1962, and Kovalev, 1964a.

10. The traditional Western numbering of quadrants of an input-output table is used in this paper:

|      |     |
|------|-----|
| II   | I   |
| III  | IV  |

The Soviet usage reverses the numbering of the first and second quadrant—thus final demand is quadrant II.

final purchasers' prices, the allocations of transportation, communications, and trade services to final demand are zero. Earlier studies had indicated that the available CSA and Gosplan statistical and planning data could not be used in the construction of the table, and a sampling survey was resorted to for the 73 industrial sectors and one construction sector. The survey covered about 20 percent or 11,000 of all industrial and construction enterprises and was stratified to reflect different scale enterprises; sampling within these subgroups was random. The flow and coefficient data for agriculture and services, as well as the national income data for the first, third, and fourth quadrants, were taken directly from census records and income accounts of the CSA. The basic statistical sector classification employed by Soviet statistical agencies was used in the construction of the table. However, in Soviet general statistical practice the sectors are defined on an administrative basis and often include secondary products or products normally manufactured elsewhere, while the input-output sectors are "pure" sectors producing homogeneous output. The necessary adjustments were made by a method similar to the one employed in Japanese input-output tables: "nonsectoral" products were removed from sectors for which they are secondary and added to sectors for which they are primary; the input flows (columns) were adjusted proportionally to output transfers. The overall magnitude of these adjustments is not known but it appears to be substantial.[11]

The density of the technology matrix is fairly high, with nonzero entries comprising about 61 percent of the total and with a high degree of concentration of flows in some key sectors. Thus, some 500, or approximately 12 percent, of all

11. According to one Soviet source, "nonsectoral" output as percentage of unadjusted gross output in the value table ranged from a high 35.1 percent in hoisting and transporting equipment, 34.1 percent in forging equipment, 27.8 percent in transportation machinery, to a low 1.8 percent in electrical power generation and 0.4 percent in coal mining. Eidel'man, 1963b, p. 17.

nonzero entries in the interindustry flow table account for about 95 percent of all interindustry transactions.[12]

Subsequent studies have also shown that the Soviet table in value terms displays an inner structure expected of an industrial nation of the Soviet size and level of development. The interindustry transactions matrix shows a high degree of decomposability—the matrix lends itself readily to rearrangement into three distinct blocks, or a triangular matrix.[13]

The algebraic properties of the Soviet input-output models do not offer anything new. The flow table shows the equality of row and column sums for all sectors, or for any sector k:

$$\sum_{j=1}^{n} x_{kj} + Y_k = \sum_{i=1}^{n} x_{ik} + V_k \qquad (i, j = 1, 2, 3, \ldots n)$$

where $x_{kj}$ are sales of sector k to sector j; $Y_k$ is final demand in sector k; and $V_k$ is value-added in sector k. Value-added includes wages, income-in-kind, profits, and taxes, as well as capital consumption allowances. Final demand comprises personal and public consumption, government expenditures, and gross investment. A column vector of export entries completes the first quadrant, and a row vector of imports completes the third quadrant. As the second step a table of direct material input coefficients is prepared (coefficients $a_{ij}$ defined as the input of sector i into production of sector

12. Berri, Klotsvog, and Shatalin, 1962a, p. 55.

13. The three blocks are as follows: (a) fuel, chemicals, and woodworking, (b) mining, metallurgy, and machine building, and (c) agriculture, food, textiles, and apparel. The degree of independence of the three blocks is indicated by the fact that 79 percent of all interindustry transactions (omitting rows of services) are found within the blocks and only 21 percent of flows constitute interblock transactions. The structure within blocks is triangular. Further rearrangement of the sector order brings about a triangular matrix with 92 percent of all interindustry transactions located on or below the main diagonal. Leibkind, 1963a.

j per ruble of gross output of sector j, or $a_{ij} = x_{ij}/X_j$). Finally, the table of direct material input coefficients is transformed into a table of full material input coefficients showing all direct and indirect requirements of sector j production for inputs of sector i. In matrix algebra notation the latter table can be described as

$$R = (I - A)^{-1}$$

where I is an identity matrix and A is a square matrix of direct material input coefficients $a_{ij}$. The so-called Leontief's inverse R makes it possible to calculate a set of gross output levels (X) necessary to sustain production of any set of final demand levels (Y),[14] or

14. In their attempts to establish the Russian origin of input-output techniques, Soviet economists for some time operated with a different type of inverse matrix tracing the concept of a full input coefficient to the work of prerevolutionary Russian mathematically oriented economist V. K. Dmitriev. Somewhat rearranging the original Dmitriev equation of full labor costs and expanding it to cover all costs, Soviet economists write the following equation for any $ik^{th}$ element:

$$d_{ik} = \sum_{j=1}^{n} d_{ij} \cdot a_{jk} + a_{ik} \qquad (i, j, k - 1, 2, 3, \ldots, n)$$

The above can be written in matrix algebra notations for the entire table as $D = DA + A$ where D is a square matrix of full input coefficients and A is a matrix of direct input coefficients. Rearranging

$$D - DA = A$$
$$D(I - A) = A$$
$$D = A(I - A)^{-1} \text{ or } D = A(I + A + A^2 + A^3 \ldots)$$
$$D = A + A^2 + A^3 + \ldots.$$

Since Leontief's inverse $R = (I - A)^{-1}$ can also be written as $I + A + A^2 + A^3 \ldots$ we see that

$$D + I = R.$$

The only difference between Leontief and Dmitriev's inverses lies in the value of diagonal elements which are larger by one in Leontief's inverse. The crucial problem is, of course, whether the original Dmitriev concept of direct and indirect labor costs can be legitimately expanded to all costs and transformed into $D = DA + A$. The question

$$(I - A)^{-1}Y = X$$

The 1959 table in value terms was further extended in 1962 by the addition of a vector of labor input coefficients expressed in man-years, with the average annual employment figures corrected to reflect the adjusted "pure" sectors.[15] Rather than presenting the employment data as a complementary row vector of primary inputs, Soviet framers of the table expanded them into a full table showing direct labor expenditures embodied in material flows, and hailed the new table as the "first of its kind" and a "revolutionary new" labor input-output table.

The table of interindustry flows in value terms is transformed into the "embodied labor" table by simple multiplication of each row i by the appropriate labor input coefficient $c_i$, defined as employment in man-years per ruble of gross output, or $c_i = L_i/X_i$. Thus the Soviet 1959 labor input-output table appears as follows:

| | | | | | | |
|---|---|---|---|---|---|---|
| $c_1x_{11}$ | $c_1x_{12}$ | $c_1x_{13}$ | ... | $c_1x_{1n}$ | $c_1Y_1$ | $c_1X_1$ |
| $c_2x_{21}$ | $c_2x_{22}$ | $c_2x_{23}$ | ... | $c_2x_{2n}$ | $c_2Y_2$ | $c_2X_2$ |
| $c_3x_{31}$ | $c_3x_{32}$ | $c_3x_{33}$ | ... | $c_3x_{3n}$ | $c_3Y_3$ | $c_3X_3$ |
| ... | ... | ... | ... | ... | ... | ... |
| $c_nx_{n1}$ | $c_nx_{n2}$ | $c_nx_{n3}$ | ... | $c_nx_{nn}$ | $c_nY_n$ | $c_nX_n$ |
| $L_1$ | $L_2$ | $L_3$ | ... | $L_n$ | | |

It must be noted that the traditional column-row sum equality does not hold true for the labor flow table where each row sum $(= L_i)$ is smaller than the column sum

$$\left( = \sum_{i=1}^{n} c_ix_{ij} + L_j \right).$$

---

itself is of academic interest only, as Dmitriev's inverse soon disappeared from Soviet writings and the traditional Leontief's $(I - A)^{-1}$ is now being used. Aganbegian and Belkin, 1961, pp. 28–34; Zauberman, 1962, pp. 437–45.

15. Eidel'man, 1962a, 1963a, and 1963c.

The ability to calculate the total labor cost of output, i.e., the direct "live" labor and the labor embodied in material purchases, was hailed as an important addition to more traditional tools of labor planning in the Soviet Union. The next step in the manipulation of the labor flow table is the calculation of full labor input coefficients analogous to full material coefficients, showing all direct and indirect labor requirements per unit of output. The full labor input coefficient for any sector j is calculated as:

$$t_j = \sum_{i=1}^{n} c_i r_{ij} \qquad (i = 1, 2, 3, \ldots, n)$$

where $r_{ij}$ stands for the $ij^{th}$ element of the Leontief inverse R. Soviet economists treat full labor input coefficients as Marxian socially necessary labor per unit of output. However, they relate these coefficients not only to final demand as is done in Western models but to gross output as well. Thus the total socially necessary labor expended in production of the output of any sector j is calculated as

$$W_j = \sum_{i=1}^{n} c_i r_{ij} X_j \qquad (i = 1, 2, 3, \ldots, n)$$

or, for the entire system, the socially necessary labor becomes (in matrix algebra notation):

$$W = c(I - A)^{-1}X$$

Calculations like this were actually performed for the entire 1959 labor input-output table but the analytical or operational applicability of the "full socially necessary labor cost" is not clear and has not been further discussed.

The 1959 table (in physical units) was never published in the U.S.S.R., but a large segment of the second quadrant of the table in value terms appeared in the *1960 Statistical Abstract of the U.S.S.R.* No data for the remaining three quadrants were released. In the following year, the *1961*

*Statistical Abstract of the U.S.S.R.* carried a similarly truncated segment of the labor table.[16] It was possible, however,
to estimate the omitted flow and final demand entries, using
the published truncated segments of the second quadrant as
well as other interindustry data scattered in professional
journals, reports, and books. Because of omissions and the
nature of the available data, some sectors had to be aggregated, and the final reconstructed 1959 table shows 66
productive sectors instead of the original Soviet 83.[17]

It would be useful at this point to summarize Soviet economists' own assessment and criticism of the first Soviet
venture into input-output analysis. Aside from purely technical points, such as errors in data and the problem of the
reliability of the data obtained by the sampling survey,[18]
the criticism centers on two somewhat related points.

Many Soviet economists feel that the choice of purchasers'
over producers' prices was unfortunate. The use of purchasers' prices leads to double counting of trade and transportation costs, and this distorts the distribution of the gross
social product, making the row and column sums of an
input-output flow table not comparable to or directly translatable into values used in statistical reporting and planning.
Furthermore, the use of purchasers' prices means that the
flows are substantially distorted by the incidence of the
turnover tax, which is highly differentiated for different
groups of consumers in the U.S.S.R.[19] These distortions also

16. *Nar. khoz.*, 1960, pp. 103–43; *Nar. khoz.*, 1961, pp. 77–117.

17. Treml, 1964a and 1964b.

18. Eidel'man in the discussion reported in "Soveshchanie," 1962,
pp. 117–18; Riabushkin in the discussion in Nemchinov, 1962a, p. 329.

19. Berri, Klotsvog, and Shatalin, 1962a, p. 59; Aganbegian and Belkin,
1961, pp. 55–58; Solovev, 1964, p. 25. It may be added that the use
of purchasers' prices in the 1959 Soviet table ruled out international
comparison of structure of production and in 1962 the Economic
Research Institute found it necessary to approximate the flows in
terms of producers' values by removing trade and transportation costs.
Berri and Shvyrkov, 1963, pp. 133–44.

compound the difficulty of correlating the tables in value terms with tables expressed in physical units. Those who support the use of purchasers' prices generally, or at least for ex-post input-output tables, retort by pointing out the almost insurmountable difficulties of obtaining the flow data in producers' prices.[20]

The second point of criticism concerns the noncorrespondence and definitional discrepancies between input-output tables in value terms and those in physical units. In addition to the fact that the commodity coverage and classification employed were different in the two tables and that a certain noncorrespondence was introduced by the use of purchasers' prices, the two types of tables differ in their definitions of intrasectoral turnover and in their categories of final demand. The table in physical units, as some critics have noted, does not identify gross investment allocations but divides final demand entries into "market" and "other needs." [21]

Some discussants have expressed dissatisfaction with the layout of the fourth quadrant, which is designed to show the redistribution of national income through fiscal agencies of the state to sustain the "unproductive" (in Marx's vernacular), activities presented in the final demand quadrant.[22] We may note that, following the layout of the Polish and Hungarian input-output tables, the fourth quadrant was left blank in the 1962 Soviet planning input-output table. Finally, the treatment of capital consumption allowances in the table in value terms has also drawn repeated criticism.[23]

20. Eidel'man, 1964, p. 12; Kossov, 1964, pp. 68–69.
21. Nemchinov, 1963a, p. 3; Vairadian, 1964, pp. 237–38.
22. Aganbegian, 1962, p. 49.
23. Conforming to Marxian price theory, Soviet framers of input-output tables suggest that the column sum of the second quadrant corresponds to Marxian c (constant capital), and that the sum of value-added entries of the third quadrant corresponds to v (variable capital) plus m (surplus value). This treatment calls for inclusion of depreciation in the second quadrant which, needless to say, cannot

It is interesting to note that the general tenor of the critical evaluation of the pioneering Soviet excursions into input-output analysis has been rather restrained. Most larger theoretical issues have been either completely avoided or dismissed in a few short sentences. The reluctance to discuss them can probably be explained by the dogmatic rigidity of Soviet economics. For instance, the implications of the linearity assumption were not discussed at all until well into 1963 when M. R. Eidel'man raised the problem of fixed and variable costs in the context of input-output models.[24] When two other economists, Boiarskii and Dzhaparidze, continued the discussion of linear models and the related problems of fixed and variable costs, they hastened to disavow the concept of "Malthusian type diminishing returns" and unequivocally stated that input coefficients decrease with increasing output levels.[25] Another case in point is the assumption of stability of the input coefficients, which has never been questioned or even discussed in connection with input-output tables. The latter is particularly puzzling as numerous Soviet economists are on record with criticism of the assumption of stability of coefficients made in the studies of national balance sheets in the 1920s in the U.S.S.R. or in Western input-output models.[26] This lack of

---

be done without a corresponding offsetting column of replacement entries. To circumspect the problem, Soviet authors show depreciation neither with the second nor with the third quadrant but as a row separating the two. Dissatisfied with this they call for a better solution. Eidel'man, 1962b, p. 275; Vairadian, 1964, p. 226; Aganbegian, 1962, p. 51.

24. Eidel'man, 1963b, pp. 18–19.

25. Boiarskii and Dzhaparidze, 1963, pp. 10–11.

26. One source states that "since the thirties the use of static and dynamic coefficients has been compromised and the assumption of stability of coefficients came to be associated with the old, discarded economic relations which could only handicap the progress of socialist reconstruction." Vairadian, 1964, p. 211. For similar statements see Riabushkin, 1957, p. 236, and Sorokin, 1961, p. 38.

interest in the problem of stability can possibly be explained by the fact that Soviet economists consider input-output analysis primarily as a tool of planning. Input coefficients in planning models should be based not on past records but on projected changes in technology.[27] The list of possible issues can be continued—the discussion of possible distortions introduced by aggregation has never gone beyond a simplified statement of the problem. The implications of the no-substitutability assumption have never been discussed, nor has the problem of joint products been raised.

Of great interest are Soviet experiments in constructing regional and, recently, interregional input-output tables. The work on these tables is centered in the Moscow and Novosibirsk branches of the Laboratory on Applications of Mathematical Methods in Economic Analysis and Planning of the Academy of Sciences of the U.S.S.R., headed until recently by Academician V. S. Nemchinov.[28] Nemchinov has long been known to be particularly interested in problems of regional development of the country generally and in regional input-output tables. As early as 1957, when even the term input-output analysis was not yet acceptable to the profession, he urged the All-Union Conference of Statisticians to give more attention to regional models and subsequently published several papers on the subject.[29] The efforts of the Laboratory's staff have been extensive—working in special teams or in cooperation with local planning and statistical agencies, they have completed 20 regional input-output tables and three more are in preparation. (See Table 1.)

Soviet regional input-output tables, both the ex-post and the planning type, do not significantly differ from their na-

27. Al'ter et al., 1962, p. 75.

28. The Laboratory was merged in 1963 into a newly created Central Institute of Mathematical Economics of the Academy of Sciences of the U.S.S.R. under the directorship of academician N. P. Fedorenko.

29. Riabushkin, 1959, p. 167.

## Table 1

### REGIONAL INPUT-OUTPUT TABLES IN THE U.S.S.R.

(completed or in preparation)

| Region | Year | Number of sectors | Type | Units of measurement |
|--------|------|-------------------|------|----------------------|
| 1. Mordovskaia A.S.S.R. | 1958 | 14 | Ex-post | Purchasers' prices |
| 2. Mordovskaia A.S.S.R. | 1959 | 86 | Ex-post | Purchasers' prices |
| 3. Tatar A.S.S.R. | 1959 | 165 | Ex-post | Purchasers' prices |
| 4. Tatar Sovnarkhoz | 1960 | 150 | Ex-post | Purchasers' prices |
| 5. Kalinigrad oblast' | 1960 | 15 | Ex-post | Purchasers' prices |
| 6. Latvian S.S.R. | 1961 | 239 | Ex-post | Producers' prices |
| 7. Lithuanian S.S.R. | 1961 | 239 | Ex-post | Producers' prices |
| 8. Estonian S.S.R. | 1961 | 239 | Ex-post | Producers' prices |
| 9. Three Baltic republics | 1961 | 239 | Ex-post | Producers' prices |
| 10. Karelian A.S.S.R. | 1961 | 75 | Planning | Purchasers' prices |
| 11. Tatar Sovnarkhoz | 1961 | 150 | Ex-post | Purchasers' prices |
| 12. Tatar Sovnarkhoz | 1961 | 56 | Planning | Purchasers' prices |
| 13. Tatar Sovnarkhoz | 1962 | 56 | Planning | Purchasers' prices |
| 14. Lithuanian Sovnarkhoz | 1962 | 180 | Planning | Purchasers' prices |
| 15. Byelorussian S.S.R. | 1962 | 500 | Planning | Physical units |
| 16. Tatar Sovnarkhoz | 1963 | 56 | Planning | Purchasers' prices |
| 17. Moscow economic region* | n.a. | n.a. | n.a. | n.a. |
| 18. Azarbeidzhan S.S.R.* | 1964 | n.a. | Ex-post | Physical units |
| 19. Georgian S.S.R.* | n.a. | n.a. | n.a. | n.a. |
| 20. Armenian S.S.R. | 1963 | 91 | Ex-post | Purchasers' prices |
| 21. Latvian S.S.R. | 1970 | 150 | Planning | Producers' prices |
| 22. Lithuanian S.S.R. | 1970 | 150 | Planning | Producers' prices |
| 23. Estonian S.S.R. | 1970 | 150 | Planning | Producers' prices |

* In preparation.

tional counterparts. With two exceptions they are all constructed in value terms, probably reflecting Nemchinov's predilection for value balances and input-output models. Most of the tables were prepared in purchasers' prices and this, as is the case with the national studies, is explained by the difficulty of obtaining the necessary data in producers' values. We may note, however, that in the case of three Baltic republic tables which were later combined into an interregional model, producers' values were used. In this case the regular flow table was supplemented by a set of tables of interregional deliveries in physical units, and producers' values were used in the main table to insure correspondence among the tables.[30]

30. Kossov and Mints, 1964, pp. 18–19.

The regional tables place greater emphasis on identification of separate noncompeting imported products—most of the published Soviet tables contain special matrixes relating import flows to separate sectors, while the national input-output tables present one row of imports. The framers of the regional tables also seem to have been less rigid in their classification of services into "productive" and "unproductive"; and such sectors as communal and residential services, all of transportation and communications, and other services found in the final demand column of the national tables are shown in the interindustry quadrant in the regional tables.[31] The prospects for adaptation of the regional and interregional models to the needs of planning are impossible to assess at this time and will probably depend on the future of input-output techniques, but the work will be continued. A recent conference of the Scientific Council of the Academy of Sciences of the U.S.S.R. recommended construction of regional tables for all constituent republics of the U.S.S.R.[32]

## PLANNING INPUT-OUTPUT MODELS

The general outline of the scope, organization, and administration of Soviet economic planning, as well as the shortcomings of the planning methods, need not detain us at this point. They have been discussed recently in several excellent, detailed, and up-to-date works, and only a brief summary is needed here.[33]

There is sufficient evidence to suggest that Soviet planning today is experiencing its deepest crisis. This can be seen in the continuous and significant changes in output and investment targets, in the perennial reshuffling of priorities, in the "freezing" of large construction projects, and in the growth of unfinished construction and of the park of uninstalled capital equipment. There are delays in the formula-

31. Cherniak, 1962, pp. 118–23; Kossov, 1964, pp. 157–200.
32. "Plenum nauchnogo soveta," 1964, p. 151.
33. Levine, 1962a, pp. 47–66; Bergson, 1964. For an admirably frank criticism of the present planning methods, see Nemchinov, 1965.

tion of state plans and marked inconsistencies in different
planning indicators and measures. The consumer goods industry, while still unable to satisfy the demand for all commodities, is nevertheless plagued by inventories of unsold
goods which grow at an alarming rate. There is also some
evidence of growing frictional unemployment and difficulties with labor allocations. Some of these problems are
new, e.g. the buildup of inventories or frictional unemployment, and the traditional planning methods offer no solutions. At the same time the post-Stalin liberalization of
academic discussion has intensified both criticism of the
current state of affairs and the search for new planning
methods.

A crucial issue of special relevance to our discussion of the
applicability of input-output techniques is the problem of
overall balancing and internal consistency of various production and distribution plans. Stalin's planning methods
assigned rank priorities to selected key industries and accepted, almost invited, shortages and strains in nonpriority
sectors. This procedure was abandoned in the late 1950s
in favor of a more balanced approach.[34]

The Gosplan work with balance sheets of the economy in
the early 1930s came to a complete standstill for at least 20
years. Since 1951, Gosplan reportedly has been constructing
overall ex-ante balances, but the work remains in an experimental stage, and there is enough evidence to conclude that,
as of now, the Soviet planning apparatus works without an
operational balance sheet for the entire economy.[35]

34. Hardt, 1959, pp. 121–42.

35. A. Ziborov, chief of the Balance section of the Central Statistical
Administration of the R.S.F.S.R., described the situation as follows:
"The theoretical and methodological study of the balance sheet of the
national economy is progressing very slowly. We have many versions
of the Balance—the Gosplan version, or the CSA version but no single
accepted version of the model of socialist reproduction. Discussions
of correct prices for the construction of balances last for years"
(Ziborov, 1962, p. 16). The same theme was repeated in an editorial

The main tool of Soviet planning of supply and distribution has been and remains the method of material balances, i.e. balance sheets for specific products usually expressed in physical units. The balance sheets show stocks at the beginning of the period, imports, and levels of current production as well as main deliveries, exports, and additions to inventories. As with most other aspects of Soviet planning, a detailed description of the operational side of planning by material balances is lacking, or is at best rather vague. We do not know how detailed is the list of suppliers and consumers, nor how extensive is the itemization by product type in a single balance. Nor do we find in the literature a detailed description of methods insuring or approximating some degree of internal consistency in the projected levels of gross output. The magnitude of the problem and the cumbersome Soviet apparatus of material supply planning would seem to preclude a high degree of internal consistency in the plan. At present the central (all-union) Soviet planning agencies prepare and administer more than 18,000 material balances in a complex multilayer system.[36] The information we have is incomplete, but the overall picture appears to be as follows. Gosplan prepares 1,200 or more material balances for key products; in the process of preparation of these balances, input requirements of tens of thousands of products are considered. The estimation and setting of these input coefficients, or *normativy,* is also a direct responsibility of Gosplan. An additional 18,000–20,000 material balances are prepared by the Council of the National Economy of the U.S.S.R., the main administrations

---

of *Planovoe khoziaistvo* ("Stroitel'stvo kommunisma," 1962, p. 4). Another prominent Soviet statistician notes that "the problem of construction of the national plan in a form of the balance sheet was raised a long time ago but this task has not been accomplished so far" (Vairadian, 1964, p. 232).

36. This is the figure most frequently cited in the general discussion on the subject. Birman, 1963a, p. 7; Kovalev, 1964, p. 192; Cherniavskii, 1965, p. 9.

of interrepublic deliveries, and the republic supply administrations.[37] The available Soviet literature on the subject
does not explain the methods of aggregation and disaggregation of balances at different levels of the planning apparatus, but there is sufficient evidence to suggest that the
system lacks cohesion and that the material balances at
different levels are not completely collated.[38]

Furthermore, the trend seems to lie in the direction of extending the list of products manufactured and distributed
in the centrally planned manner. Extension of the coverage
of centrally planned products is paralleled by a continuous
increase in the number of centrally determined input coefficients.[39]

Academician V. S. Nemchinov, who has urged planners to
decentralize the distribution of industrial products and to
substitute a direct buyer-seller arrangement for the present
system, has been very critical of the method of material
balances employed in the construction and administration
of the supply plan. He points out that shortages of some
products have become almost permanent under the system,
a situation which, he feels, is caused by the lack of internal
consistency in the material balances. As he puts it, "we have

37. Alekseev, 1965, p. 70; Dudkin and Ershov, 1965, p. 60.

38. One source gives a very interesting illustration of this lack of
correspondence. Thus, to cite but one example, the Gosplan nomenclature of energy machinery and equipment lists 122 positions,
while the Council of the National Economy of the U.S.S.R. operates
with a list of 322 positions. However, only 21 positions in the two
nomenclatures coincide. Similar discrepancies are noted in the nomenclature used by the Central Statistical Administration. Kovalev, 1964a,
p. 304.

39. Birman notes that the number of centrally planned products increased from 13,105 in 1960 to 18,000 by 1962 (Birman, 1963a, p. 7). The
October 1961 Decree of the Central Committee of the CPSU and the
Council of Ministers of the U.S.S.R. stressed the importance of extension of the coverage of centrally determined input coefficients to all
resources used in the U.S.S.R. (Pugachev, 1964b, p. 59).

the rows of material balances but not the table—the row is balanced but the column is not." [40]

Western scholars who have examined the Soviet methods of approximating internal consistency of material balances discount the possibility of any extensive employment of iteration; in all probability the process of balancing a set of material balances does not extend beyond a few major elements of the matrix and a rough adjustment for second order effects among these. [41] The best answer the planners can offer at present to provide for possible imbalances in the supply plan has been to allow for a reserve of up to five percent in all material balances—a rather crude method at best. [42]

Generally speaking, the process of iteration does not have to be too extensive. If the matrix of interindustry transactions can be made triangular by rearrangement of sector order in such a way that each sector sells only to sectors of lower order number and buys only from sectors of higher order number (i.e. no two sectors are selling to and buying from each other), then planners can arrive at a consistent set of gross output targets and interindustry requirements in one set of computations. Only in cases of indecomposable matrices with a substantial number of entries above the diagonal would the framers of material balances have to resort to several iterations. But even then, as John Montias has proved in a very interesting study, the existence of indecomposable groups would not pose unsurmountable problems as long as the circular interdependence is restricted to sectors with capacity limitations. [43] As was pointed out above, the 1959 Soviet input-output matrix can be rearranged into a block triangular format but the decomposability is

40. Nemchinov, 1964a, p. 9.
41. Levine, 1959, pp. 164–66; Montias, 1959, pp. 974–76.
42. *Entsiklopediia*, 1964, pp. 386–87.
43. Montias, 1962, pp. 280–87.

far from perfect.[44] At present there is no evidence that Soviet planners make use of this characteristic of interindustry transactions matrices. Probably one of the explanations lies in the fact that material balances, prepared and administered by different agencies, with differing commodity classifications and in varying degrees of detail, do not constitute a uniform matrix.

Supply planning based on material balances has another built-in potential source of error—error introduced by aggregation. Production flows and individual entries, e.g. the $x_{ij}$, shown in material balances are prepared on the basis of input coefficients, $a_{ij}$, and gross output requirements, $X_j$. Since the central planning agencies operate with a limited number of products, the input coefficients used in construction of material balances are averaged (*svodnyi* in Soviet terminology) and branch or sector coefficients are weighted (in most instances) by gross output weights from the previous period. Thus, any change in the product mix of an aggregated sector could lead to distorted allocations.

Needless to say, the crucial problem is and has been the point of departure in drawing up state plans. The difficulties described above are directly related to the time-honored Soviet practice of initiating production planning by specifying certain, in most cases exogenously determined, rates of growth of gross output of key sectors and industries. In spite of some criticism of "steel eaters" made by Khrushchev, the Soviet leadership was and probably still is guided primarily by objectives of high industrial growth and considers the rapid development of such industries as steel, fuel, electrical power, and machinery as an aim in it-

44. Thus, according to one Soviet source, estimation of gross output levels on the basis of direct input coefficients located on and below the main diagonal only lead to understatement of actual gross output values by 23 percent in the extracting, fuel, and chemicals block, by 34 percent in the machinery and metallurgy block, and by 6 percent in the agriculture, food, and apparel block. See note 13 above and Leibkind, 1963a, pp. 172–73.

self.[45] Thus rates of growth of gross output of these industries are set at maximum attainable levels, subject only to capacity constraints and some considerations of interindustry requirements. The political leadership and the planners make no clear distinction between intermediate and final products and, once certain investment targets and national defense needs have been allowed for, the remaining elements of net product, especially its consumption component, are determined as residuals.[46]

The deficiencies of this approach are receiving greater and greater recognition in the Soviet Union, especially among the younger, mathematically oriented economists and statisticians. The search for new answers centers on a discussion of prerequisites for "optimal planning," a new, widely used, but vaguely defined term. Probably most critics of the present system would define "optimal planning" as planning and control methods that would insure the most efficient allocation of resources while optimizing some welfare criterion of the Soviet state. The quest for the "optimality criterion" has so far left the field wide open, with more conflicting opinions emerging as the discussion encompasses wider and wider circles of academic economists, statisticians, and planners. At a special round-table discussion on current problems of Soviet economics and planning, one speaker after another raised the problem of the optimality criterion. Academician V. M. Glushkov, the leading Soviet specialist on cybernetics, submitted that the search had taken too long and that his research group had chosen the expedient method of considering time minimization as the criterion. I. S. Malyshev, Deputy Director of the Central

45. Levine, 1962a, p. 132; Wiles, 1962, pp. 282–83.

46. V. S. Nemchinov describes the situation in these terms: "The gross output targets are specified first, followed by subtraction of intermediate products to obtain the national income (net product) magnitudes. Finally, subtraction of the accumulation and investment funds from the net product leaves the consumption fund of the population." Nemchinov, 1964b, p. 82.

Statistical Administration, suggested labor productivity as the criterion. L. M. Gatovskii, chief editor of *Voprosy ekonomiki* and chairman of the conference, expressed the opinion that it appeared to be impossible to formulate this criterion, and he questioned the need for a single criterion.[47]

Thus no agreement is in sight yet. As one Soviet economist puts it: "indisputably, the optimality criterion can be defined as maximum output at minimal costs. However, Soviet economists cannot agree on what constitutes the minimand and the maximand." [48]

The economic debate extends to such related topics as: recognition of the allocative functions of interest and rental charges, problems of price formation, criteria of successful economic performance at the micro-level, and many others; but no consensus on any of these problems has emerged yet. A resolution of these problems, provided it were forthcoming and provided it were acceptable to the political leadership, would result in the formulation of new planning methods. In the meantime, Soviet planners are marking time, vacillating between modest improvements in traditional methods (such as that of material balances) and guarded explorations of new approaches utilizing value relationships in the resource allocation problem.

From the very beginning of their studies, Soviet economists and statisticians have viewed input-output techniques primarily as a tool of planning and control. In very summary fashion the static planning input-output models envisaged by the proponents of the new methods can be

47. Davidov, 1964, pp. 90–94; "Ekonomisty i matematiki," 1964, pp. 63–110. It is interesting to note that Gatovskii's original statement questioning the need of a single criterion of optimality was omitted from subsequent reports on the conference. "Ot redaktsii," 1964, p. 95.

48. Cherniavskii, 1963, pp. 114–15. We could add parenthetically that this clear recognition of the need of a single optimality criterion signifies important progress in Soviet economic science. Fifteen years ago even the simple principle of maximum output at least cost was considered alien to Soviet economics. Novozhilov, 1963, pp. 132–33.

described as follows. Two matrixes of direct input coefficients, defined as requirements for inputs i per unit of output of sector j, will be constructed on the basis of past experience and projected (planned) technological progress. The first n × n matrix A will show direct material input coefficients for n products or sectors; the second m × n matrix B will show direct input requirements in m primary resources, such as labor of various grades, capital equipment, etc. As the next step these two matrixes will be transformed into matrixes of full input coefficients, i.e. coefficients reflecting all direct and indirect requirement per unit of final demand. The matrix of full material coefficients R will be obtained by inversion of matrix A, in the traditional Leontief form:

$$R = (I - A)^{-1}$$

The matrix of full primary resource coefficients T will be obtained by multiplication of the B matrix of direct coefficients and the inverse R:

$$T = B(I - A)^{-1}$$

The set of full primary resource coefficients of matrix T will enable the planners to establish a "production possibility curve" for the economy so that alternative mixes of final or autonomous demand (consumption, gross investment, defense, exports) can be considered, and the mix, maximizing some predetermined preference function of the political leadership and/or the population, can be chosen. Once this feasible mix of elements of final demand Y has been determined for all n products, a mutually consistent set of gross output targets X will be calculated as the product of multiplication of the n × n inverse of the coefficient matrix A and the final demand vector Y:

$$(I - A)^{-1}Y = X$$

The advantages of this method are several. First, it would enable the planners to consider alternative feasible bills of final goods and to have on hand "trade-off" data showing the opportunity cost of alternatives. The latter would be particularly important for adjusting plans for unexpected changes in exogenous variables outside the control of the planning apparatus, e.g. foreign trade changes, weather, etc. The present-day planning methods, in which the output target for many industries is determined on the basis of the previous period, do not allow for consideration of alternatives of any significant scope, nor are they sufficiently flexible.

Secondly, the new method would provide for a mutually consistent set of gross output targets—again a major improvement over present methods which do not insure overall balancing to an acceptable degree. In this connection we may note that the degree of interdependence of economic variables and hence the difficulty of equilibrating gross and net product targets are not constant. As suggested by Western scholars, the degree of interdependence is increasing, and the growing technological sophistication reduces factor substitutability and hence the flexibility of the Soviet system.[49] Soviet scholars have also come to recognize this phenomenon. One of the most ardent advocates of planning reforms, A. G. Aganbegian, recently commented on the growing dependence of production levels on the mix of final goods. Critical of the inflexible and deterministic nature of Soviet planning, he notes that "it is becoming more and more difficult to balance the national economy and to control it. Actually it is impossible to fully balance the plan." [50]

Lastly, the new method would greatly reduce the labor and time necessary for construction of various state plans (at present between seven and eight months) and would bring Soviet planning one step closer to "continuous planning," i.e. planning without terminal dates and with continuously made adjustments.

49. Hardt, 1962, pp. 1–31.
50. Aganbegian, 1964a, p. 65.

Proponents of the new methods were convinced of the feasibility of complete integration of input-output techniques with more traditional tools of planning. At the April 1960 Conference on Applications of Mathematical Techniques to Economic Analysis and Planning, V. D. Belkin, one of the earliest advocates of input-output, presented an approved "Plan of Scheduled Priority Projects" according to which the studies of applications of input-output techniques to planning were to begin in 1960. The first stage, that is, the construction of the state plan on the basis of input-output tables, was to be completed by 1965.[51] Apparently, a great number of Soviet economists (especially of the older school) and planning officials did not share the enthusiasm of the proponents of input-output techniques and censured them on several occasions for trying to replace all planning by manipulations of input-output tables.[52]

The work on planning input-output models began almost immediately after completion of the two ex-post flow and coefficient tables for 1959. An unexplained division of labor in preparing planning tables was effected at that time. Starting with the 1962 models, the Economic Research Institute of Gosplan assumed the task of preparing the planning tables in value terms, while the preparation of tables in physical units became the responsibility of the Main Computer Center of Gosplan.[53] This separation has probably contributed to continuous and possibly even increasing differences in the classification, coverage, and structure of the two types of models.

The shift from ex-post to planning models appears to have been somewhat too hasty, especially in the light of shortcomings of the ex-post tables and the fact that major

51. Belkin, 1961b, pp. 134–35.
52. Bor, 1960, pp. 42–43; Kovalev, 1961a, p. 22; Vairadian, 1964, pp. 231–32.
53. Berri, Klotsvog, and Shatalin, 1962b, p. 35; Kovalev, 1964, p. 198.

theoretical problems besetting planning have not been resolved. It is interesting to note that in this respect Soviet
proponents and framers of input-output models differ from
their colleagues in other countries of the Soviet bloc. Input-
output studies were pioneered in the bloc by the Poles and
Yugoslavs, followed by the Hungarians and now by all the
other countries; but among the 20 input-output tables constructed or in preparation in the bloc outside the Soviet
Union we find only two planning models—the 1964 Ger-
man and the 1965 Hungarian. The latter was designed for
very limited objectives and not for "overall planning for the
whole economy," according to one Hungarian source.[54] (See
Table 2.)

An important shortcoming of all planning input-output
exercises reported in the Soviet literature has been the absence of primary resource constraints from planning models.
Soviet framers of input-output models recognized from
the outset the importance of at least basic capital and
labor coefficients. The "Plan of Scheduled Priority Projects"
referred to above projected construction of ex-post and
planning labor input vectors for the 1960–64 period and of
the capital vector by 1964. Central Statistical Administration
and Gosplan officials repeated at a 1961 conference that construction of capital and labor constraints must be the next
order of business.[55] A labor input vector (in man-years) was
added later to the 1959 ex-post table in value terms, and
there is some evidence of the subsequent addition of a fixed
capital vector.[56] However, all discussions of and reports on

54. Horvath, 1963, p. 219.

55. Belkin, 1961, pp. 132–35. Eidel'man and Kovalev in discussions reported in "Soveshchanie," 1962, pp. 115–21.

56. I was able to find only two references to the fact that a capital
vector has been constructed for the 1959 ex-post table in value terms:
Belousov, 1963, p. 74, and Iaremenko, 1964, pp. 37–40. Neither source
elaborates on the nature of capital data used, but Iaremenko at least
presents some statistical data. For 13 industries he published full, i.e.
direct and indirect, requirements for capital defined as $P = k(I - A)^{-1}$

Table 2

## INPUT-OUTPUT TABLES IN THE U.S.S.R. AND OTHER COUNTRIES OF THE SOVIET BLOC
(completed or in preparation)

| Country | Year | Number of sectors or products | | Type | Units of measurement |
|---------|------|-------|------------|------|---------------------|
| | | Total | Industrial | | |
| U.S.S.R. | 1959 | 83 | 73 | Ex-post | Purchasers' prices |
| U.S.S.R. | 1959 | 157 | 157 | Ex-post | Physical units |
| U.S.S.R. | 1962 | 83 | 73 | Planning | Purchasers' prices |
| U.S.S.R. | 1962 | 346 | 323 | Planning | Physical units |
| U.S.S.R. | 1963 | 372 | 344 | Planning | Physical units |
| U.S.S.R. | 1963 | 435 | 407 | Planning | Physical units |
| U.S.S.R. | 1964–65 | 438 | 408 | Planning | Physical units |
| U.S.S.R. | 1970 | 124–29 | 112 | Planning | Purchasers' prices |
| U.S.S.R. | 1970 | 600 | n.a. | Planning | Physical units |
| Bulgaria | 1960 | 75 | n.a. | Ex-post | Value terms |
| Czechoslovakia | 1961 | 97 | n.a. | Ex-post | Value terms |
| Czechoslovakia | 1961 | 216 | n.a. | Ex-post | Physical units |
| Czechoslovakia | 1962 | 267 | n.a. | Ex-post | Physical units |
| Czechoslovakia | 1962 | 96 | 87 | Ex-post | Purchasers' prices |
| Czechoslovakia | 1963 | 479 | n.a. | Ex-post | Physical units |
| East Germany | 1959 | 27 | 21 | Ex-post | Purchasers' prices |
| East Germany | 1964 | 27 | n.a. | Planning | Purchasers' prices |
| Hungary | 1957 | 40 | 31 | Ex-post | Purchasers' prices |
| Hungary | 1959 | 100 | n.a. | Ex-post | Purchasers' prices |
| Hungary | 1965 | n.a. | n.a. | Planning | Purchasers' prices |
| Poland | 1957 | 20 | 14 | Ex-post | Purchasers' prices |
| Poland | 1961 | 56 × 74 | 56 × 74 | Ex-post | Purchasers' prices |
| Poland | 1962 | 130–50 | n.a. | Ex-post | Value terms |
| Romania | 1961 | 63 | 55 | Ex-post | Purchasers' prices[2] |
| Romania | 1963 | 110 | 70 | Ex-post | Purchasers' prices[1] |
| Romania | 1963 | 110 | 70 | Ex-post | Physical units[1] |
| Yugoslavia | 1955 | 27 | 15 | Ex-post | Producers' prices |
| Yugoslavia | 1958 | 76 | 59 | Ex-post | Producers' prices |
| Yugoslavia | 1961 | n.a. | n.a. | Ex-post | n.a.[1] |

1. In preparation.
2. The table was never completed.
Sources: For sources on input-output tables in the countries of the Soviet bloc other than the U.S.S.R., see primarily Lukacs, 1962. For sources of Soviet tables, see text.

---

where k is a row vector of capital/gross output ratios. I repeated Iaremenko's exercise using the 66-sector Soviet 1959 input-output table (Treml, 1964b) and different types of Soviet capital data. The tentative conclusion of these tests indicates that the Soviet capital vector was constructed in terms of capital buildings, structures, and equipment (Soviet *osnovnye fondy*) valued at replacement cost as of January 1, 1960. The correspondence between Iaremenko's and my indexes is measured by Kendall's rank correlation coefficient of +0.92.

exercises with planning input-output models give no evidence of the use of labor, capital, or any other type of primary resource constraints in planning models constructed in the 1961–65 period.[57]

We may now summarize the available information on planning input-output exercises. As with the two 1959 ex-post tables, the first set of Soviet planning flow and coefficient tables (labeled "experimental" by their framers) was prepared in two versions—one in physical units showing 346 products and another in value terms (in current 1962 purchasers' prices) with 83 productive sectors.[58] Since practically no information on the table in physical units is available, we must concentrate our attention on the value table. This table was identical to its 1959 ex-post predecessor in terms of its layout and structural features, with two exceptions: the fourth quadrant was left blank and the value-added quadrant showed only one row of entries combining labor income with taxes, profits, and other forms of net income. The construction of the planning table can be summarized as follows. A table of planned direct input coefficients $a_{ij}$'s was prepared on the basis of the 1959 ex-post table. The framers of the planning table felt justified in restricting the adjustments in coefficients for technological, price, and other changes to some 500 coefficients, or 12 percent of all nonzero coefficients. Because of 1959–62 price changes and the nature of the data on projected technological changes, the 1959 value input coefficients had to be converted to coefficients in physical units, adjusted for technological changes, and then converted into value input co-

57. At the spring 1964 conference, both Kovalev (Main Computer Center of Gosplan) and Al'ter (Economic Research Institute of Gosplan) indicated work in progress on capital, labor, and other resource constraints for the future planning input-output models. "Ekonomisty i matematiki," 1964, pp. 100 and 102; Belousov, Komina, and Komarov, 1965, pp. 27–28.

58. Gatovskii and Kovalev, 1962, pp. 44–45; Berri, Klotsvog, and Shatalin, 1962b, pp. 34–43.

efficients. Considering the short span of four years, the magnitude of some of the reported adjustments appears to be surprisingly high. For instance, input of coke into ferrous metals decreased by 13.7 percent, while input of electrical power into ferrous metals increased by 9.4 percent; input of coal into machine building decreased by 20 percent, offset by a 5 percent increase of input of petroleum products. These substantial changes can probably be explained by changing technology and changes in the output mix within the aggregated sectors. The use of purchasers' prices adds another source of instability of coefficients—changes in the distribution pattern and the incidence of commodity taxes are reflected in the coefficients. After the adjusted coefficient table was completed, a table of full input coefficients was obtained by matrix inversion of the $(I - A)^{-1}$ form.

The planning model was formulated by starting with the vector of final demand. The control totals for various sectors contributing to consumption, investment, and exports were taken directly from the national income data of the 1962 plan, although the framers of the planning model reported substantial difficulties which had to be resolved before national income data could be fitted into the input-output framework. Finally, a set of gross output values was obtained as the product of multiplication of the final demand vector and the inverse of the technology matrix. The terminal task of the exercise was comparison of the gross output levels projected in the state plan with the gross output values derived from the input-output table. Since the two sets of gross output vectors were not directly comparable, growth rates for the 1959–62 period were chosen for this test. According to published reports, the comparison tests produced satisfactory results: for such important industries as metallurgy, fuel, lumber and woodworking, paper, and food, rates of growth in the plan and in the input-output table proved to be almost identical (with differences ranging from 0.4 to 1.3 percentage points). Generally it was felt that the experiment was successful, as it proved that the input-output approach can provide essentially the same data as the more traditional planning methods, but of course much faster and with less effort. It also appears that the exercise enabled the input-output team to pinpoint certain strains and bottlenecks in the plan and to detect sectors in which the final product could have been increased without corresponding increases in inputs. However, the description of this aspect of the experiment is rather vague.

Apparently the position of those who advocated the application of input-output techniques in planning was strengthened by the successful completion of the first sets of 1962 models; and the planning models for 1963 were ambitiously and somewhat prematurely described as designed to "practically implement the construction of the State Plan" by such economists in positions of authority as L. Gatovskii, chief editor of *Voprosy ekonomiki,* and N. Kovalev, director of the Computer Center of Gosplan.[59] Discussion of input-output techniques appeared in several elementary texts on statistics and planning, and the uninitiated reader could easily have believed that input-output analysis had been an integral tool of Soviet planning for some time.[60]

Unfortunately, less and less information is being made available, and we have only glimpses of the planning models constructed for 1963 and later. Two separate planning tables in physical units were constructed for 1963—one showed 372 and the second 435 products.[61] There is also a brief reference to the construction of a planning table in value terms; but there is no further mention of it and no evidence that it was ever completed.[62] Contrary to the expectations

59. Gatovskii and Kovalev, 1962, p. 45.
60. Malyi, 1963, pp. 360–62; Breev, 1963, pp. 100–09.
61. Kovalev, 1963, pp. 76–77.
62. "Stroitel'stvo kommunisma," 1962, p. 4.

of the framers of planning balances, the two 1963 models in physical terms were not integrated with the 1963 state plan; and soon after the completion of the tables the adjective "experimental" was used again. The Main Computer Center of Gosplan followed with another experimental planning model for 1964–65, showing 438 products.

Completion of a planning input-output model in value terms for the terminal year of the next (1966–70) five-year plan has been recently reported. The table shows some 125 sectors,[63] and there is some evidence that labor and capital input coefficients are being prepared for this model. For the first time since the beginning of experiments with input-output techniques, the framers of the model considered alternative final demand mixes. According to one report, the model generated 20 alternative bills of final goods, subject to projected labor and capital capacity constraints. Two versions were chosen, "reflecting the politico-economic goals of the next five-year period." [64] The Main Computer Center of Gosplan is in the process of preparing a parallel planning model for 1970, with some 600 commodities expressed in physical units.[65]

To what extent the input-output exercises and the two 1970 planning models will be used to implement the preparation of the state plans is, of course, difficult to say, but discussion in the professional literature leads one to believe that all the exercises are still essentially experimental.

## PROSPECTS AND PROBLEMS

Impressive as the efforts and accomplishments of the advocates of new techniques may be, the fact remains that

63. The exact number of sectors has not been determined yet, and different authors give different numbers ranging from 124 to 130. Efimov, 1964, pp. 16–20; Klinskii, 1964, pp. 92–93; Shatalin, 1965, pp. 25–26; Shvyrkov, 1965, p. 16.

64. Klinskii, 1964, pp. 92–93.

65. Dudkin and Ershov, 1965, p. 60.

after eight to nine years of experimentation and exploration, after construction of two large ex-post, nine large
planning, and twenty-three regional tables, input-output
techniques have neither replaced the planning apparatus nor
been integrated with it. It is probably safe to conclude that
by now most ideological obstacles have been overcome, that
the shortage of cadres of mathematically trained economists
has been somewhat alleviated, and that Soviet computer
hardware and data processing facilities have improved.
Nevertheless, as both the advocates and the opponents of
the new techniques testify, "input-output analysis remains
in an experimental stage." [66] In a searching paper, Iu. I.
Cherniak, a prominent input-output specialist, summarizing
Soviet input-output studies, regretfully notes that so far the
new methods have not found concrete applications in
planning and calls for a "completely new interpretation of
input-output techniques." [67] This disappointment echoes
the general frustration being expressed with increasing frequency by Soviet advocates of the application of mathematical techniques in planning.

At an important policymaking conference of the Scientific
Council on Applications of Mathematics and Computers in
Economics and Planning of the Academy of Sciences of the
U.S.S.R. held in October 1963, the record of construction
and experience with ex-post and planning models was carefully evaluated. The numerous and far-reaching empirical
and theoretical studies reported at the conference point to a
continuing and intensive interest in input-output techniques. At the same time, the summary of the proceedings

66. Modin, 1964, p. 112. V. D. Belkin notes that "input-output techniques have been sufficiently perfected but are not being used in actual
planning," "Koordinatsionnoe soveshchanie," 1963, p. 112. A veteran
planner, director of the Institute of Norms of Gosplan, and one of the
chief spokesmen of "dogmatists," M. Z. Bor, recently commented on
"the paucity of results of input-output studies" and criticized the
planning input-output exercises for methodological errors. Bor, 1963, p.
5, and 1964, p. 116.

67. Cherniak, 1964, pp. 190–91.

regretfully notes that "several important problems in the field of practical applications of mathematical methods in planning remain unresolved." An illustration of the type and magnitude of these problems is provided in the same report. When the problem of price determination in the context of mathematically formulated planning models was raised at the conference, two irreconcilable positions emerged. One group of participants suggested that prices would be generated in the process of constructing the optimal plan and that therefore there was no need for an independent price formation formula. The second position was that determination of prices reflecting both the "value" and the "demand" side must precede rather than follow the formulation of the plan.[68]

We may now examine some of the difficulties which have so far prevented direct implementation of planning by input-output techniques. It should be stressed, however, that at least some of these difficulties are not uniquely related to the input-output framework but have a much larger scope.

As correctly foreseen by Herbert Levine, one of the controversial issues in the discussion of the adaptability of input-output techniques has become the point of departure in drawing up the plan.[69] As noted above, the traditional Soviet method of planning consists in extrapolation of growth rates of gross output levels in key industries and sectors, with most elements of the net product being determined as a residual after all interindustry requirements have been met.[70] This method is not inconsistent with the

68. "Plenum nauchnogo soveta," 1964, pp. 151–52.

69. Levine, 1959, pp. 171–73.

70. One author describes the situation as follows: "at present planning in the U.S.S.R. is based on measures of gross output without due considerations for requirements of final consumption of the society. Gross output levels of steel, fuel, power were used as points of departure in construction of plans and these were not balanced with planning of levels of final output or national income. Plans for expansion of output of different industries were often based on past records without considerations of society's needs." Shatalin, 1965, p. 23.

usual manipulations of input-output models.[71] However, most, if not all, Soviet specialists insist on reversing this procedure—national income levels (subject to given resource constraints) are determined first, and gross output levels are calculated as a product of the vector of national income levels and the inverse of the technology matrix.[72] The opponents of the new methods consider it a "major methodological sin" to start planning with the net product.[73] From defenses offered by advocates of the new methods, we can conclude that they are being accused of a "consumption-oriented approach" and of supporting techniques that would lead to retardation of economic growth.[74] One is led to believe, therefore, that the issue does go beyond the purely technical aspects of the problem and touches upon the basic conflict of the traditional growth orientation of the Soviet system and the gradually emerging emphasis on consumption.[75]

71. Lange, 1959, p. 226. N. I. Kovalev correctly suggests the feasibility of three alternative approaches: construction of the plan starting with gross output levels as it is now practiced in the U.S.S.R.; starting with net product levels and deriving the vector of gross output levels as the product of the final demand vector and the technology matrix; finally, a combination of the two methods whereby some sectors would be planned starting with gross and some starting with net product levels. Kovalev, 1964, pp. 196–97.

72. Berri and Efimov, 1960, pp. 38–39; Aganbegian and Belkin, 1961, pp. 13–14; Nemchinov, 1962b, p. 23; "Ekonomisty i matematiki," 1964, p. 102; Shatalin, 1965, p. 23.

73. Iu. A. Kronrod in the discussion reported in *Trudy*, 1961–62, *1*, 179. On a recent occasion he spoke of "the hopelessness of exogenous determination of final consumption levels" (Kronrod, 1965, p. 14). M. Z. Bor, in a critical review of input-output techniques, also rejects planning starting with national income and stresses the primacy of production over consumption (Bor, 1964, p. 118).

74. Berri, Klotsvog, and Shatalin, 1962b, p. 42; Arzumanian, 1964a, p. 3.

75. Even greater difficulties loom ahead. In the first comprehensive discussion of a dynamic input-output model, A. D. Smirnov indicates that the only rational exogenously determined vector of the model is

But even if consumption were to be upgraded on the planners' priority scale, the difficulties inherent in the new approach would not be immediately resolved. A crucial question would be whether, in the absence of consumer sovereignty, the Soviet political leadership would be willing to commit itself to a national priority scale and, if so, how this preference scale would be transmitted.[76] A prominent Hungarian statistician, Gy. Cukor, at the 1961 Budapest Conference on Input-Output Analysis recognized the preference of proponents of input-output analysis for planning that starts with national income levels; but he pointed out that the neglected problem in this issue is how to plan final demand, a problem on which input-output analysis offers no help.[77]

Demand theory has been long neglected in the Soviet Union. The very concepts of a utility function and of price and income elasticities of demand have been rejected as basically alien to Soviet economics. To be sure, the general revival of Soviet economic science has finally touched even upon this area. For instance, in a new volume, *Economic Models and Theoretical Problems of Consumption*, highly interesting papers on consumer's utility by Nemchinov and Volkonskii appear alongside Eugene Slutsky's 1915 pioneering paper, which has finally been translated into Russian.[78]

---

consumption constrained by investment (Smirnov, 1964, pp. 104-12). Needless to say, this unequivocal balancing of consumption versus growth would be unpalatable to the Party.

76. Montias, 1964, p. 174.

77. Cukor, 1962, pp. 135-36.

78. Vainshtein, 1963. Eugene E. Slutsky's paper, "Sulla teoria del bilancio del consumatore," published originally in Italian in *Giornale degli economistie e revista di statistica*, No. 1 (1915), was rediscovered in the early 1930s by J. R. Hicks (*Value and Capital*, 2d ed. Oxford, 1946, p. 19). Slutsky's paper represents a further extension of the ordinal utility approach to problems of consumer's choice and constrained maximization of consumer's utility. Until now the paper has been completely ignored in the U.S.S.R.

Two alternative approaches seem to be emerging at the present time. G. M. Geller, speaking at the November 1961 Conference on Applications of Mathematics in Economics, submitted that planning of food consumption could be based either on a set of "normatives" or on statistical studies of actual consumption patterns. Geller rejected the latter approach because it reflects patterns determined by random forces and supported the method based on scientifically determined norms of an optimal food diet. The Nutrition Institute of the Academy of Medical Sciences of the U.S.S.R. worked out an optimal diet for 1965 differentiated for regional differences, age distribution, and three basic income groups.[79]

But the "statistical approach" finds more and more supporters. In the volume referred to above, Volkonskii advances the "revealed preferences" approach, suggesting that the "only reliable objective expression of consumers' preferences is to be found in the market behavior of consumers themselves." V. F. Pugachev, addressing himself to the problem of the optimality criterion, constructs an objective function weighted by consumers' and the state's preferences and supports Volkonskii's revealed preferences approach. A novel aspect in Pugachev's welfare function is explicit recognition of the time element and a suggested discounting of the utility of future consumption.[80] However, the discussion is still very abstract and is essentially restricted to academic circles. Even among academicians a consensus is far from realization. For instance, a prominent statistician who actually pioneered in the study of consumer demand in the U.S.S.R., Professor P. P. Maslov, was highly critical of the Volkonskii and Pugachev papers referred to above and censured the authors of the volume for uncritical acceptance

79. "Koordinatsionnoe soveshchanie," 1962, pp. 79–80.
80. Volkonskii, 1963, pp. 210–40; Pugachev, 1963b, pp. 63–106. For a more extensive discussion of Pugachev's welfare function see Chapter 4.

of bourgeois theories of consumption.[81] But even were the academicians to agree on what constitutes consumer's utility, the necessary reorientation of planning practitioners could be expected to be a prolonged and painful process.

Another important factor that impairs the development of more rigorous control techniques and particularly the adoption of input-output methods to planning has to do with the organization, availability, and processing of economic information in the U.S.S.R.[82] By now virtually everybody even remotely concerned with planning reforms, the use of mathematical techniques in economic analysis, or input-output studies is on record with demands for complete revision of the present system of information.[83] Soviet statistical and planning agencies process a mass of data—a total of about 40 billion bits of economic information are handled monthly and the volume is expected to increase 1.5 times in the next 10 years.[84] However, as some of the most prominent specialists in this field recently testified, the rate of utilization of this information is very low.[85] The avail-

81. "Ekonomisty i matematiki," 1964, p. 90. Maslov also questions the applicability of the concept of income elasticity of demand in a socialist economy. Leifman, 1963, pp. 293–94.

82. For a more detailed description of the Soviet system of information see Chapter 1.

83. Nemchinov, 1962a, p. 5; L. V. Kantorovich as reported in "Obshchee sobranie," 1964, p. 76; Modin, 1964, p. 112; Efimov, 1963, p. 19; Kovalev, 1963, p. 110; Gatovskii and Kovalev, 1962, pp. 42–43.

84. Kozlov, 1962, p. 8.

85. Academician N. P. Fedorenko, director of the Central Institute of Mathematical Economics of the Academy of Sciences, describes the situation as follows: "The existing system of economic information, methods of collection, transmission, and processing of data can only approximately insure construction of a balanced plan in aggregate terms. The basis of this information is provided by data collected by the Central Statistical Administration and data obtained by innumerable telephone calls and conferences of planning and control agencies. Not more than 10 percent of these data, collected belatedly, is used in planning and administration." ("O rabote instituta," 1964, p. 6.) N. I. Kovalev, director of the Main Computer Center of Gosplan, similarly

able information is deficient in more than one respect: the data in physical units and in value terms are not strictly comparable; definitions of gross output, especially the intrabranch and intraplant components, differ from industry to industry; conversions from constant to current prices cannot be done simply by price indexes but necessitate costly recalculations; commodity classification systems are haphazard. A fundamental problem is generated by classificational and definitional discrepancies among data collected and used by Gosplan, the Central Statistical Administration, the Council of National Economy (Soviet Narodnogo Khoziaistva), and agencies of the Ministry of Finance.[86] The shortcomings of the system are apparent. The Soviet information system is designed primarily for effective transmittal of command signals from above or for control purposes[87] and not for assisting managerial micro-decisions or multivariate analysis of the input-output type. Thus this problem extends beyond economics to the general question of the allocative efficiency of the system versus effective control from above. It is therefore not surprising that the available data could not have been employed in the construction of the two 1959 ex-post tables and that sampling surveys and independent estimates had to be used.

An important defect of the planning and census statistics for the purposes of input-output studies lies in the principle of organization of economic information which follows ad-

---

indicates a very low level of utilization of economic information. (Kovalev, 1964, p. 300.)

86. Drogichinskii, 1964, p. 221; Usatov, 1964, p. 6; Kovalev, 1964a, p. 304. Even within the same agency, such as Gosplan, different subdivisions and departments employ different and quite often unreconcilable systems of classifications. Shvyrkov, 1965, p. 13.

87. Campbell, 1963, p. 258. Campbell's position finds support in Eidel'man, an important functionary of the Central Statistical Administration, who notes that "the presently employed system of economic information is primarily designed for . . . control over plan fulfillment." Eidel'man, 1960, p. 66.

ministrative (enterprise) rather than commodity lines. Since input-output tables must be constructed in terms of sectors producing homogeneous products, this organizational feature of Soviet statistics necessitates the artificial creation of "pure" sectors with costly recalculations of available data.[88]

In recent years more and more attention has been focused on the study of cybernetics and related fields, and a vast data collection and processing system is on the drafting boards of the Institute of Cybernetics of the Academy of Sciences of the U.S.S.R. A new commodity classification system is being prepared by Gosplan and various research groups. An important feature of the new system being designed is that the prime criterion of classification is homogeneity of output and not the administrative lines of control. But the project is still in the drafting stage and progress is very slow.[89] Furthermore, Soviet planning and statistical methods are rather resilient. It will be recalled that we were told at the time of the 1957 reorganization and reform that this very feature of Soviet statistics, i.e. an administrative rather than a commodity basis for accounting, would be corrected, but the change was never put into effect.[90]

The successful introduction of a completely overhauled and revised system of economic information envisaged by Soviet specialists will be contingent, among other factors, on significant improvements in and enlargement of mechanized data processing capacity. In 1962 the Soviet Union had approximately 300,000 desk-type calculating machines and 5,000 sets of electronic, punched-card type data processing

88. Nemchinov, 1963a, p. 4. Some Soviet economists advocate reorganization of all planning indicators and statistical reporting along "pure-sector" lines: Eidel'man, 1963b, pp. 16–17; Shvyrkov, 1965, pp. 16–18. However, no agreement has been reached yet and others recommend retention of the present system and construction of input-output tables in two forms—on the basis of "pure" sectors and on the basis of administrative lines. Bor, 1964a, pp. 121–22.

89. Lalaianets, 1963, pp. 106–07.

90. Ezhov, 1960, p. 98.

equipment capable of handling not more than 25 percent of the total flow of economic information.[91]

Today, as in the past, the input-output specialists do not have readily available the data necessary for construction of flow and coefficient tables. As was described above, the direct material and labor input coefficients for the 1959 ex-post tables were obtained by direct sampling of industrial and construction enterprises. While the overall accuracy of the data so obtained is probably acceptable, there has been some criticism. M. R. Eidel'man, for instance, pointed out that the sampled enterprises did not base the reported data on actual information but estimated them. Major errors were subsequently discovered in the processing of the collected data.[92] The situation with input-output type data for planning models is similar—no directly available data exist, and planning coefficients are prepared on the basis of extensive and time-consuming studies. Soviet planning agencies continuously generate projected input coefficients for planning purposes, but these cannot be used in planning input-output tables. The *normativy* are based on projected technological process requirements, i.e. do not take into account material and other costs outside of productive shops. Coefficients used in input-output tables must reflect all requirements, and the difference between these and the *normativy* can be as great as 10–15 percent.[93]

A promising approach to the problem of data availability is being explored at the former Laboratory on Applications of Mathematical Methods in Economics of the Academy of Sciences of the U.S.S.R. The staff working on regional models bypassed the aggregate census and planning statistics and went directly to planning and accounting data of industrial enterprises. After several pilot studies they con-

91. Kovalev, 1964a, p. 352.

92. Eidel'man as reported in "Soveshchanie," 1962, pp. 117–18; Kovalev, 1964, p. 346.

93. Buzunov, 1964, pp. 26–27; Kovalev, 1964a, p. 199.

cluded that the *tekhpromfinplans* of individual enterprises contain all the data necessary for the construction of ex-post and planning input-output tables. The new method was tested in several regional studies, culminating in the construction of a 450 × 450 planning matrix for the Byelorussian Republic for 1963.[94] This method is different from the questionnaire sampling employed in the two 1959 ex-post national tables in the sense that it offers a direct link between operational planning documents at the enterprise level and the center preparing input-output tables. The *tekhpromfinplan,* or at least a part of it, is modified and transformed into a four-quadrant matrix or a small input-output table for the enterprise. The various subtotals and totals of this matrix are transmitted to planning agencies to be incorporated into the ex-post or planning input-output tables. However, as the proponents of the new method hastened to add, the present-day preparation of *tekhpromfinplans* leaves much to be desired: methodology differs from one branch to another, there is no uniformity of index construction and, furthermore, there is a substantial gap between individual *tekhpromfinplans* and industry or branch-wide operational planning.[95] Thus the application of the new method also has to wait for the promised revision and overhaul of the entire information system.

The problem of generation of input coefficient data, for both models in physical units and in value terms, is crucial. Soviet planning, statistical, and administrative agencies as well as manufacturing enterprises have long experience in estimating input requirements and have amassed substantial empirical data. The fact that the technical *normativy* used in current planning are not directly employable in input-output tables is only one part of the problem. Even the most ambitious proponents of input-output techniques

94. Linkun and Sokolovskii, 1963, p. 154; Polonskii and Ippa, 1963, p. 96.

95. Modin, 1964, p. 113 and 123; Cherniak, 1964, pp. 192–200.

do not envisage technology matrixes of larger order than 1000 × 1000, but the present Soviet planning system encompasses tens of thousands of products. Aggregation of input coefficients, whether obtained by sampling surveys or estimated on the basis of *tekhpromfinplan* data, will thus always be required. The problem, so far unresolved in Soviet literature, is the choice of weights for the necessary aggregation. As was pointed out above, an exercise with a planning input-output model starts with the preparation of a table of direct input coefficients, and at this stage the framers of the model do not have the vector of gross output levels which could be used as weights in aggregation. The use of previous-period weights will introduce some error into the aggregated coefficients.[96]

A separate problem facing the Soviet input-output specialists today is the dichotomy between models in value terms and models in physical units. Needless to say, construction of two tables simultaneously, be it of the ex-post or the ex-ante variety, is wasteful, but apparently no clear-cut case could be made for one type over the other. To date (excepting the pre-1959 pilot studies), a total of nine large tables have been constructed—three in value terms and six in physical units. Among the 23 regional models the picture is different—only two tables were constructed in terms of physical units. Parenthetically, we may note that with respect to national models, the Soviets differ from their Eastern colleagues: among the 20 tables constructed or in preparation in the Soviet bloc outside the Soviet Union, only three are in physical units. (See Table 2.)

The advantages, at least from the perspective of operational planning agencies, of working with input-output

---

96. A recent Soviet paper outlined an iterative procedure for deriving gross output weights needed for coefficient aggregation on the basis of projected net output (final demand) levels (Dudkin and Ershov, 1965, pp. 59–63). Needless to say, this is only a partial solution which rules out consideration of alternative bills of final demand.

models in physical units are clear. In the first place, this would represent a more or less painless modification of the time-honored method of material balances. The formulation of direct material input coefficients either for ex-post or for planning models should also be relatively easy.[97] The results of various manipulations of the matrix would be easy to translate into output targets, supply and distribution quotas, shipping orders, etc., none of which would drastically depart from the currently used planning methods. Lastly, the greatest advantage of models in physical units is that they would avoid all deficiencies, shortcomings, and unresolved difficulties of operating with Soviet price data.

The most important limitation of models in physical units is that they cannot cover the entire range of commodities produced in the economy. The Soviet ex-post and planning models constructed so far have covered from 60 to 85 percent of the gross social product (Soviet definition).[98] But to achieve even this level the framers of input-output tables have had to resort to measuring some flows of heterogeneous commodities in value terms. In the 1959 table in physical units, 12 out of 181 positions were in value terms, but they comprised from 6 to 7.5 percent of the gross industrial product.[99] The impossibility of having

97. The ease of preparation of direct input coefficients for models in physical units should not, however, be overstressed. The 435-product 1963 planning model had 13,000 nonzero coefficients which were estimated on the basis of 18,000 material balances specially prepared for this purpose. For estimates of direct input coefficients of fuels and lubricants in agricultural production, special maps showing distribution and technology of production of 32 agricultural basic cultures (and 42 products) had to be prepared. Kovalev, 1963, pp. 76–77, and 1964, pp. 201–02.

98. The lower figure of the range is estimated. See also Kovalev, 1963, p. 79, and 1964, p. 198.

99. My estimate on the basis of the original commodity classification list used in the sampling survey. *Forms and Instructions*, 1959. The actual table was prepared in a somewhat aggregated form with 157

complete coverage leads to possible distortions in the model. As some Soviet specialists point out, the reduced coverage results in understatement of the "true" full input coefficients (elements of the inverse of the technology matrix).[100] Faced by this problem, the Soviet framers of tables have continued to enlarge the matrix, going from 157 commodities in the 1959 ex-post table to 438 in the 1964–65 planning table. Needless to say, there is a limit to the size of the matrix; one Soviet author suggests that 800 × 800 is the largest matrix that can be handled by domestic computers.[101] The fact that models in physical units cannot show value-added elements or the generation and redistribution of national income, and cannot be used for overall balancing of flows, adds to their limitations.

One can conjecture that the emphasis placed on these models has been essentially a matter of expediency. Faced with an increasing lack of consistency in material balances, Gosplan has been anxious to explore new methods which could conceivably bring a degree of coherence into planning of material supplies.

Theoretically, input-output models in value terms integrated with national income accounts would appear to be superior to models in physical units. In practice, however, the hybrid nature of the Soviet price system severely limits the usefulness of models in value terms. The shortcomings of the Soviet price system, now frankly admitted and discussed by Soviet economists, need no enumeration here.[102]

---

commodities. The percentage coverage of the gross industrial product has been estimated on the basis of comparable sectors in the 1959 table in purchasers' prices. There is a discrepancy in Soviet literature, and we do not know what type of prices were used for aggregated sectors in the 1959 table in physical terms. V. S. Nemchinov indicates the use of constant 1955 prices in one paper (Nemchinov, 1963b, p. 178) and the use of purchasers' prices in another paper (Nemchinov, 1962c, p. 70).

100. Aganbegian and Belkin, 1961, pp. 55–57.

101. Shvyrkov, 1962, p. 36.

102. Bornstein, 1964.

The quest for a more rational price system continues unabated, but no resolution of the problem of "the law of value and price formation" is in sight. If anything, the liberalization of the academic debate observed in recent years has led to more divergent positions.

The purest case of prices generated as indexes of relative scarcity—Kantorovich's "objectively determined valuations" —is finding more and more support among academic economists but is adamantly opposed by the older, more dogmatic school and by such ideological watchdogs of the profession as Gatovskii.[103] Perhaps the award of the coveted Lenin Prize in Science to Kantorovich, Novozhilov, and Nemchinov (posthumously) in the spring of 1965 signifies an important turning point in the debate.[104] But we must realize that even unreserved acceptance of the price formation model advocated by these three would constitute, at best, an important breakthrough in official Soviet economic doctrine, and the actual implementation of the proposals will take considerable time. Realizing this, the younger, mathematically oriented economists lend equal support to a more operationally feasible concept of "production price," i.e. price based on average cost plus a uniform charge on fixed and revolving capital. In a recently published book,

103. "Ekonomisty i matematiki," 1964, p. 110. The members of the older school such as L. Gatovskii, A. Boiarskii, A. Kats, P. Mstislavskii, and M. Kolganov reject Kantorovich's "objectively determined valuations" essentially for two reasons. Firstly, Kantorovich's prices are formed at the margin and thus the theory is formally akin to the concepts of "vulgar bourgeois marginalism." Secondly, his prices are clearly determined by interaction of supply and demand, which makes the process of price generation incongruous with the operations of central planning. For the assessment of criticism of the older school, see Novozhilov, 1963, pp. 107–27.

104. The award of the prize is more than symbolic. Kantorovich, Novozhilov, and Nemchinov were the only economists among some 900 scientists nominated for the Lenin Prize. In the discussion of the nominations sponsored by the editors of *Ekonomicheskaia gazeta,* criticism centered almost exclusively on Kantorovich's "objectively determined valuations." "Za i protiv," 1965, pp. 9–10.

appropriately entitled *Prices of Uniform Levels and Economic Calculations Based Upon Them*, V. D. Belkin uses input-output techniques to illustrate and analyze alternative models of price formation and to show distortions introduced by other than "production price" prices.[105] However, the Belkin-proposed price reform model drew an immediate negative response from A. Komin, a Gosplan functionary engaged in actual price setting.[106]

The 1959 ex-post table in value terms, used in conjunction with the table of labor flows, was employed in the analysis of shortcomings of the Soviet price system, and the results have reportedly been used to implement the ongoing revision of wholesale industrial prices.[107] The results of this study have never been published, but we can form some idea of the methodology from the following illustration. It is a well-known proposition that, in a system in which labor is the only constraint on production, a vector of relative equilibrium prices would be proportional to the vector of "full" labor input coefficients,[108] or

$$t = c(I - A)^{-1}$$

where c is the row vector of direct labor input coefficients expressed in labor-time per unit of gross output; t is the row vector of "full" labor input coefficients tracing all direct and indirect labor requirements; and $(I - A)^{-1}$ is the Leontief inverse of the matrix of direct material coefficients A. If we were to take this vector of ideal "labor only" prices and use it to transform the original input-output table in physical units into a table in value terms, then all elements of the vector of "full" labor input coefficients would

105. Belkin, 1963, pp. 50–134.

106. Komin, 1964, pp. 31–33. Komin raises the question of feasibility of calculations of "tens of thousands" of prices on the basis of a limited number of prices generated in an input-output model.

107. M. R. Eidel'man as reported in "Soveshchanie," 1962, p. 117; Berg, 1962, p. 2.

108. See, for example, Chenery and Clark, 1959, pp. 60–61.

be equal to unity (that is, the equilibrium price in terms of labor units per labor unit value of a product would equal one for all products in the system).

Making use of this proposition the staff of the Economic Research Institute of Gosplan examined the divergence of actual prices from "true values" by measuring the dispersion of actual "full" labor coefficients. In an ideal case with labor being the only scarce resource and prices reflecting only direct and embodied labor, all "full" labor coefficients per ruble of output would be identical. Not surprisingly, the discovered dispersion was rather substantial. Taking the weighted average as 100, the actual "full" labor input coefficients ranged from 33 for the gas industry to 198 for animal husbandry.[109] If the entrenchment of the Marxian labor theory of value is as strong as illustrated in this approach, it is doubtful that a meaningful revision of prices can be achieved on the basis of input-output tables.

What is happening has been predicted before. Eidel'man, discussing the 1959 table in value terms, suggested that it should be employed in an analysis of the price system and as an aid in an empirical model of price formation. But as he noted, the economic profession must first agree on the mode of price formation.[110]

As could be expected the actual revision of Soviet prices has fared no better than the theoretical debate on price formation. The July 1960 plenary session of the Central Committee requested "a revision of wholesale producer goods prices to insure full reflection of costs of production" to be completed in the 1961–62 period. Gosplan and the Ministry of Finance of the U.S.S.R. followed through in October 1961 with a detailed set of instructions for revising wholesale prices and freight rates.[111] The reform is

109. Belousov, 1963, pp. 68–70.
110. Eidel'man, 1961b, p. 61.
111. *Plenum Tsentral'nogo Komiteta*, 1961, p. 326; Maizenberg, 1961, p. 42.

proceeding very slowly; publication of new price catalogues is continuously postponed, and some observers recently suggested that at best it would be completed in 1966 (though in fact it was not).[112] But the reform is under way and the new price catalogues are almost complete. Of course this is disappointing to advocates of a radical change in the Soviet price system. The new prices, while adjusted for certain structural changes, will probably retain most attributes of the old price system.

In the context of input-output analysis, the presently used hybrid price system poses some additional problems. The turnover tax is highly differentiated for various groups of consumers, and hence the actual commodity flows are substantially distorted in an input-output table expressed in terms of purchasers' prices. The three basic Soviet distribution systems, i.e. wholesale and retail consumer trade, the intraindustry supply and distribution system, and the system of procurement of agricultural products, have different markup margins, which again would lead to distortions of actual flows in a table expressed in purchasers' prices. The use of purchasers' prices will pose additional complications in the context of interregional input-output tables, construction of which is envisaged for the future. At present about 70 percent of all consumer goods (mainly foodstuffs) prices are differentiated by geographic regions.[113] This means that regional input-output tables prepared in terms of average regional purchasers' prices cannot be brought together into interregional tables without distortions of actual flows. The use of purchasers' prices also in-

112. Il'iushin and Rutenburg, 1965, p. 58.

113. The system is rather complex. Essentially there are three "price belts," but the geographic definition of a belt differs for different commodities. Thus the Byelorussian Republic is classified with Belt I for meat products and with Belt II for wines. Compared with average Belt I prices, Belt II prices are higher by 8–10 percent and Belt II prices are higher by 16–18 percent. Bauman and Tolkushin, 1965, pp. 31–33; Riauzov and Titel'baum, 1961, pp. 182–84.

creases the possible instability of input coefficients; changes in the latter reflect not only changing technology and changes in the output mix of aggregated sectors, but changing patterns of distribution and the incidence of commodity taxes. Under the circumstances, the use of producers' prices would be clearly preferable but, as was pointed out above, collection of the necessary flow and coefficient data in terms of producers' prices is very difficult if not impossible.[114]

An equally difficult problem is that of current versus constant prices. As noted above, the 1959 ex-post input-output tables and the subsequent planning tables in value terms have been prepared in current prices. This precludes any comparison and collation of tables over time and also makes the tables not directly comparable or translatable into planning data, which are expressed in constant prices. Because of sector aggregation, changing commodity mix within given sectors, and again because of the use of purchasers' prices, recalculation of tables from current into constant prices poses almost unsurmountable difficulties. The only solution to this problem offered so far has been to construct tables simultaneously in current and constant prices, with both types of data obtained directly from individual enterprises.[115]

We have covered only the major problems that have so far prevented successful integration of input-output techniques and planning. Additional difficulties loom ahead. We could mention the inadequacy of Soviet capital capacity data and the shortcomings of depreciation accounting which would reduce the usefulness of a capital capacity

114. In this respect, an additional problem lies in the fact that for some Soviet industries "pure" producers' prices are not available at all. In such industries as ferrous metals, petroleum products, lumber, or glass, price catalogues list wholesale enterprise prices (i.e. producers' prices) f.o.b. point of destination.

115. Eidel'man, 1963b, p. 24.

vector in a static model. Similarly, the present-day calculations of effectiveness of capital investment and the shortcomings of the available data on incremental capital-output ratios would handicap preparation of dynamic input-output models.

The problems discussed here are in most instances uniquely Soviet in the current institutional setting of the Soviet economic system. But we should not forget other general limitations inherent in input-output analysis, such as the possible distortions introduced by aggregation, implications of the linearity assumption, treatment of joint products, and others.

A fascinating aspect of the Soviet involvement with input-output analysis, not discussed in this paper, is found in what we may call the "feedback effects" of explorations of rigorous mathematical models. There is sufficient evidence to suggest that some of the most sacrosanct postulates of Marxian dogma (or, to be exact, of the traditional Soviet interpretation of it) are being successfully challenged in the context of Soviet input-output studies. The adaptation of input-output techniques to the needs of central planning has produced no results so far, but the mere fact that the two were found to be incongruous led to examination of planning techniques and accelerated demands for reform.

In conclusion, we may suggest that a substantial gap exists between the potential use of input-output techniques and actual opportunities to apply them. The Soviet economic profession, gradually and hesitantly, does seem to be approaching some solutions, and the pace of the search is accelerating. But unless and until Soviet economists find the solutions to the problems outlined above, and unless these solutions are accepted by the political leadership, input-output techniques will remain on the fringes of the planning apparatus.

## COMMENTS

### Abraham S. Becker

"Socialism is calculation," Lenin is reported to have said. Having recently discovered the primacy of economics over politics in the current stage of development, the Soviet Union is eager to calculate. But how? To Lenin on the eve of the seizure of power, it appeared a simple thing, a task for clerks. Whatever else they may dispute, the present generation of Soviet planners is in accord on the complexity of the task. Many of them would probably also concur in the judgment on the existing system rendered by the Czech economist Josef Goldmann: "The higher the level of economic development already attained, the more complex the process of extended socialist reproduction, the more outdated necessarily will become the traditional system with its detailed output targets, centrally determined and compulsorily imposed, and its corresponding technique of factor allocation." [1]

Vladimir Treml has provided an insightful report on the history and present state of the reform effort in input-output techniques. After all the research already done, he asks, why has input-output not been integrated into the planning apparatus? His conclusion is that application of input-output techniques has been hindered by systemic barriers.

The comments to follow bypass the history of input-output studies in the Soviet Union, as there is little to add to Treml's cogent account. Instead, expanding a bit on his perceptive critique, my remarks are addressed to the present state of affairs and the conditions for future development. The scope of these observations ranges somewhat

1. Goldmann, 1964, p. 88.

Views expressed in this paper are my own. They should not be interpreted as reflecting the views of the RAND Corporation or the official opinion or policy of any of its governmental or private research sponsors.

beyond the narrow focus of input-output, but, as will presently be indicated, it is doubtful that the future of input-
output can be discussed apart from the fate of mathematical
economic planning in general.

This is not to say that more proximate reasons cannot
be found for the detention of input-output in the stage
of experimentation. Treml mentions a number of trouble
spots—among others, quantitative and qualitative gaps in
the availability of computers, mathematicians, and programmers, as well as the universally recognized defects of
the current information system. Given the enormous cost
of input-output tables based on the existing information
system, it would not be surprising if adoption of input-
output were held up pending an information reform alone.[2]
Academician Fedorenko put it bluntly: "The radical rationalization of the system of economic information is the
necessary precondition for the effective penetration of computer technology."[3] I have little to add other than to indicate possible institutional rivalries among the new emerging forces in mathematical economics as an additional
obstacle to progress.[4] But even if these obstacles were sud-
denly overcome, the role of input-output in Soviet planning
would yet be difficult to foresee.

## THE PREDICAMENT OF SOVIET PLANNING

To set the framework for the discussion it may be helpful to take a preliminary overview of Soviet planning. Obvi-

2. The fact that several hundred research and project-making institutions are said to have been involved in the elaboration of the
1970 input-output tables is itself a reflection of both the difficulties and
the costliness of such studies under present conditions (Gusev, 1964, p.
100). For a recent analysis of aggregation problems posed by the supply
system and its accompanying norms, see Dudkin and Ershov, 1965.

3. Fedorenko, 1965, p. 2.

4. There seems to be an overtone of jealousy regarding the "empire"
of the new Central Economic Mathematical Institute of the Academy
of Sciences expressed in "O rabote instituta," 1964, pp. 12–13.

ously we follow here along a beaten path, but the short detour may aid in charting less familiar territory later.

A central concern of Soviet planning has been to infuse local execution with central purpose and motivation. The dichotomy between the goals of the directing force and the translation into action reflects a number of breaks in the chain:

1. The center may have a reasonably clear vision of the goal and the path by which it is to be attained, but both differ from that for which much of the society would opt. Hence the regime's preferred path must be maintained forcibly and there are obvious incentives to stray therefrom. This is a classical problem of Soviet society. In the contemporary setting, it is exemplified in such phenomena as the short-circuiting of resources from central to local purposes and illegal private enterprise.

2. Even if the center knew what it wanted, the instruments at hand would prevent the smooth execution of its will. For reasons minutely dissected in recent years, the planning and management system is frequently out of step with the leadership or tripping over its own cumbersome bulk.

3. The center itself may be uncertain of its goals and transmits its own hesitations to the system.

The relationship between economic ends and planning means may be clarified by a pair of distinctions—first, between consistency and efficiency-cum-optimality of an output program, and second, between planning algorithms and perspectives. We recognize the existence of processes in Soviet short-run planning which, at least in principle (although frequently and possibly increasingly not in practice), are capable of yielding consistent output programs—consistent in the sense of a balanced input-output transactions table. Soviet writers candidly concede that even a consistent output program is unlikely to be efficient, in the sense of location on the economy's production frontier. As to optimality, no one is sure yet just what the criterion should be.

The second distinction is closely related to the first. The theoretical attainability of consistency is the result of the existence of a planning algorithm in the method of material balances. But for determination of resource allocation, Soviet planning has had nothing but a set of perspectives. Now the relatively simple priorities scheme of Stalinism is obsolete, and the emperor's clothes of "economic laws of socialism," which in an uncritical age dressed up this scheme, evokes increasing embarrassment. As the Stalinist perspectives have been found wanting, a search has begun for replacements. To a considerable extent, this has taken the form of exploration of mathematical models.

The search for the elusive goals is also bound up with the perennial problem of securing their realization. The central dilemma of Soviet economic organization has been, and still is, centralization versus local autonomy. Does the union of computer and mathematical model imply inexorably complete centralization? Can it be achieved and at what cost? Alternatively, is greater local initiative, with all its advantages in easing the burden of bureaucracy, compatible with central purpose?

In this setting, what is the role of input-output to be? Merely an improved tool for the attainment of consistent output targets, or possibly also a means to clarifying and attaining higher-order objectives? In what form of economic organization must it be imbedded, and does its function in planning change with the economic system itself?

### THE STARTING POINT OF PLAN MODELS

"The crucial problem," says Treml, "is and has been the point of departure in drawing up state plans." To begin with the technical point, it is undoubtedly clear to all the participants in the Soviet debate that an input-output plan model may begin with final demand, *or* gross outputs, *or* a combination of the two. The controversy, such as it is, must be over substance.

What explains the fervor of the appeal to and from final demand? Treml alludes to the charges of consumptionism leveled at proponents of final demand. The charge is manifestly untrue, if being a consumptionist means favoring a slow rate of growth of investment and output. But if the final demand school is not consumptionist, it does wish to see the consumer accorded more than a residual crumb from the allocation table. In theory, one could assure consumption its "fair" share even when starting from gross output, by rejecting output targets that generate less than adequate consumption flows. This is cumbersome, and one runs the risk of tiring of the exercise short of the desired basket. Moreover, if a criterion of adequacy already exists, why not begin by stipulating a bill of consumption goods?

Indeed, although the defenders of final demand occasionally refer to the charge, it is difficult to find an actual example of such criticism in the published literature of recent years. The few available defenses of gross output as the starting point focus instead on the difficulty of estimating final demand and on the presumed importance of the relation between Departments I and II of the social product, a relation obtainable only from gross output.[5]

It is precisely this old-line argument—the necessity for keeping the two-sector relation in center stage—that has convinced many of the advisability of beginning from final demand. The operational guidance to be derived from the "law" of the faster growth of Department I than of Department II appears increasingly doubtful. In consequence, focus on the two-sector relation must appear to many to have obscured the whole issue of balance and optimality.[6]

5. Bor, 1964a, pp. 72, 118; Kronrod, 1965, pp. 13–15. A. P. Bechin is a great believer in final product as an analytical category but not in planning from final demand. Bechin, 1964 and 1965, pp. 46–47.

6. Efimov, 1964, p. 14.

As one academic group of Soviet writers put it, appropriate structural analysis has been delayed by making a fetish of the role of balances.[7] It is coming to be recognized that all notions of efficiency in the use of resources are wide of the mark if they do not get at what it costs to obtain what you want.[8] As regards the latter, it seems to be clear (at least to the scholars and perhaps even to many policy-makers) that steel, coal, and cement are intermediate products even in a nonconsumer-oriented society. Final demand planning would then have the additional, heuristic advantage of forcing planners and policymakers to face up to the problem of objectives.[9]

The veteran planner M. Z. Bor denies the possibility of stipulating final demand: "There is not and cannot be ex-ante a given commodity structure of the utilization of national income. In the final analysis, that structure is a product of the level and structure of production." [10] Whatever may be said about the problem of stipulating final demand, it seems clear that Soviet policymakers are disenchanted with the existing methods of setting production levels. One of the basic themes of the discussion surrounding the preparation of the 1964–65 plan and now of the next five-year plan is the necessity to plan other than on the basis of "inherited proportions." Khrushchev proposed an alternative criterion, that of "progressive branches," with chemicals as his case in point. Kosygin's speech on the draft five-year plan is equally concerned with pushing "progressive branches." [11] It seems inherently difficult to plan a "progressive" structure starting from gross outputs.

In the optimizing models that are presently being put

7. Leont'ev, Mukasian, and Kanygin, 1964, pp. 23–24.

8. Gromov, 1964, pp. 65, 74.

9. This is not to dispute the fact that some devotees of final demand planning continue to emphasize the importance of the Department I–Department II relation. For example, see Shatalin, 1965, pp. 22–24.

10. Bor, 1964a, p. 118.

11. Kosygin, 1965.

forward as part of the national economic cybernetics program (on which more presently), final demand is the starting point. "Noneconomic needs," in Glushkov and Fedorenko's phrase, are to be set by the "competent bodies," who will also stipulate the trade-off between present and future consumption.[12]

If final demand, or part of it, is to be stipulated, some of the most intriguing questions relate to the consumption bill of goods. Treml takes note of the yet undeveloped state of empirical research in the U.S.S.R. on consumer demand and of the existence of a second strand of consumption theory—"scientific norms" of consumption. Several years ago a review of the discussion on stipulation of consumption levels showed little on the horizon *but* "scientific norms." [13] However, life demonstrated, as the Russians are fond of saying, that that was unnecessarily restrictive. Norms are still to be one of the sources for construction of the consumption vector.[14] Nevertheless, the theoretical case for consumption plans based on household market behavior has been stated with increasing boldness.[15] More importantly, the recent transfer of parts of light industry to planning on the basis of direct ties with suppliers and retail outlets appears to have rendered at least some of the scientific norm research obsolete. How far these arrangements will be carried is, of course, another matter, to which we will return shortly.

The problem of supply organization brings us back to the opponents of final demand planning. Although the objection has not been explicitly framed, it may be that fear of the abolition of the administrative system of intermediate goods supply lies at the core of the opposition.

12. Glushkov and Fedorenko, 1964, pp. 90–91.
13. Becker, 1963, pp. 12–13.
14. Pugachev, 1964, p. 95.
15. Vainshtein, 1963. See also the review of papers by Dudkin and Girsanov in Montias, 1964, pp. 172–74.

The moment the demand for intermediate goods is derived from final demand in an activity model, the raison d'être of the whole system of material balances, along with the existing administrative supply system, comes into question. The necessity for a quasi-market rather than administrative organization of supply has been pushed most notably by Nemchinov.[16] The forcefulness of the opposition[17] may reflect a real fear that the control over resource allocation would thereby slip away.

## THE NATIONAL CYBERNETICS PROGRAM

Thus, if the controversy over the starting point of plan models is partly to blame for the retarded development of input-output, it is not so much on account of direct fears of consumptionism as over the larger issue of control of the economy and formulation of its objectives. This larger issue is a more significant aspect of the discussion on programming models that have come to occupy a greater share of attention.

Indeed, in the last few years there appears to have been a subtle shift in the role of input-output in the general discussion of Soviet planning. The centrality of both input-output and the macro-balance problem to which it is a solution appear diminished in favor of growing attention to micro-planning, macro-optimality, and the interrelations of the two. Soviet literature on mathematical applications to national planning has been focused in the last two years on a revolutionary vision. Both adjective and noun are used advisedly: the potential transformation resulting from schemes which are yet on paper is enormous; the whole thing may be utopian, and its boldness and integral structure certainly command esthetic appreciation. I refer to the six-point program whose spiritual father is Academician

16. E. g. Nemchinov, 1964e.
17. Snabzhat', 1964.

Nemchinov and whose current prophets are Academicians Glushkov and Fedorenko.[18] The program encompasses:

1. Radical recasting of the information system;

2. Creation of the Unified State Network of Computer Centers, a three-layered network with a projected minimum capacity, according to one version, of close to the present U.S. level;[19]

3. Routinization and algorithmization of ordinary processes of administration and control;

4. The kingpin of the system—a dynamic national economic optimizing model of continuous planning;[20]

5. Elaboration of the mathematical methods required for solution of specific problems arising from the general model;

6. Development of the concrete administrative and planning system—institutions and behavior rules—consistent with the general model.

Any discussion of the future of Soviet planning and of the place of mathematical techniques in it must take account of the existence of this program. For convenience the program is referred to as the "national economic cybernetics program," using the broader Russian sense of the term "cybernetics."

In this vision, input-output is but one of an arsenal of techniques and an auxiliary stage in a step process of plan formulation. Precisely what its role will be cannot yet be clear, for the discussion on the overall optimizing model is just beginning. Much will also depend on the pace at which the parts of the program are introduced.[21] There is considerable discussion of the advisability of a piecemeal

18. The principal exposition is in "O rabote instituta," 1964, pp. 3–10. See also Glushkov and Fedorenko, 1964; Pugachev, 1964; Bezrukov and Venikov, 1965. On the role of Nemchinov, see Cherniak's paper in Akademiia nauk, 1964, pp. 188–209.

19. Pugachev, 1964a, pp. 100–01.

20. Ibid., and Glushkov and Fedorenko, 1964.

21. Experimental applications are under way in Leningrad, Moscow, and the upper Volga regions. Evenko, 1965.

approach versus a policy of waiting until the complete system or complete subsystems can be put in place.[22] A third factor to be considered is suggested in a sagacious remark by Nemchinov. Commenting on the program, he warned of a potential danger: The economy was an organic whole; would the proliferation of partial models make up an organic unity too?[23] If the grand optimizing model proves troublesome, will the input-output table assume a more central role as the most viable organic representation of the economy?

## THE ROLE OF THE ENTERPRISE

Nevertheless, the focus of public interest recently has been elsewhere, on the experiments at the Bolshevichka and Maiak enterprises, on the tentative efforts to decentralize direction of light industry and trade. Is this not an alternative to the cybernetics program?

Shortly after the Party Plenum of November 1962, at which Khrushchev was cryptic on the subject of Libermanism and planning reform, the issue of enterprise management dropped out of public view. The year 1963 saw the first formulations of the national economic cybernetics program discussed above and the organization of a system of agencies for pursuit of the required research. Liberman and Libermanism were conspicuous by their absence from public discussion. By the spring of 1964, and subsequently,

22. For example, Kobrinskii of Gosplan declared himself firmly against the piecemeal approach ("O rabote instituta," 1964, p. 12). Oblomskii, also from Gosplan, is for gradualism ("Kibernetika," 1964, p. 17). At the time of formation of the Central Economics-Mathematics Institute, Glushkov favored immediate recasting of the information system even before the major planning models and algorithms had been developed (Glushkov, 1963, p. 13). Evidently unbalanced growth is taking place: "Life shows that computer centers are created faster than the mathematization of economic tasks can be carried out" (Sobolevskii, 1965, p. 59).

23. "O rabote instituta," 1964, p. 10.

the enterprise and Liberman are back as a focus of discussion. What has not been so generally noted is the return of Kantorovich and shadow prices.[24]

The theme that connects this discussion with that on optimal national planning is, of course, the search for behavior rules guaranteeing coincidence of the economic interests of the enterprise with those of the national economy. The primacy of the national interest is never questioned and the national economic cybernetics program is in part designed to achieve that end.

For this reason there is no necessary relation between division of opinion on the issue of the cybernetics program, on the one hand, and that of enterprise autonomy, on the other. Academician Trapeznikov, a decentralizer à la Liberman, has attacked the extreme computationists.[25] On the other hand, Nemchinov insisted on the need for what he called true *khozraschet* planning—production plans based on contracts and considerable flexibility in pricing. By implication at least, Nemchinov would have had the enterprise maximize profits subject to contract fulfillment.[26] Belkin and Birman are cyberneticists but decentralizers, if only because optimum plans would founder on the shoals of current managerial rules of the game.[27] The same position has been taken by Academician Fedorenko.[28]

It is not surprising that most informed Soviet discussion locates somewhere along the middle of the centralization-decentralization continuum. Given the role of central planning as an article of Soviet faith and the ability of the regime to overcome its distaste for Western-tainted mathematical tools, it seems natural for planners and policy-makers to seek solutions to the crisis of central planning in

24. Nemchinov, 1964e, pp. 74 ff.
25. Trapeznikov, 1964.
26. Nemchinov, 1964e.
27. Belkin and Birman, 1964.
28. Fedorenko, 1965.

cybernetics. A measure of skeptical reserve with regard to the omnipotence of models and machines would seem sufficient to keep the regime from succumbing to the lure of what Peter Wiles called "perfect computation." Nemchinov expressed the compromise position with respect to both centralization and computerization: "The socialist economy demands not less than two mechanisms of regulation: a centralized purposeful mechanism of economic administration and a decentralized mechanism of self-adjustment and self-regulation of the economic system. The correct decision consists in a choice of that system optimally combining both regulating mechanisms." [29] Thus, through Nemchinov and the stage form of the Glushkov-Fedorenko cybernetics program, we see a possible link between the computer and Libermanism.

Nonetheless, it is by no means clear how much and what kind of enterprise autonomy there will be. How far will the current experiment in direct linkage of consumer goods plant with trade outlet be carried? Will it embrace all intermediate goods distribution? It is interesting, though not necessarily indicative, that the majority of letters reacting to an *Ekonomicheskaia gazeta* article on the question in the middle of 1964 opposed "trade" or direct links and favored "supply" or the existing method.[30] Even if the experiment spreads, how will prices be set in this kind of relationship?

At this point we are back to Kantorovich, or rather Kantorovich and Novozhilov together. At a 1964 conference which devoted much of its attention to them, Novozhilov offered a semantic sword to cut the Gordian knot. There are two forms of centralization, he said, direct and indirect. Indirect centralization "consists in the setting of such prices and coefficients for the calculation of outlays and effects as will enable the local unit itself to find the variants

29. Nemchinov, 1964b, p. 86.
30. "Ne uprazdniat," 1964.

most appropriate to the national plan and to the general minimization of production outlays." [31]

There has, of course, been considerable opposition to the Kantorovich-Novozhilov position. Academician Khachaturov grumbled at the prospect of having "prices call the tune." [32] Academician Ostrovitianov doggedly protests that shadow prices assume a scarcity of goods whereas the Soviet Union is marching toward abundance.[33] But, hopefully, the sign of things to come may be the mathematician Golanskii's contemptuous dismissal of objections that Kantorovich's objective valuations are not compatible with Marxist value: "This is scholasticism. Value and objective valuations are completely different and incommensurable things. Value is a category of political economy and objective valuations are an algorithmic formula for the calculation of equilibrium prices in an optimal plan." [34] With the official recognition of a Lenin prize awarded to Kantorovich, Nemchinov, and Novozhilov in April 1965, it begins to appear that the attention accorded Liberman should perhaps be redirected at the Lenin laureates.

It has been often noted that input-output in the Leontief

31. "Kibernetika," 1964, p. 9.
32. Ibid., p. 8.
33. "Za i protiv," 1965, p. 9. Ostrovitianov's is not a lone voice in the wilderness. It is slightly sobering to consider the following passage from a critique of Novozhilov written by Kolganov (Kolganov, 1964, p. 111): "For the sake of facilitating the use of known mathematical methods we may not renounce such fundamental principles of the labor theory of value as the contradiction between exchange and use value, the absence of dependency between utility and value, the qualitative difference and incommensurability of heterogeneous use values. We may not do this because without them all mathematical formulas and equations cease to express any objective economic regularities (*zakonomernosti*) and are turned into a free exercise of the mind. Evidently, the way out must be sought elsewhere, in the development of new methods of mathematical analysis, and not in the renunciation of practically verified theoretical principles."
34. "Za i protiv," 1965, p. 10.

mold with fixed coefficients is peculiarly appropriate to the pure command economy. If prices become truly active at the enterprise level, will the place and function of input-output be radically altered? Again, the movement to decentralization and the future of the national economic cybernetics program are inextricably linked among themselves and with the fate of input-output.

## THE POLITICAL FACTOR

I hope to be forgiven a breach of discipline if I conclude with a few speculations on what is perhaps the most important though clearly the most elusive factor in the future of mathematical-economic planning—the political factor. Are the indicated directions of Soviet planning viewed by the regime as entirely consistent with its self-image, with the maintenance of the hegemony of the Party?

There has been a certain amount of sensitivity in Soviet and East European writing to Chinese charges of revisionism and to Western announcements that the Russians are abandoning Marx.[35] The noncommunist observer cannot help being amused by Soviet indignation at being forced to eat their own words. After all it was they who in the Stalin era denounced similar planning schemes in precisely the indicated terms. However, it seems clear that Western chortling and Chinese ranting alone will not drive the Russians back to dogmatism.[36]

Ota Sik was correct when he defended the current Czech reform as "*planned* use of *Socialist* market relations between *Socialist* enterprises for the benefit of the whole *Socialist*

35. See for example the reply to the *Time* cover article on Liberman (Gatovskii, 1965). Also the comments by Sobolev and Kantorovich in "Ekonomisty i matematiki," 1964, pp. 76–78.

36. Nemchinov described articles by Campbell and Zauberman as efforts to drive a wedge between Soviet mathematicians and economists. "Konferentsiia," 1963, p. 83. See also Sobolev's remark in "Ekonomisty i matematiki," 1964, p. 76.

society." [37] But it was not to oversee this kind of arrangement that the Soviet Communist Party evolved in the images of Stalin and Khrushchev. Did not at least some *apparatchiki* shudder when they read Birman's assurance that "by orienting oneself on *profit* it is possible to distribute everything that needs to be distributed, including labor, in a planned manner, on the basis of *objective computation*"? [38] Can a party secretary keep computers in "petty tutelage"? Will such change-resistant forces have a significant impact on the direction and pace of reform?

There is, moreover, the question of the manageability of change itself. In a perceptive essay on the theory of the command economy, Gregory Grossman joins Peter Wiles in believing that "there is no half-way house between a market economy and a command economy." Grossman believes that with time, as the economy grows and is modernized, the dilemma becomes ever starker. It can be relieved only by a fundamental relaxation in the regime's attitude toward resource mobilization and enforcement of priorities. "But then," he concludes, "such a hybrid structure might prove to be only a transitional stage, for the same political developments would probably make it more difficult to resist the lure of a thoroughgoing Socialist market economy à la yougoslave. But we are now on very 'iffy' ground." [39]

Kantorovich once estimated that optimal planning would raise national output by a third. Fedorenko hopefully looks to doubling the rate of growth.[40] The promise of such an output explosion from the combined efficiency and growth effects of the mathematical-economic reforms must be heady indeed. It will be fascinating to see whether this lure held out to the Party is sufficient to overcome all its doubts on the erosion of its own raison d'être.

37. Sik, 1965.
38. Birman, 1964. Emphasis supplied.
39. Grossman, 1963, pp. 118–23.
40. "O rabote instituta," 1964, p. 10.

## Michio Hatanaka

As Vladimir Treml points out, the material balance method has been used in Russia for many years, primarily as a technique for establishing the feasibility of the Soviet plan. More specifically, the internal consistency between the planned output of a product and the national demand for the product is investigated for a short-term economic plan. The indirect industrial demand component raises a serious problem for the investigation of internal consistency. And the input-output model is particularly suited for solving this kind of problem. I would like to restrict my consideration here to the use of an open, static input-output model as a replacement for the material balance method.

It should be noted that a comparison between the input-output technique and the material balance method is only a matter of academic interest at the present time. The use of an input-output model for economic planning requires a far more advanced computer than the Soviets now have. Furthermore, in order to understand the working of the economy, a device is needed to relate the different sectors, each having a highly disaggregated description, by certain aggregate variables. Such a device would present a number of aggregation problems for which there are no solutions as yet. Moreover, the use of an input-output model would require a complete reorganization of the Soviet administrative system of economic information. The present paper assumes that all these problems are somehow solved.

I would like to begin with one obvious advantage of the input-output technique. We are told that the Party leaders are reluctant to write down their objective function. Therefore it would be useful to prepare a number of different plans. This cannot be done by the material balance method

A discussion with Norman Kaplan aided in the preparation of this paper. He suggested a comparison between the material balance method and the input-output model in reference to the production possibility frontier.

as it is so time-consuming. By using a computerized input-output model, the planning authority could prepare a number of different plans corresponding to a number of different bundles of feasible final demands. Another advantage of computerization is that as the execution of the plan proceeds a sequence of revised plans can be issued based on the improved information fed back to the planning authority from the production enterprise.

The main problem with which this paper is concerned is a comparison between the material balance method and the input-output model from the standpoint of production system efficiency. The framework of the economy that we are considering has final demands, production functions, and constraints. Therefore it also has what might be called the final-demands-possibility frontier. This is shown symbolically in a two-dimensional diagram in Figure 1. The coordinates are for the final demands. Since we are discussing a short-term plan, the capacity limitation forms an important part of the constraints.[1]

In considering the practical side of economic planning it is important to distinguish between model and reality. Let us assume that the final-demands-possibility frontier in Figure 1 is the true frontier for the planned time period. Only God knows precisely where it is located. One can imagine the set of points that are feasible according to the input-output model or according to the material balance method; these sets are not necessarily the same as the set of points on and inside the true frontier. It is true that if the input-output model is an accurate representation of the real economy, then any point outside the true frontier would not be chosen as a feasible point. But we know that

1. One of the problems discussed by Treml and others is whether the final demand should be used to determine outputs, or the outputs used to determine final demand. This problem seems to be irrelevant to a check of internal consistency, although it might be relevant to an optimization problem.

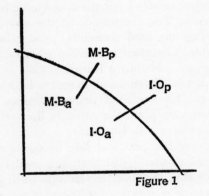

Figure 1

the input-output model is based on a number of mathematical simplifications of reality. With the use of computers, some of the errors in the input-output model can be corrected fairly easily. Assuming that a wrong prediction has been made on the capacity of some industry or on the effect of technical progress upon an input coefficient, all that is necessary is to obtain a new answer on the basis of new data. However, errors due to the linearity assumption or aggregation are more difficult to correct. Therefore, on a priori grounds alone, the selection of points outside the true frontier is equally as possible as the selection of points inside the true frontier. The material balance method will later be shown to have a consistent bias toward the infeasible region, but it is not entirely impossible that the method selects the points inside the true frontier.[2]

Suppose that a point outside the frontier has been selected by the planning authority. As the execution of the plan starts and the actual performance is reported back to the planning authority, they will know that they have selected an infeasible point. In the case of the material balance method, a part of the infeasibility might be eliminated by discussions between the planning authority and the production managers. Another part might be dissolved simply by letting the planning authority throw up its hands and letting individual production managers do whatever they want. In the case of the computerized input-output model there should be some computerized correction method by which the infeasible point can be brought to the feasible region. The correction method should use priority ranking on different bottlenecks. If the infeasibility is to be resolved by the throwing up of hands, it is difficult to make a strong argument for the input-output model.

2. Benjamin Ward has commented that the plan would have some impact on the location of true frontier. This problem would be important for long-term economic plans, but not for short-term economic plans.

Treml reports that no Russian studies have appeared investigating the extent to which the input-output model
represents reality.[3] Therefore, it can be assumed that they
have not developed the correction method which I propose
to consider. I am inclined to take this as indicative of im-
maturity in their study of the practical applications of
mathematical methods. However, if a conjecture which I
later make is correct, the necessity for the correction method
is less serious in the input-output model than in the material balance method.

In Figure 1, $M - B$ and $I - O$ are used to abbreviate the
two methods under comparison. The points with subscript p
represent the points chosen in the plans, and those with
subscript a represent the positions which the economy
would actually attain if the corresponding plans were used.
Even if the original plan turned out to be feasible, the
position at which the economy actually arrived could be
different from the planned position. What kind of comparison can be made between the input-output model and the
material balance method? Probably the most important one
is to compare the deviations of $M - B_a$ and $I - O_a$ from the
true frontier, but it is obvious that we cannot make this
comparison unless we know a great deal about the two
methods, First, we do not know how $M - B_a$ and $I - O_a$ are
determined. Second, unless the two points are placed in a
specific way (such as one northeast of the other), we do not
know how to compare the deviations.

To avoid this dead end, it could be assumed that, given
the long-term economic goal, the Party leaders have chosen
a given direction of movement from the present position in
Figure 1 as the most desirable for the short-term plan. Un-

3. There have been a number of studies investigating the work-
ability of the United States input-output models. However, I do not
think that any of them deals with a model as disaggregated as the
Russians would need for economic planning.

der this assumption, a guess could be ventured as to the relation between $I - O_p$ and $M - B_p$.

In comparing the mechanisms of the input-output model and the material balance method, one notices that both use the concept of input coefficients, but that the similarity stops there. I would like to discuss the production functions, aggregation, iteration, and coverage of goods, in this order, using a sort of *ceteris paribus* approach. When discussing a possible difference between the two methods in regard to one of these four aspects, I am assuming that the two methods are identical with respect to the other three. The identity can be established either by changing the material balance method to the input-output or vice versa.

When the input-output model is used for economic planning, the input coefficients are the predicted values of the ratios between inputs and outputs. The production function assumed in the input-output model is such that if the technology is correctly predicted, there is a unique value of the input coefficient which does not depend upon anything (especially not upon output and scarcity of resources).[4] The material balance method used here is the one described by Levine.[5]

It seems that the subjective probability distribution formed by the production manager is different from that formed by the planning authority. The difference reflects a polarity in interests. Therefore the input coefficients are made an object of bargains between them, neither one thinking that the input coefficients are determined solely by the technology. Input substitution based on scarcity is taken into consideration in the determination of the coefficients by the planning authority as part of the process of balancing the output and the national demand.

4. Incidentally, the substitution theorem cannot be introduced because of a number of constraints due to capacity limitations.

5. Levine, 1959 and 1962a.

Therefore, the view of the production function implicit in the material balance method differs from that of the input-output model. Perhaps the material balance method tends to attribute greater flexibility to input coefficients than the input-output model does, particularly when input substitution is introduced. Suppose that the coefficients chosen by the input-output model can also be chosen by the material balance method, but not vice versa. Then some points in Figure 1 that are not considered to be feasible by the input-output model could be considered feasible in the material balance method. Suppose that in the neighborhood of the point in Figure 1 where they are at a given time, the Party leaders think that a given northeast direction of movements is the most desirable. Then the point selected by the material balance method is likely to be on the northeast side of the point selected by the input-output model.

However, the difference between these two points should not be overemphasized. Since the input coefficients in the input-output model have to be predicted, the coefficients might become an object of bargains. The distance between the two points selected by the two methods would not be very great.

Another topic to be considered is aggregation. The material balance method goes through different levels of aggregation both commodity-wise and region-wise. It starts with aggregated variables that are subsequently broken into disaggregated variables and brought back to aggregates for the approval of the top government officials. Then the aggregates are again broken into disaggregates as the plans are sent to individual production plants. It is possible that the application of the input-output model would also have to go through aggregation and disaggregation. There will probably be no great difference due to aggregation between the plans made by the two methods. If there is a substantial difference, it is hard to see any consistent tendency for the direction of the difference.

One difference between the input-output model and the material balance method is that while $I + A + A^2 + \ldots$ is calculated in the input-output model, the material balance method stops roughly at $I + A$. The failure to iterate causes a nonrandom error, actually underestimating the outputs that are consistent with the final demands.

Retaining the *ceteris paribus* approach, let us assume that both methods have the same coverage of commodities. Let us also assume that the two methods use the same input coefficients, $A$, which are absolutely constant. Under these assumptions, the lack of iteration in the material balance method can be investigated. The following is a crude version of the material balance method where the output target is set as

$$x_{t-1} + (y_t - y_{t-1})$$

where $x_{t-1}$ is the actual output in the previous period and $y_t - y_{t-1}$ is the change in the final demand. This version of the material balance method is more sophisticated than the above, and uses predictions of the increase of capacities in order to set the output target. The above crude material balance method computes

$$A\{x_{t-1} + (y_t - y_{t-1})\}$$

as the indirect, industry demand. Thus

(1) $$A\{x_{t-1} + (y_t - y_{t-1})\} + y_t$$

is the estimate of the nation's total demand. Let us compare this with the nation's demand as calculated by the input-output model, i.e.

(2) $$(I - A)^{-1}y_t.$$

Provided that all the simplifying assumptions for the input-output model hold true and hence $x_{t-1} = (I - A)^{-1}y_{t-1}$, we have

(3) $$(2) - (1) = (A^2 + A^3 + \ldots)(y_t - y_{t-1}).$$

As the economy grows, most of the components of the vector $(y_t - y_{t-1})$ are positive. Comparing the estimates by the two methods for the outputs that are consistent with the same final demands, we see that the estimates by the input-output model are mostly greater than the estimates by the material balance method. Therefore, when the same constraints rather than the same final demands are given to the two methods, some of the points in Figure 1 that are feasible according to the material balance method are not considered feasible according to the input-output model. Practically all of the points that are feasible according to the input-output model are also feasible according to the material balance method. Here is another reason why we might expect that the point selected by the material balance method tends to lie on the northeast side of the point selected by the input-output model.

However, there is the danger of overemphasizing the difference between the two methods due to the iteration. Even with the crude material balance method used above, the magnitude of (3) is not likely to be great unless $y_t - y_{t-1}$ is great. We know that the convergence of the infinite sum $I + A + A^2 + \ldots$ is fairly rapid. When the increase in capacities is taken into consideration in the material balance method, they have something like $(1 + \lambda)x_{t-1}$ instead of $x_{t-1}$, where $\lambda > 0$. When this change is made in (1), the extent to which (2) is greater than (1) becomes generally smaller; in fact, it is possible that (2) becomes smaller than (1).

Finally, there is the matter of coverage of commodities. While the entire production system is covered in the input-output model, the material balance method treats only a part of it, though it is a substantial part. Suppose that the entire production sector is split into two subsectors I and II, and the material balance method treats only the products of subsector I. The matrix A is subdivided as

$$\begin{bmatrix} A_{I,I} & A_{I,II} \\ A_{II,I} & A_{II,II} \end{bmatrix}$$

I would like to venture a conjecture that $A_{II,I}$ is nearly zero. Treml reports that the whole matrix A is nearly triangular. Then A must be even more nearly decomposable. This does not mean that $A_{II,I}$ would be nearly zero for the *particular numbering* of industries used above. However, as an additional argument, it could be conjectured that the commodities not treated in the material balance method are mostly near the stage of consumption. It might be difficult to check due to the difference in the aggregation used in the material balance and the presently available input-output table. At any rate, assume that $A_{II,I}$ is nearly zero.

The input-output model becomes

(4)
$$\left.\begin{array}{r} A_{I,I}x_I + A_{I,II}x_{II} + y_I = x_I \\ A_{II,II}x_{II} + y_{II} \approx x_{II} \end{array}\right\}$$

As for the material balance method, again we use the *ceteris paribus* approach and assume that it iterates within the range of commodities with which it deals explicitly. Furthermore, assume that both methods use the data for $A_{I,I}$ and $A_{I,II}$. Then the material balance method specifies the target of $x_{II}$ and uses the first half of (4) to determine $x_I$. On the other hand the input-output model uses all the equations in (4). Then the difference between the plans obtained by the two methods is due to the difference between the target of $x_{II}$ in the material balance method and the solution of $x_{II}$ from the second half of (4). This difference does not appear to be great, particularly if $x_{II}$ consists mostly of goods near consumption.

Summarizing these guesses and conjectures:

1. The points in Figure 1 that are selected by the two methods are not very far apart, and

2. The point selected by the material balance method is likely to be located on the northeast side of the point selected by the input-output model, i.e. the input-output model tends to be more conservative.

To these two conjectures can be added a generally observed fact:

3. The material balance method tends to choose a point outside the true frontier.

By the northeast relation stated in (2) the point selected by the input-output model has a better chance of being inside the true frontier. The small distance between the two points stated in (1) prevents the input-output model from moving too deeply inside the true frontier. The conclusion is that *the input-output model has a better chance of feasibility without going too deeply inside the frontier.* If the input-output model has a better chance of feasibility, then we can say that perhaps the distance between I—$O_a$ and I—$O_p$ is likely to be smaller than the distance between M—$B_a$ and M—$B_p$.[6]

6. Since I know very little about the material balance method, the hypothetical identity between the two methods for the *ceteris paribus* method was established primarily by changing the material balance method to the input-output model. Though some parts of my consideration involved linear relations, some others involve more complex relations. Hence the interaction effects could be serious, and it is certainly desirable to study the other way of establishing the identity.

# 3. Linear Programming and Soviet Planning

*Benjamin Ward*

For the quantitatively inclined, an economy is not an organism but a disparate collection of problems. It is not a unified search of the like-minded for some objective truth but a large number of separate decisions, each based on its own distinct set of data and criteria. But the problems for which there are solutions are never unique in *every* respect. The kind of data needed, the size of the problem, and the kind of theory used in its solution are natural bases for similarity among problem decisions and so for classifying the whole collection of quantifiable economic problems.

This view of an economy, it is no exaggeration to say, is an essential part of the intellectual equipment of those who use modern quantitative methods in economics. It not only provides practitioners with a general procedure for attacking problems (including, of course, those they do not succeed in solving) but also with a view as to what should be done in areas adjacent to the problem at hand. For these disparate problems are by no means seen as mutually independent. The solution of one problem generates the data for others, and where the methodology of problem solving is similar the data are more likely to be transferable to other problems. Since in economics it is a commonplace that "everything depends on everything else," this pressure

I should like to thank Gregory Grossman for his many comments and suggestions, Alan Parker for research assistance, and the Center for Slavic Studies, University of California, for financial assistance in preparing this paper.

toward a common approach to problems among quantitative economists quickly leads to a common orientation toward the most all-embracing aspects of economics. And since the language spoken by these practitioners is only partly understood by other economists and policymakers, and since the practitioners are likely to be youthful, an aura of revolution and mystery tends to surround their work.

Can such an interpretation of the economy be fully translated into Soviet practice? The implicit pragmatism of the approach, with its possible threat to traditional views, also offers the prospect of clearly perceived gains, perhaps the most promising way to circumvent and even discredit tradition. But for the Soviet thinker, there is perhaps another way of viewing the economy which entails the use of mathematical techniques and yet is based on an organismic interpretation of economic reality. The description of a fully automated economy, in which each part is linked to the whole (and conversely) by a chain of functional relations which are formalized and installed in some grand program of plan making and execution, is more than a dream—it is a set of current Soviet research projects.[1] Though still far in the future at best, there are those who believe that its long shadow should already encompass current decisions. Its implications for the Soviet economy would be truly revolutionary.

All societies, however, have developed defense mechanisms against innovation, and most observers have a healthy respect for the quality of these mechanisms in Soviet society. And innovations themselves often have a way of disappointing in practice. Also, the major constraints that seem likely to be effective in limiting Soviet economic application of mathematical techniques are not confined to the inertial drag of traditionalists. There are a half dozen ways in which limitations to further advance in this direction may be encountered.

1. Belkin, 1962; Glushkov and Fedorenko, 1964; Pugachev, 1964c.

1. Intrafirm production scheduling, enterprise decision-making, interfirm supply planning, long-range plan making: these terms suggest broad classes of economic problems for which mathematical models have been developed. However, in none of these areas has a definitive mathematical procedure for solving all problems of the given class been achieved. Instead there are, at best, procedures presently available in each area for practical application for solving only a few of the many problems that occur. Indeed, there are many types of problems for which mathematical economists are in sharp disagreement over such fundamental aspects as: whether static procedures will suffice, or whether aggregative variables are sufficiently stable, or whether uncertainty must be formally incorporated into the models. Despite the very rapid developments over the last two decades, I suspect few would claim that mathematical economics has reached maturity as an applied discipline; some would argue that it is still in its infancy. And Soviet achievements in this area are quite modest when contrasted with those in the United States. In a word, existing mathematical descriptions of economic reality are often so crude as to be a serious handicap to successful problem solving.

2. The capacity of data processing machines to handle large-scale problems is still a major bottleneck in U.S. practice. Many of the problems posed by Soviet needs are of far larger scale than any hitherto computed in this country. But existing Soviet machinery is extremely crude by current U.S. standards, especially with respect to speed of operation and size of memory units; also the number of computers available for economic calculations is very small. This appears to be more a matter of backward production technology than of theoretical knowledge, but the surprisingly slow rate of improvement over the past four years raises doubts about the prospects, at least for the immediate future.

3. There has been a good deal of comment on ideological barriers to the application of mathematical methods in the

Soviet Union. Clearly, much progress has been made in lowering this barrier since the days when mathematical economics was condemned as bourgeois apologetics and statistical analysis was restricted to the natural sciences. Even in the last five years there has been a notable relaxation, as can be seen by comparing, say, Nemchinov's comments in the preface to Kantorovich's 1959 book with Gatovskii's opening remarks to a 1964 round-table conference of economists.[2] Extra-enterprise production and distribution problems, price calculations, intertemporal comparisons by means of interest rates: all these once disputed areas are now open for discussion and application. Of course it is always possible that strict control of thought will be reintroduced, but at this writing there are no signs of a serious counterattack on the modernizers.

4. Together with the operation of the machines, a great deal of skilled labor is needed to administer a programmed economic system. But, more important, the stage of "capital construction," of preparation of models and programs and initial data, is especially labor intensive. In this area the Soviets have clearly made considerable progress. The first class of specialists in mathematical economics has just been graduated from Moscow University.[3] The general extent of interest in the subject is suggested by printings of books dealing with linear programming: Kantorovich's previously mentioned book was given an initial printing of only 3,000 copies in 1959, while a standard text of 1963 appeared in 26,000 copies.[4] Of course, many purchasers of these books will not become successful practitioners, and current complaints about shortages of skilled cadres are frequent.

5. The introduction of a mathematical procedure in making any given decision has consequences like those of any change in administrative routine. Inertia and vested

2. Kantorovich, 1959, and Konferentsiia, 1964.
3. Nemchinov, 1964d.
4. Iudin and Gol'shtein, 1964.

interests must be overcome; new information must be collected and, of course, processed in new ways. The latter can often be a serious problem. Accountants, clerks, foremen, and other lower-level employees must have some understanding of the requirements of the new routine if they are to generate or collect the most useful information. Typically, existing information flows are inadequate for successful solution by new methods. Hence some measure of co-operation by an often considerable number of people must be obtained before even a test of the new procedures can be made. High-level approval in principle of the methods no doubt makes changes easier, but by no means eliminates the challenge to established position. Passive resistance is as old as bureaucracy.

6. Even with successful removal of the above-mentioned constraints, there remain the problems of control and incentives. Each routine requires a number of complex and specific actions by a great many people. Once the plan is made, there must be a willingness, as well as a capability, for fulfilling it. This has always been a serious problem for Soviet economic organizations, and it is not axiomatic that good plan making and plan fulfillment go hand in hand.

In summary, it appears that problems relating to ideology and the training of cadres are relatively less serious today than they were five years ago, while technical and organizational constraints remain critical. This paper is primarily concerned with only one aspect of the technical problem: the extent to which linear programming techniques have been applied in Soviet planning practice and their prospects for future use. However, it has seemed desirable to devote considerable attention to the organizational problem as well.

Linear (and to some extent nonlinear) programming offers some of the best opportunities for immediate application to the economy, since it is a well-developed technique for which literally hundreds of applications have already been made by Western economists and operations researchers. In addition, it makes fewer demands on both computers and trainees, in comparison with most alternative procedures. And it provides a basis for comparatively simple and "natural" interpretations of the environment, which are a considerable help in the process of conversion of real world problems into mathematical ones (and conversely). For all these reasons the present state of Soviet work in linear programming provides a useful indicator of short-run Soviet capabilities in the whole area of quantitative planning.

But a survey of the applications and pilot studies to date is of limited use for this broader purpose unless the developments are related to existing planning practice. For only then can one discover the areas that are amenable, from an organizational point of view, to application of the new techniques. And only by reference to existing control procedures can one form an estimate of the quality of the information that will serve as inputs to the new procedures.

Consequently, the next section contains a schematic and somewhat idealized picture of the Soviet short-run planning system. The following sections survey some applications of linear programming techniques to Soviet problems and describe briefly an attempt at formulating an overall planning scheme for the economy as a whole, and the concluding section attempts to infer prospects for the near future from these developments.

## Soviet Plan Making[5]

The short-run planning process can be thought of as comprising two overlapping stages. The first is a learning process in which the planning board collects the information it expects to need in making a plan. This includes derivation of an initial set of final demand targets from the perspective

5. This section is based in considerable measure on Western studies of Soviet-type planning, particularly those of J. M. Montias (1959) and H. Levine (1959), though it differs from these in several important respects.

plan and current performance data. The second stage consists of making and adjusting the plan figures until a consistent and acceptable plan has emerged. The stages overlap because, for example, the board must have some idea of the magnitude of the task to be faced by an industry before it knows what part of the industry's production functions to find out about. The second stage requires some learning, as the plan figures indicate changes in tasks for various industries.

The first step in the planning process is to announce to all firms that they are to produce at the formally designated capacity rate for each product in the next plan period and are to determine their requirements for achieving this target. The choice of capacity operation is based on the assumption that the long-run plan is a good one and that it has hitherto been fulfilled, so that existing capacities are roughly those needed to continue on the optimal long-run path. Of course there is some flexibility in the definition of "capacity." This is to allow for differences in gestation periods among industries and to take account of any special information about the quality of the poorer plants, customary practices as to the number and intensity of shifts, and the like.

The next step, collecting information on recent performance, is construed to be essentially the collection of input coefficients. Formally, the firm's estimate of its input coefficients is simply the ratio of each required amount of input to the capacity level of output. But because of bargaining that goes on between the plan board and the enterprise, these coefficients are generally not those accepted by the board. The board, in effect, constructs a set of coefficient distributions. These might appear in the internal work of the board as a pair of numbers ("mean" and "standard deviation") to represent each coefficient or in some more complicated form depending on the shape of the distribution, i.e. on the relative likelihood that upward or downward biases dominate. Thus the nature of the distribution depends on the values of the coefficients actually reported, information relating to the bargaining process (recent revisions, changes during the course of the reporting, possibly even reports on the personalities concerned), and information collected in other ways. From this information the coefficient distributions are constructed by the planning board, say by the appropriate product sections.

Armed with these distributions, the plan is then made. The interaction (administrative iteration) now is between the planning board and its own product sections. The board first reports a bill of gross outputs and final demands to each product section. If these balance for the set of "mean" input coefficients showing uses of the relevant product, this fact is reported back to the board. If not, the production section must choose from among other possible input coefficients within some prescribed range of the coefficient distributions. Product sections will generally have some discretion in reassigning coefficients. This discretion is defined and limited by a criterion, assigned the product section by the center, which takes account of the relative priorities of the various industries and the effectiveness of changes (i.e. the amount of saving of product available per standard unit of reduction in coefficients). Of course revision may be forbidden for some uses, so that in effect the coefficient distribution is a point. Success in balancing product supply and allocation would be reported to the board at the completion of this step, possibly with some summary statement as to the adjustment made.

Should this step fail to yield a balance, the product section reports that the plan is infeasible and by how much. The board then may choose one of three courses of action: first, it may simply reduce the required final demand for the product by an amount that will bring gross requirements down to gross output; second, it may lower some aspects of the coefficient-adjustment criterion; or third, it

may raise the target level of production of gross output for
that product. The implications of this procedure may be
illustrated now. The material balances for a two-sector
economy, in which the $x_i$ are gross supplies (requirements)
of the commodities, $\bar{x}_i$ are targeted gross outputs (capacities),
$y_i$ are final demands and $a_{ij}$ the mean coefficients of input of
$i$ per unit of output of $j$ desired, are:

(1) $$\bar{x}_1 = a_{11}\bar{x}_1 + a_{12}\bar{x}_2 + y_1$$
(2) $$\bar{x}_2 = a_{21}\bar{x}_1 + a_{22}\bar{x}_2 + y_2$$

Equations (1) and (2) show a consistent set of gross outputs
for the given estimates of technical coefficients and final
demands. Suppose now that section (1) is not in balance, the
gross output targeted being too low to cover all needs, as
described on the right side of the equation. This situation is
shown in Figure 1. The line $\alpha$ is equation (1) with gross supply, $x_1$, substituted for gross-targeted output, $x_1$. Line $\beta$
shows equation (2), with sector (2)'s material balance in
order. If both equations were in balance, P would define the
consistent bill of gross outputs; but they are not. The first
product sector, if it follows the first of the above possibilities, will shift equation $\alpha$ to the left so as to bring about
a new intersection at Q, consistent with the targets but at a
lower final demand, $y'$. If this is not permitted or does not
suffice, norm adjustment may be tried. $\alpha'$ shows the result of
reducing $a_{12}$ (the amount of product 1 needed by sector 2
in producing a unit of product 2). If permissible rotations
of this kind will not bring the sector into balance at targeted
output levels, the product sector reports failure.

Note that the advantage of operations of these kinds is
that they have no effect on material balances elsewhere in
the system. Even though a change in $a_{12}$ has some impact on
sector 2, it does not directly affect the balancing work of this
product sector, which is concerned with targeted gross output and allocations of product 2 only. But if the board is
forced to change gross output levels, the impact on other

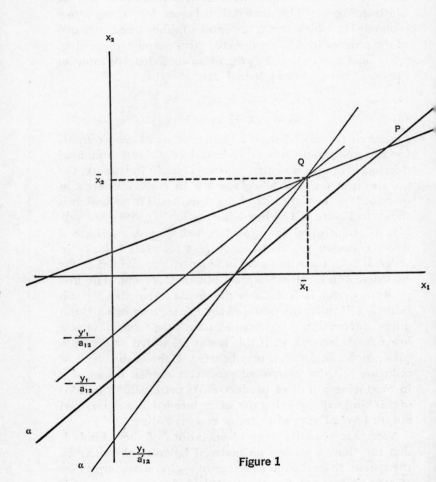

Figure 1

product sections may be widespread. A standard iteration, or perhaps even two, involving the reporting and summation of additional requirements, will then be necessary in most cases. However, the damping of this process by adjustments in all sectors of the first two kinds described above sharply limits the overall impact on the plan.

The result of this process is a bill of some hundreds of gross outputs that are mutually consistent in terms of a bill of final demands and a technology matrix, both of which are somewhat altered as a result of the planning process. The final step is to convert this highly aggregated bill of goods into production targets and input quotas for each enterprise in the country. Again, the conventional capacity levels, modified in conformity with the plan adjustments, form the basis for disaggregation. At this point, scarcities relating to the transportation system come into play for the first time in a serious way (though transportation appears as one or several sectors in the aggregate plan). But with much of the problem already solved, ad hoc adjustments of a kind similar to those made by the product sections of the planning board must again be made. That is, further adjustment of input assortments to sectors, regions, and enterprises are made by means of a criterion composed by the transport planning sector (ministry) and applied to coefficient distributions constructed by regional and sectoral procurement agencies. At the end of this step the short-run plan is completed, insofar as extra-enterprise activity is concerned. Of course the disaggregation process outside the enterprise does not assign inputs and output targets for every product to every enterprise. Some of this work is left to enterprise supply and procurement organizations.

Leaving aside the informational aspects of coefficient and final demand construction, the remainder of the planning process just described does not impose overwhelming tasks of communication or calculation on any of the participants. Indeed, the assistance of calculating machines more powerful than the abacus and slide rule is unnecessary. The product sections are required to make calculations essentially on the balance for their own product alone. The central board solves no large-scale problems internally; instead it constructs criteria for norm adjustment and serves as an aggregator and communication link in the iterative reconstruction of gross output targets. Lower levels in the hierarchy deal with problems of limited scope and comparable arithmetic complexity in more or less routinized ways.

The most surprising aspect of this scheme is the implicit transposition of a basic stability assumption about the environment. On its most rigid interpretation there is no substitution of activities permitted in input-output models. If this assumption is relaxed, the natural approach is to assume that each product may be produced in several ways, which may be described by alternative columns of input coefficients. In this case, the process of constructing an optimal bill of gross outputs requires at some stage a choice among column vectors in the technology matrix. It is always assumed that any allocation of the output among sectors (and final uses) is permitted by the environment. Requirements for allocation to any one sector are set by the conditions in that sector alone.

In our interpretation of the Soviet model, this assumption is transposed. That is, product sections of the planning board choose alternative row vectors, alternative vectors of allocation coefficients, while the formal model itself assumes that any bill of allocations of inputs to production sectors is permitted. The justification of this assumption cannot be that Soviet production technology differs fundamentally from that in capitalist countries; rather it stems from the special institutional features of the Soviet case. The existence of a hierarchy means that organizational constraints enter into any alteration of allocations among sectors. Individual firms or industries are often not in direct contact with firms or industries which supply them with inputs, but, to a considerable extent, establish their relationships through vertical communication within the hierarchy. Also, each reallocation calls for considerable activity in the form of aggregation and disaggregation to take some account of the implications for various levels of the economy. Consequently there are real restrictions on shifts in the intersectoral allocation of output. Of course there are limits to the extent to which production technology is ignored in this stage of the planning process. In evaluating the outputs of the process, one should be aware both of the oversimplifications entailed by application of the usual input-output model and of the special features of Soviet operation.

There are three ways in which normative, optimizing features are built into this planning scheme. The first is simply that the output of the process is a formally consistent plan. This means, in the normative sense, that some account is taken of the interdependence that abounds in any developed modern economy. The second feature is the gearing of short-term, operational plans to the long-run aims of the leadership, as spelled out in the perspective plan. This enters the planning process by way of the setting of initial capacity targets and of an initial bill of final demands. Finally, the formal accounting for uncertainty about the environment and sectoral priorities by means of readjustment of capacity (gross output) targets brings current information into the short-run plan-making process, permitting some interactions with the long-run goals as translated into initial data.

Though the damping features insure the convergence of this planning process to a consistent (aggregate) plan, there is clearly no reason to believe that the final product is optimal, or even feasible. And yet when the constraints of uncertainty and plan-making costs are taken into account, the system does make some sense. If the long-run plan is a good one (and ignoring the effects of different gestation periods in expanding capacities), the capacity approach to assigning gross outputs does seem fairly reasonable. There is no point in producing capacity that will not be needed. Also the needs for standby capacity, the greater likelihood of breakdowns of older equipment, even the number of shifts to be employed, all can be, and in fact are, taken into account in setting the initial "capacity" output targets.

Coefficient forcing implies either that there are opportunities in terms of alternative linear activity functions which have not as yet been taken into account, or that there is a smaller social cost to underfulfilling targets in non-priority sectors than there is in carefully constructing a consistent plan for those sectors. Experience presumably provides some evidence to the material balancers on the former question. Indeed, errors will be most likely to occur when the balancers are ignorant of the nature of their ignorance, a situation which is a large step removed from simply choosing coefficients at random or solely on the basis of priorities. As for the second alternative, there is no good basis for comparing the two costs. But at least there is some reason to appreciate the significance of plan-making costs, as well as reason for some skepticism about the gains from more formally detailed plan making when information is limited and unreliable.

## Two Studies of Transport Planning

The relative simplicity of the transportation problem of linear programming makes it especially attractive to the economic planner. The ease of large-scale calculation stems from two properties of the problem: first, the initial very large matrix of constraints (m × n by m + n for m markets and n supply points) can be telescoped for purposes of calculation (to m by n) and secondly, calculations on this matrix are further shortened because every basis of the problem is triangular, so that each stage in the solution requires a minimum of computation.

The organization of Soviet planning also makes application of the transportation problem attractive. Earlier stages in the planning process produce production targets for enterprises and bills of requirements of enterprises for these outputs. The problem then faced by, for example, union and republican supply-procurement organizations, is to assign these supplies to consumers. This problem is the simplest form of the transportation problem, in which both supplies and demands are fixed.[6]

The results of calculations for the distribution of coal using this format have been reported by Tret'iakova.[7] Two series of calculations were made. The first dealt only with allocations within Siberia and the Far East and was performed for nine supply points and eight demand points; these were then disaggregated to ten supply points and thirty demand points. The second series of calculations allocated coal throughout the Soviet Union, using 30 × 98 cost matrices and data from 1957 and 1960.

Data for the regional model and for the 1957 union model were based on actual production and consumption for 1957. The 1960 data were based on the plan. Statements of requirements (zaiavki) provided the raw data in terms of tons of coal of each type requested from each basin by each consumer. Caloric equivalents were also provided for each type of coal, and these coefficients were used to convert all coals into conventional units. Coking coal was excluded from the model.

Some aggregation of supply and consumption points was necessary. Oblast administrative centers were generally taken as demand points and the major shipping center from each coal deposit was taken as the supply point. In a few cases, more than one shipping point was assigned to a basin; for example, where coals of quite different caloric

6. As will be seen below this is not quite true, since alterations in initially given planned requirements and availabilities are frequently made at a later stage in the planning process.

7. Tret'iakova, 1962; see also Birman, 1962, pp. 196–200.

contents were shipped from that basin. A table of distances was constructed, based on the assumption that the shortest route from any supplier to a consumer was the route actually taken.

Excluded from the calculations, in addition to coking coal, were exports, imports, and shipments by other than rail transport. Coking coal amounted to about 21 percent of the total amount of coal extracted in 1960 while export and import of hard coals was relatively insignificant.[8] In these cases the procedure was to subtract the relevant quantities from availabilities and requirements at appropriate points; e.g. for exports, an administrative center close to the point of export was designated the demand point for those exports.

Three alternative criteria were used in calculations. In one, the problem was simply to minimize the total number of ton-kilometers of coal haulage. In another, the problem was to minimize transport cost based on official freight rate schedules. The construction of these cost matrices posed no serious difficulties. A third criterion, direct cost of transport (including costs relating to size of trains, loading and unloading costs, and costs of required empty-wagon hauls), was more complex, though a study by a transportation institute attached to the old Gosekonomsovet S.S.S.R. greatly simplified this task.

The results of these calculations with actual and planned data for the union models are summarized in Table 1. Thus substantial, if not spectacular, savings in calculated transport cost would result from using any of the formal schemes. In general terms, the major difference between the calculated schemes and the others is a reduction in the average length of hauls in the former cases. As can be seen from Table 2, which compares 1960 data, another difference is the reduction in the number of suppliers attached

8. *Nar. khoz.*, 1962, pp. 154, 545–46.

Table 1

## RESULTS OF COAL TRANSPORT STUDY

| Criterion of optimality | Actual | Calculated | Saving (%) |
|---|---|---|---|
| 1957: calculated vs. actual data | | | |
| Direct cost (million rubles) | 8,800 | 7,903 | 10.2 |
| Ton-kilometers (millions) | 277,166 | 249,727 | 9.9 |
| Freight rates (million rubles) | 7,157 | 6,570 | 8.2 |
| 1960: calculated vs. plan data | | | |
| Direct cost (million rubles) | 7,444 | 6,714 | 9.8 |
| Ton-kilometers (millions) | 201,364 | 187,665 | 9.3 |
| Freight rates (million rubles) | 6,021 | 5,558 | 7.7 |

*Source:* Tret'iakova, 1962, p. 51.

to any given consumer, and vice versa. In the table, both suppliers and consumers are arranged in rough order from west to east. This form shows clearly the irrational deliveries in the upper right and lower left-hand corners of the table. The consolidated summary shows 51 deliveries according to plan data but only 30 in the "optimal" calculation.

A final aspect of the calculation consists of producing the shadow prices. In the problem at hand, these constitute delivered prices and locational rents attaching to each supply point. Tret'iakova presented the following table (Table 3) of price comparisons generated by the regional model, her main purpose being to illustrate (and condemn) the wide variation in purchasers' prices at a single demand point. Also noteworthy is the wide variation between actual and calculated purchasers' prices. On the assumption that locational rent is zero at the Raitsikhinskii supply point, the ratio of calculated to actual purchasers' prices varies, for the data presented, from .60 to 3.49. Thus, if uniform purchasers' prices were introduced, as Tret'iakova advocates, and production costs and freight rates remained unchanged,

## Table 2

## COMPARISON BETWEEN THE "OPTIMAL" PLAN AND ACTUAL DELIVERIES OF COAL

("optimal" delivery as percentage of actual)

| Region (market) | Basin | | | | | | | | | | | | | |
|---|---|---|---|---|---|---|---|---|---|---|---|---|---|---|
| | Donetskii | Podmos-kovnyi | Petert-skii | Kizelov-skii | Tseliabin-skii | So. Ural | Kuznet-skii | Karagan-dinskii | Ekiba-stuzskii | Tserem-hovskii | Kanskii | Khakas-skii | Zabal Kal'skii | Far Eastern |
| North | 0 | 0 | 123 | 0 | | | | | | | | | | |
| Northwest | 237 | 0 | 71 | 0 | | | | | | | | | | |
| West | 110 | 0 | | | | | | | | | | | | |
| Center | 96 | 105 | 0 | 90 | 0 | 0 | 105 | | | | | | | |
| Povolz'e | 62 | | | | | | 165 | 172 | | | | | | |
| North Caucasus | 100 | | | | | | | | | | | | | |
| Zakavkaz'e | 100 | | | | | | | | | | | | | |
| South | 98 | | | | | | | | | | | | | |
| Urals | | | | 265 | 102 | 111 | 12 | 92 | 0 | | | | | |
| Western Siberia | | 0 | 0 | | | | 94 | 2 | 9282 | 127 | 0 | 0 | | 0 |
| Eastern Siberia | | | | | | | 0 | | | 97 | 128 | 153 | 102 | |
| Kazakhstan and Central Asia | | | | | | | 58 | 99 | 666 | | 0 | 0 | | |
| Far East | | | | | | | | | | | | | | 101 |

*Source:* Tret'iakova 1962, p. 53.

*Note:* A "zero" entry means that there was an actual delivery though not an "optimal" one. A blank means no delivery in either case.

Table 3

PRICE COMPARISONS BETWEEN OPTIMAL CALCULATION
AND ACTUAL 1957 DATA
(rubles per ton of conventional fuel)

| Supplier-market | (1) Freight rate (R./T.-km.) | (2) Actual supply price | (3) Actual delivered price | (4) Calculated supply price* | (5) Calculated delivered price | (6) Column (5) ÷ Column (3) |
|---|---|---|---|---|---|---|
| Tseremhovskii (shaft)-Mariinsk | 51 | 93 | 144 | 189 | 241 | 167 |
| Tseremhovskii (strip)-Mariinsk | 60 | 67 | 127 | 180 | 241 | 189 |
| Khakasskii (strip)-Mariinsk | 23 | 68 | 91 | 218 | 241 | 264 |
| Tseremhovskii (strip)-Krasnoiarsk | 47 | 67 | 114 | 180 | 228 | 199 |
| Kanskii (shaft)-Krasnoiarsk | 16 | 62 | 78 | 211 | 228 | 290 |
| Kanskii (strip)-Krasnoiarsk | 16 | 49 | 65 | 211 | 228 | 349 |
| Tseremhovskii (strip)-Irkutsk | 12 | 67 | 79 | 180 | 193 | 242 |
| Tseremhovskii (strip)-Buriatiia | 31 | 67 | 98 | 180 | 212 | 215 |
| Zabaikal'skii (shaft)-Buriatiia | 37 | 92 | 129 | 174 | 212 | 163 |
| Gusinoozerskii-Buriatiia | 13 | 98 | 111 | 199 | 212 | 190 |
| Raitsikhinskii-Blagovestsensk | 27 | 75 | 102 | 75 | 102 | 100 |
| Raitsikhinskii-Habarovsk | 41 | 75 | 116 | 75 | 116 | 100 |
| Primorskii-Habarovsk | 44 | 128 | 172 | 71 | 116 | 67 |
| Primorskii-Primorskii krai | 14 | 128 | 142 | 71 | 86 | 60 |
| Zabaikal'skii (shaft)-Tsita | 19 | 92 | 111 | 174 | 193 | 174 |
| Zabaikal'skii (strip)-Tsita | 10 | 109 | 119 | 183 | 193 | 162 |
| Raitsikhinskii-Tsita | 119 | 75 | 193 | 75 | 193 | 100 |
| Bureinskii-Tsita | 93 | 96 | 189 | 100 | 193 | 102 |

Source: Tret'iakova 1962, pp. 58–59. There is some rounding error.
* Note: Assuming zero rent at Raitsikhinskii station.

very substantial differential rents would be earned by some mines.

The second study was a somewhat more detailed model of cement allocation for the Ukraine. The work was performed by the Institute of Construction Economics in 1962, the calculations made at Gosplan S.S.S.R.'s Computer Center, and the work reported by A. M. Loginova.[9] The data were taken from the first half of 1961 and again the calculated "optimal" plans compared with the half-year plan. Alternate calculations assumed 12 or 25 supply points, and 25 or 184 consumption points.

There were in 1961 twelve factories in the Ukraine producing cement. Two of these were excluded because their entire output was consumed on the spot. Three import points were fixed and, with a minor consolidation, twelve supply points were assigned. It was determined from the 11,000 supply orders (*nariady*) that cement was to be delivered to some 961 railroad stations in the Ukraine (as in the coal study, water transport was excluded). These were aggregated into 184 demand points by first grouping demands by *oblast* and then choosing major consumption points within each *oblast* and aggregating all other consumption points within a 60-kilometer radius of the major point. For some calculations a further aggregation into 25 consumption points was made, with each *oblast* administrative center serving as the aggregate demand point.

A special aggregation problem was created by the fact that Ukrglavsnabsbyt was responsible only for intrarepublican supply while Soiuzglavstroimaterialy made interrepublican allocations of cement.[10] Because of uncertainty

9. Loginova, 1963.

10. Ukrglavsnabsbyt—the Chief Administration for Supply and Procurement of Construction Materials, an agency of the Council of the National Economy of the Ukrainian S.S.R. Soiuzglavstroimaterialy—the Chief Administration for Interrupublican Supplies of Forest and Construction Materials, an agency of the Council of the National Economy of the U.S.S.R.

as to the effects of the different allocation procedures used by these two organs, calculations were made both for matrices including and excluding the union-allocated cement. The latter, more inclusive tables accounted for 96.5 percent of all cement consumed within the republic.

There are several types and grades of cement which are, within limits, mutually substitutable. One set of calculations assumes in effect that all cements are perfect substitutes and simply allocates "natural" tons in accordance with the criteria. In the other calculations, account is taken of the fact that higher-grade cements are more productive of concrete per unit of weight. All cements, regardless of type, were converted into conventional units based on their grade, and these conventional tons assigned in accordance with the criteria. Two criteria were used, ton-kilometers and transport cost as measured by freight rates.

The results of these calculations and comparisons with the plan data are shown in Table 4. Loginova points out that the savings are very high in comparison with the usual results of such calculations. This is attributable in part, she asserts, to the complexity of the Ukrainian rail system, which offers an overwhelming number of alternative routes among which the intuitive planner must choose. One important result of the revised transport scheme, and an explanation for the substantial difference in the savings offered by the two criteria, is shown in Table 5. Both calculated schemes very substantially reduce the average length of hauls in comparison with the plan scheme. Indeed, some 13.3 percent of the cement is hauled more than 700 kilometers in the plan, while neither calculated scheme has any hauls of that distance. Since unit transport costs are higher for short than for long hauls, the increasing concentration of hauls in the shorter range reduces the value of the freight-rate criterion relatively less than that of the ton-kilometer criterion.

Neither of these studies is more than experimental in

## Table 4

### RESULTS OF CALCULATIONS OF OPTIMAL SCHEMES OF TRANSPORT OF CEMENT FOR THE UKRAINE FOR THE FIRST HALF OF 1961

| | "Ukrainian" matrix | | | | "Union" matrix | | | |
|---|---|---|---|---|---|---|---|---|
| | 12 × 25 tons | 25 × 25 conventional units | 12 × 84 tons | 25 × 184 conventional units | 12 × 25 tons | 25 × 25 conventional units | 12 × 184 tons | 25 × 184 conventional units |
| Cost, cost-matrices expressed in distances (millions of ton-kilometers) | | | | | | | | |
| planned | 989 | 989 | 959 | 959 | 1720 | 1720 | 1697 | 1697 |
| calculated | 596 | 583 | 588 | 556 | 1028 | 1000 | 1094 | 1028 |
| saving in percent | 39.8 | 41.1 | 38.7 | 42.1 | 40.2 | 41.8 | 35.5 | 39.4 |
| calculation time (minutes) | 4.5 | 5 | 100 | 150 | 4–5 | 5 | 100 | 150 |
| Cost, matrices expressed in terms of freight rates (thousand rubles) | | | | | | | | |
| planned | 4180 | 4180 | 4102 | 4102 | 6699 | 6699 | 6636 | 6636 |
| calculated | 3243 | 3203 | 3185 | 3118 | 5013 | 4929 | 4996 | 4920 |
| saving in percent | 22.4 | 23.4 | 22.4 | 24.1 | 25.2 | 26.4 | 24.7 | 25.8 |

*Source:* Loginova, 1963, p. 155.

## Table 5

## PLANNED AND OPTIMAL DISTRIBUTION OF CEMENT CLASSIFIED BY DISTANCE HAULED
### (thousand tons)

| Suppliers: cement factories and stations | Planned distributions of cement classified by distances (kilometers) | | | | | | | Total amount of cement (thousand tons) | Optimal distribution of cement classified by distances | | | | Optimal distribution of cement classified by freight rates | | | |
|---|---|---|---|---|---|---|---|---|---|---|---|---|---|---|---|---|
| | to 100 | 101–300 | 301–500 | 501–700 | 701–900 | 901–1100 | 1101–1300 | | to 100 | 101–300 | 301–500 | 501–700 | to 100 | 101–300 | 301–500 | 501–700 |
| Ambrosievskii | 446 | 158 | 226 | 120 | – | 15 | | 965 | 544 | 114 | 255 | 52 | 544 | 62 | 307 | 52 |
| Kramatorskii | 39 | 98 | 21 | 4 | 1 | | | 163 | | 159 | 3 | | | 107 | 55 | |
| Enakievskii | 60 | 133 | 16 | 17 | 2 | 2 | | 230 | | 178 | 52 | | | 230 | | |
| Dnepropetrovskii | | 3 | 4 | 12 | 12 | 7 | 2 | 40 | 40 | | | | 40 | | | |
| Dneprodzerzhinskii | 37 | 26 | 36 | 64 | 35 | | 1 | 199 | 199 | | | | 199 | | | |
| Krivorozhskii | 33 | 190 | 64 | 88 | | 66 | 9 | 450 | | 321 | 62 | 68 | | 321 | 108 | 21 |
| Har'kovskii | 57 | 21 | – | | | | | 77 | 77 | | | | 77 | | | |
| Nikolaevskii | 32 | 25 | 4 | 18 | 10 | 158 | | 247 | 97 | 151 | | | 97 | 143 | 8 | |
| Zdolbunovskii | 34 | 40 | 198 | 1 | 7 | | | 279 | 17 | 54 | 208 | | 21 | 46 | 213 | |
| Vadul-Siret | 10 | 20 | 14 | 18 | 2 | – | | 65 | 21 | | 43 | | 21 | | 43 | |
| Kovel' | 5 | 9 | 3 | | | | | 16 | 12 | | 5 | | 16 | | | |
| Frikatsei | | | 28 | | 37 | 8 | | 73 | | | 73 | | | | 73 | |
| Total (thousand tons) | 752 | 723 | 613 | 343 | 106 | 256 | 12 | 2805 | 1008 | 977 | 701 | 120 | 1015 | 909 | 808 | 73 |
| percent | 26.6 | 25.8 | 21.5 | 12.2 | 3.8 | 9.1 | .4 | 100 | 35.9 | 34.8 | 25.0 | 4.3 | 36.2 | 32.4 | 28.8 | 2.6 |

Source: Loginova, 1963, p. 157.

nature. Indeed, I am aware of no evidence that supply allocations for any product have as yet been made on a broad scale by this method. Nevertheless, there is much interest in the approach, and protagonists seem to feel that it is about ready for practical application. As a partial technique it has weaknesses, of course, so that a question worth asking is how much of an improvement over previous administrative techniques it offers.

Perhaps the most obvious weakness of these schemes is their failure to consider alternative patterns of production and consumption in addition to alternative patterns of deliveries of the goods. In principle, it seems perfectly possible to expand the framework of the problem to consider alternative production levels up to some capacity limit without transcending the formal framework of the transportation problem. There is precedent for this approach in a coal industry study for the United States.[11] Several factors have inhibited this approach in Soviet work to date. The first is the limited capacity of available computers, a minor constraint since the expanded problem would require only $m$ additional variables and one more disposal activity. The second is organizational; transport planning comes at a late stage in the plan-making process, so that feedback to earlier stages of the plan would cut across existing lines of authority and would considerably lengthen the already excessive time period required to produce a plan in final form. A third might be the difficulty of collecting data on production costs in appropriate form (see below). But the second consideration is probably decisive.

Even if the assumption of perfectly inelastic supply and demand are accepted, there is some doubt as to whether *zaiavki* or *nariady* provide a good estimate of consumers' requirements. The well-known incentive to overstate requirements in anticipation of reductions in allocations and erratic deliveries must have some effect on the accuracy of

11. Henderson, 1958.

the former. And the latter, representing a late-stage revision of requirements by high-level supply-procurement organizations, are possibly even less reliable indicators of "true" demand. Birman notes that this revision is rather arbitrary, is based on fairly old and inadequate information, and is often motivated by the need to keep flows of goods moving in the normative directions laid down by the Ministry of Transport.[12] The question this raises about the calculated schemes is whether they represent a significant improvement with respect to the "true" demands. If the planned and actual requirements in the *nariady* are determined partly by a desire to reduce some deliveries, the true optimal scheme may well require a different and more costly shipments plan than the reported ones. Of course, providing consumers with a more appropriate bill of inputs is a social gain for the plan as a whole, but there could be certainty that "true" demands are socially desirable ones only if the optimality of the overall plan was certain.

In the reported studies there was very little aggregation of supply points, but on the demand side there was extensive aggregation in every case. Tret'iakova felt this to be a serious weakness of the coal study, especially where *oblasts* covered a very large territory. On the other hand there is with one exception no appreciable difference in Loginova's results when the degree of demand aggregation is changed, as can be seen from Table 4. And in Tret'iakova's Siberian study, disaggregation from eight to thirty demand points increased relative savings by only two percentage points. This is especially interesting since the administrative centers for the Siberian problem are at very great distances from one another. On the other hand, the Siberian rail network is quite simple, consisting very roughly of a single east-west trunkline connected to feeder lines, so that the stability of the results may be misleading. At any rate, the

12. Birman, 1962, pp. 95–98.

question remains whether averaging distances contributes to the apparent savings in the calculated schemes as compared to planned schemes and actual deliveries in a way that would emerge only with more extensive disaggregation (or attempted execution of the scheme).

The aggregation of products appears to present a far more serious problem. Tret'iakova excluded coking coal from her model on the ground that different deposits differ in their analyses in ways that are crucial to their successful use by consumers. Thus, reassignment of deliveries of an aggregated product to reduce transport costs was undesirable with available information. She also notes that ordinary Donbass coals come in some twenty varieties with widely differing effectiveness in alternative uses. If account were taken of this fact, her calculated savings would certainly be reduced.

Cement is perhaps an even stronger case of product homogeneity than coal. But cements too come in a variety of kinds and grades. Indicators of the reduction in calculated savings when variety is taken into account were presented by Loginova. The first of these comes from the 25-supplier matrices. In this case each supplier's production was aggregated by grade of cement, of which four are recognized in the Soviet Union. These amounts were then converted into conventional units, corresponding to the effectiveness in use of grade "400" cement, and transport costs converted accordingly. Consumption requirements were also converted into conventional units. The total costs of transport on this allocation did not differ significantly from the more aggregative models. Apparently the additional costs entailed by changing the transport costs were roughly balanced by the new capability for substituting higher-grade (low transport cost per conventional ton) cements on the longer hauls.

However, Loginova made an additional calculation on the assumption that no substitution of either kind or grade was possible. That is, the assortment of requirements of each consumption point, listed on the *nariady* by grade and kind, were used as the demands to be satisfied. On this calculation (which used the freight-rate criterion), the very substantial savings are virtually eliminated, the calculated plan offering only 4 percent savings instead of 20 or more.

A final calculation uses a scheme Birman has proposed for dealing with the possibility that supplies from different supply points are not all homogeneous.[13] Nonsubstitutable cements are allocated as in the above problem. Where substitution is deemed possible for some of the consumers, the assumption is that the effectiveness of all outputs have a common measure but that some outputs are excluded for some consumers. When a consumer cannot absorb the output of one factor, this is accounted for by setting a prohibitive cost for shipments from that factor to that consumer. This does not affect the length of the computation. If one factory produces several types of product, it may appear as several supply points and the same approach applied to each. Of course this assumes that the products are produced independently, since the availability of each is a datum of the problem. On Loginova's calculation using this approach, total savings was 13.2 percent. Clearly the figures reported in Table 4 substantially overstate savings attainable in a reasonable application of the transportation problem to cement supply in the Ukraine.

In an environment in which current prices are mistrusted, the construction of a criterion for a partial problem becomes a difficult matter. As mistrust deepens, purely physical indicators of performance become relatively more attractive. For this reason the authors of transportation studies have generally used ton-kilometers of haulage as a criterion for some of the calculations. Actual freight rates are also used and divergence in results obtained by using each of these two criteria on the same problem provides

13. *Primenenie,* 1962.

a test, though rather a weak and uncertain one, of the value indices. There has been some experimenting also with the results of a study made in the Ministry of Transport, that produced measures of the direct cost of haulage for a number of commodities over a number of routes. All three criteria produced fairly similar optimal schemes, though percentage savings at times differed substantially. The assumption that transport cost over a given route is proportional to the amount hauled is subject to considerable question, as Gokhman has pointed out.[14] But the assumption is accepted in current planning practice as well as in programming calculations in the Soviet Union. Probably a better tariff schedule will be calculated before more complex criteria can usefully be applied in problem solving.

Soviet authors have placed considerable emphasis on the labor intensiveness of the work of collecting and preparing the information needed in solving problems of this type. No doubt this has been a factor in delaying widespread practical application of programming. For the coal and cement problems, the demand data actually used were more or less ready to hand at the supply-procurement offices, though they were not the data ideally needed. Supply data also came readily from planning organizations. Minimum-distance transportation routes had to be constructed and some processing of the direct cost data was necessary, while freight rates were easily available in tariff schedules. Because the problem could be neatly fitted into the existing organizational framework, data-preparation costs were, relatively speaking, minimal. That they were nonetheless substantial suggests the seriousness of this cost when piecemeal applications of programming are being carried out.

Clearly, the programming scheme has an advantage over the previous planning methods in the speed with which the delivery plan can be constructed and then periodically adjusted to data changes. The old method was not only

14. Gokhman, 1963.

a long-winded one, so that relatively old information inevitably was used in making the initial plan, but was also virtually immune to a revision more sophisticated than forcing. Here is the prospect for a gain of some significance. In addition, the prices emerging from the dual of the problem make possible some comparison of alternatives that transcend the model itself. Tret'iakova mentions the problem of supplying the Moscow area. Local coals are prescribed by both plan and calculation but they have a high pollutant effect and air pollution is already a problem in the area. The programming solution at least provides a reasonably inclusive measure of the cost of shipping cleaner coal to the area. Birman suggests, however, that the shadow prices can be quite misleading. His argument is that one would expect production capacity to be expanded most effectively where relatively high-cost products are shipped to relatively low-priced consumption areas. This is because high royalties will occur in a rational economy only at points where constraints have prevented further development. Applying this theory to the cement problem, the conclusion is that Siberian cement production should be expanded. But because of technological progress and the fact that the Siberian factories are newer, this may very well prove to be faulty development strategy.[15]

As a final comment on these studies, let me in effect repeat Nerlove's comment on a study by Henderson: from the evidence presented it is not clear that the programming solutions to these problems represent an improvement over previous practice.[16] As has been noted, there are a number of rigid assumptions and gross oversimplifications built into the models, many of which do not correspond to the assumptions made by the planners. That these assumptions

15. Note that in the problem just considered, variations in production cost have no effect on the optimal plan because supply and demand are fixed. Thus, implicitly, Birman is discussing capacity expansion alternatives using transport cost as the sole criterion.

16. See Nerlove, 1959, and Henderson, 1958.

could account for the calculated savings seems wholly within the realm of possibility. Even in Loginova's reported savings of over 20 percent, there is so much obvious misallocation (for example four entire *oblasts* are provided with no high-grade cement whatsoever) that the calculations cannot be taken as a measure of the savings to be achieved when a complex railroad network exists.

Naturally this comment cannot be taken as a prediction of results that might be attained in the future. For example, the introduction of production into the transportation scheme can, under certain circumstances, be carried out at the moderate cost of slightly expanding the size of the problem without changing its nature. The Henderson study of the U.S. coal industry, mentioned above, did take production into account, and though smaller in size was definitely more sophisticated than those studies reported here. The future still holds much promise even though the present, as represented in these studies, does not constitute a fruition.

### Long-Run Planning: The Location of Enterprises

This appears to be the first area in which the results of programming calculations more inclusive than the enterprise have been used in a formally adopted plan. Even in this case though, an independent planning scheme was derived by traditional methods. The problem was to plan the location of ceramic construction materials factories in the Republic of Kazakhstan for the period 1965–80. In 1961 the plan was drawn up in Giprostroimaterialy.[17] A team from this institute and from the Institute of Construction Economics was then assigned the task of "verifying the rationality of this scheme, and, if possible, of proposing a more perfect scheme." [18]

17. State Institute for Project-Making of Enterprises in the Construction Materials Industry.

18. Birman, 1962, p. 201.

The general lines of the problem, as conceived by these programmers, were quite similar to those formulated in the model of Nezhintsev and Rakhmanin and described below by Montias.[19] A number of possible sites for factories were identified and costs of production for alternative capacities calculated. Demand was taken as fixed for each consumption point. The problem then was to minimize the total cost of factory construction, production, and transport of products while fulfilling demand at each point. The problem differed from that of Nezhintsev and Rakhmanin in that there were no existing production facilities, the industry was assumed to produce a variety of products, and there were some complementarities associated with producing several of the products on the same site.

The many products of this industry were divided into five product groups. *Oblast* administrative centers were taken as the demand points and requirements for each product group estimated from the general directives for Kazakhstan's economic development. Estimates were made for each of four years: 1965, 1970, 1975, and 1980. The industry is strongly market-oriented, and it was assumed that feasible production points consisted of the given demand points plus two unpopulated railroad junctions and an import point (from outside the republic). Studies of alternative scales of operation assertedly revealed a roughly V-shaped average cost curve; for example, the minimum acceptable capacity for ceramic pipe was taken as 28,000 tons per year, and factory size was limited to some multiple of this amount (including, of course, zero). It was assumed that the transportation network would remain unchanged over the period and that its own capacity was sufficient to handle the increased haulage. Production and transport costs were also assumed constant over the period. In this

19. Nezhintsev and Rakhmanin, 1963. See also Chapter 4 of this volume.

way the same cost matrix could be used for calculations pertaining to a given product at different dates.

Because of the discrete variation in factory size, Birman conceived the problem as one of integer programming. Since no efficient algorithm was available (the demands not being integral multiples of capacities), a multistage and somewhat heuristic approach to a solution was adopted. Initial solutions were obtained by using the transportation problem format, with a fictitious consumer added to absorb the excess of capacity over demand. The allocation of plants for each product group was treated as an independent problem in the initial solution.

The array of initial data and the initial solution for the ceramic pipe distribution for 1970 is shown in Tables 6 and 7. On the basis of values in the optimal fictitious consumption vector, production sites were divided into three groups. The first group contained points such as Taldy-Kurgan and Petropavlovsk, in which no allocations to real consumers were made. These sites were eliminated from further consideration. The second group, containing sites such as Alma-Ata and Pavlodar, allocated all or nearly all their capacity to real consumers. These sites were accepted for the plan, the assigned capacities being accepted provisionally. In the third group fell sites like Semipalatinsk and Ust'Kamenogorsk, in which there was substantial allocation to both real and fictitious consumers.

Calculations of this kind were made for all five product groups and for each of the four years. The next stage in the calculations consisted in determining how much demand exceeded the capacity of the second group of sites, then testing each of the third group of sites in turn to see which factories could provide the additional demand at minimum additional cost. In the case of the pipe factories, the 1980 calculation showed that of the four third-group factories in the 1970 solution, Chimkent alone would be in the second group in 1980. So Chimkent was also ac-

## Table 6

### INITIAL DATA FOR THE CERAMIC PIPE FACTORY LOCATION PROBLEM

(consumption and capacity in thousand tons, costs in thousand rubles/thousand tons)

| Possible points for factory construction | Capacity | Plan Year | Alma-Atinskaia | Eastern Kazakhstan | Semipalatinskaia | Pavlodarskaia | Tselinogradskaia | Kokchetavskaia | Northern Kazakhstan | Kustanaiskaia | Aktiubinskaia | Western Kazakhstan | Gur'evskaia | Southern Kazakhstan | Kzyl-Ordinskaia | Dzhambulskaia | Karagandinskaia | Fictitious Consumer |
|---|---|---|---|---|---|---|---|---|---|---|---|---|---|---|---|---|---|---|
| | | 1980 | 20 | 16 | 10 | 37 | 16 | 13 | 14 | 39 | 6 | 5 | 10 | 27 | 5 | 10 | 53 | 207 |
| | | 1975 | 20 | 16 | 10 | 37 | 16 | 13 | 14 | 38 | 6 | 5 | 9 | 20 | 5 | 10 | 52 | 211 |
| | | 1970 | 17 | 14 | 9 | 28 | 13 | 10 | 12 | 35 | 5 | 4 | 8 | 18 | 5 | 9 | 45 | 252 |
| | | 1965 | 6 | 5 | 3 | 12 | 5 | 4 | 3 | 10 | 2 | 1 | 3 | 5 | 2 | 3 | 18 | 349 |
| Alam-Ata | 28 | | 26 | 33 | 31 | 35 | 33 | 35 | 40 | 37 | 38 | 42 | 41 | 29 | 32 | 28 | 31 | 10 |
| Taldy-Kurgan | 28 | | 28 | 32 | 30 | 34 | 35 | 37 | 37 | 40 | 41 | 44 | 44 | 32 | 45 | 31 | 34 | 10 |
| Ust'-Kamenogorsk | 28 | | 34 | 27 | 28 | 32 | 34 | 36 | 37 | 39 | 43 | 46 | 46 | 39 | 41 | 37 | 35 | 10 |
| Semipalatinsk | 28 | | 31 | 33 | 26 | 30 | 33 | 35 | 34 | 37 | 42 | 44 | 44 | 35 | 38 | 34 | 31 | 10 |
| Pavlodar | 28 | | 38 | 34 | 33 | 28 | 30 | 32 | 33 | 34 | 38 | 42 | 41 | 39 | 42 | 37 | 34 | 10 |
| Tselinograd | 28 | | 36 | 37 | 33 | 31 | 26 | 27 | 28 | 29 | 34 | 36 | 36 | 34 | 36 | 33 | 27 | 10 |
| Kokchetav | 28 | | 43 | 40 | 36 | 33 | 28 | 27 | 28 | 33 | 37 | 39 | 39 | 37 | 39 | 36 | 32 | 10 |
| Petropavlovsk | 28 | | 41 | 42 | 37 | 35 | 30 | 29 | 29 | 33 | 36 | 37 | 36 | 43 | 41 | 42 | 32 | 10 |
| Kustanai | 28 | | 39 | 42 | 41 | 36 | 33 | 35 | 34 | 30 | 36 | 29 | 29 | 42 | 38 | 40 | 34 | 10 |
| Aktiubinsk | 28 | | 44 | 42 | 42 | 42 | 33 | 36 | 33 | 34 | 26 | 28 | 33 | 34 | 31 | 35 | 35 | 10 |
| Ural'sk | 28 | | 43 | 47 | 47 | 41 | 38 | 40 | 38 | 34 | 31 | 33 | 28 | 40 | 36 | 35 | 39 | 10 |
| Gur'ev | 28 | | 38 | 42 | 46 | 35 | 33 | 35 | 33 | 34 | 31 | 29 | 28 | 39 | 36 | 40 | 34 | 10 |
| Kandagach | 28 | | 29 | 38 | 41 | 37 | 38 | 39 | 40 | 38 | 26 | 28 | 37 | 33 | 30 | 35 | 32 | 10 |
| Chimkent | 28 | | 34 | 42 | 35 | 41 | 33 | 34 | 30 | 36 | 34 | 35 | 35 | 26 | 27 | 35 | 35 | 10 |
| Kzyl-Orda | 28 | | 28 | 37 | 40 | 35 | 37 | 28 | 29 | 36 | 32 | 33 | 38 | 29 | 29 | 26 | 31 | 10 |
| Dzhambul | 28 | | 31 | 35 | 34 | 29 | 33 | 38 | 29 | 37 | 36 | 35 | 37 | 27 | 34 | 30 | 26 | 10 |
| Karaganda | 28 | | 31 | 35 | 34 | 29 | 26 | 28 | 29 | 30 | 35 | 35 | 37 | 32 | 34 | 31 | 26 | 10 |
| Angren (Uzbek S.S.R.) | 8 | | 31 | 39 | 38 | 38 | 36 | 38 | 39 | 30 | 34 | 37 | 36 | 27 | 28 | 28 | 34 | 10 |

Source: Birman, 1962, p. 206.

# Table 7

## SOLUTION OF FIRST STAGE OF CERAMIC PIPE PROBLEM
(allocations in thousand tons)

| Possible points for factory construction | Capacity | Plan Year | Alma-Atinskaia | Eastern Kazakhstan | Semipalatinskaia | Pavlodarskaia | Tselinogradskaia | Kokchetavskaia | Northern Kazakhstan | Kustanaiskaia | Aktiubinskaia | Western Kazakhstan | Gur'evskaia | Southern Kazakhstan | Kzyl-Ordinskaia | Dzhambulskaia | Karagandinskaia | Fictitious Consumer |
|---|---|---|---|---|---|---|---|---|---|---|---|---|---|---|---|---|---|---|
| | | 1980 | 20 | 16 | 10 | 31 | 16 | 13 | 14 | 39 | 6 | 5 | 10 | 21 | 5 | 10 | 53 | 207 |
| | | 1975 | 20 | 16 | 10 | 31 | 16 | 13 | 14 | 38 | 6 | 5 | 9 | 20 | 5 | 10 | 52 | 211 |
| | | 1970 | 17 | 14 | 9 | 28 | 13 | 10 | 12 | 35 | 5 | 4 | 8 | 18 | 5 | 9 | 45 | 252 |
| | | 1965 | 6 | 5 | 3 | 12 | 5 | 4 | 3 | 10 | 2 | 1 | 3 | 5 | 2 | 3 | 18 | 394 |
| Allocated to consumers | | | 17 | 14 | 9 | 28 | 13 | 10 | 12 | 35 | 5 | 4 | 8 | 18 | 5 | 9 | 45 | 252 |
| Alma-Ata | 28 | | 17 | | | | | | | | | | | 2 | | 9 | | — |
| Taldy-Kurgan | 28 | | | | | | | | | | | | | | | | | 28 |
| Ust'-Kamenogorsk | 28 | | | 14 | | | | | | | | | | | | | | 14 |
| Semipalatinsk | 28 | | | | 9 | | | | | | | | | | | | | 19 |
| Pavlodar | 28 | | | | | 24 | | | | | | | | | | | | 4 |
| Tselinograd | 28 | | | | | 4 | 7 | | | | | | | | | | 17 | — |
| Kokchetav | 28 | | | | | | 6 | 10 | 12 | | | | | | | | | — |
| Petropavlovsk | 28 | | | | | | | | | | | | | | | | | 28 |
| Kustanai | 28 | | | | | | | | | 7 | | | | | | | | 21 |
| Aktiubinsk | 28 | | | | | | | | | | 5 | | | | | | | 23 |
| Ural'sk | 28 | | | | | | | | | | | 4 | | | | | | 24 |
| Gur'ev | 28 | | | | | | | | | | | | 8 | | | | | 20 |
| Kandagach | 28 | | | | | | | | | 28 | | | | | | | | — |
| Chimkent | 28 | | | | | | | | | | | | | 16 | | | | 12 |
| Kzyl-Orda | 28 | | | | | | | | | | | | | | 5 | | | 23 |
| Dzhambul | 28 | | | | | | | | | | | | | | | | | 28 |
| Karaganda | 28 | | | | | | | | | | | | | | | | 28 | — |
| Angren (Uzbek S.S.R.) | 8 | | | | | | | | | | | | | | | | | 8 |

Source: Birman, 1962, p. 207.

cepted for completion by 1970. When each of the remaining three factories was introduced separately and in turn into the matrix, Semipalatinsk turned out to be the choice.

Additional comparisons of this kind were made to check whether the size of some factories could be increased; e.g. three pipe factories were doubled in size as a result of this calculation. Also, certain ad hoc modifications were made at this stage. Complementarities turned out to be a minor problem since each independent product group calculation assigned production to almost the same sites, though a few changes were made in the case of two product groups for this reason. The final plan turned out to be quite similar to that derived by traditional methods and was "adopted for realization."

A much larger calculation has been attempted for cement: the determination of an optimal bill of factories for the entire Soviet Union for 1970.[20] Some 125 possible production points and 135 consolidated consumption points were identified. All cement, regardless of type, was converted into conventional units. The calculation procedures and criterion appear to have been quite similar to those reported above. The resulting calculation, it is claimed, reduced the average length of haul of cement to 305 kilometers, as compared to 564 kilometers, for actual hauls in 1960 and 330 for optimal hauls made in a separate calculation for 1965.

It appears that this scheme did not become part of the plan. At a conference held to discuss the results, Loginov was quite critical of previous practice, pointing out that a number of factories built during the postwar period should be shut down according to the optimal production and distribution scheme.[21] A number of criticisms of the optimal scheme were also made and, though these were not published, they seem to have centered around errors

20. Loginov and Mints, 1964.
21. *Stroitel'naia gazeta*, Nov. 16, 1962, and Jan. 25, 1963.

in the initial data used for the calculations. In view of
the comments in the previous section, it seems likely that
there would also be grounds for criticizing the assortment
of cements allocated to individual consumption points. At
any rate, a good deal of additional work was done on the
problem in 1963, and though Loginov and Birman both
claim that the results were improved, there is no mention
of adoption of the revised scheme.[22]

Economists have generally considered the problem of
allocating investment among competing uses as rather complex. The problem at hand may offer a breakthrough in
the way of simplification; more likely it is a crude and
misplaced oversimplification. No account is taken by the
model of alternative production techniques for any given
site. At most, two alternative positive capacity limits are
assigned to a site. There is no interaction between results
for this sector and for other sectors. No account is taken of
the effects of alternative transport schemes on the transportation network itself. And, of course, the simplified
assumptions about the nature of the cement industry (described in the previous section) all apply here. Presumably
similar remarks may be made about the ceramic materials
study.[23]

Of course all development plans are fraught with uncertainty, and perhaps uncertainty may be used to justify an
approach of this kind. If it is true that transport itself is
not a bottleneck, and that alternative project costs are
dominated by transport costs and relative production costs,
then this approach may be a desirable one. But criticisms

22. Loginov and Mints, 1964, p. 117; Birman, 1963b.

23. In two respects the latter study may be more nearly acceptable.
It takes account of the multiproduct nature of the industry and it is
oriented primarily toward a region. Cement factory location in the
United States is regional-market oriented (Lichtenberg, 1960, p. 260).
The same is likely to be true of the Soviet Union. Thus a series of more
complex models of narrower scope would seem to be a preferable line
of approach.

(such as Loginov's) of past planning results may be more the result of the organizational confusion that has surrounded the cement industry than of inept planning within organizations. The apparently close coincidence of plan and calculated distribution of Kazakh ceramics suggests that this may be true. That is, it is an open question whether the calculation procedure provides a significant improvement over previous practice, given comparable problem scope and data in each procedure.

## ENTERPRISE AND INTERMEDIATE LEVEL STUDIES[24]

Enterprise and plant-level problems are not directly within the scope of this paper. However, techniques, interpretations, and successes achieved here, where ideology does not seem to be threatened by application of the approach, should have some impact on the willingness of those concerned to try similar approaches that are more inclusive in scope. For this reason, some studies at this level were surveyed.

·The machinery industry seems a natural place for early application of programming in the Soviet Union. Kantorovich has dealt explicitly with the problem of assigning tasks to a set of machines, while the problem of minimizing waste in choosing cutting patterns (e.g. in sheet metal cutting) has been studied and applied in the West. A mid-1961 conference on the use of mathematical methods in planning machinery production[25] offers an opportunity to assess the

24. An extensive but not exhaustive search of publicly available Soviet materials on the use of linear programming in economic planning was made as a part of the present study. On the basis of this survey an impression of the scope and nature of Soviet applied work through 1963 was formed. The impression gained is consistent with the impressions of recent visitors to the Soviet Union. Nor does the situation appear to have changed substantially during the two succeeding years.

25. Kozlov, 1962.

extent of use of linear programming at that time. Experimental calculations had been made in some twenty enterprises, and some of the work was put to use by the planning authorities. Nevertheless, mere formalization of problems and purely exemplary calculations dominated the work reported at the conference. Among the authors, Nelidov attacked the usefulness of linear programming for many problems of the industry (including the machine-loading problem) because of asserted substantial divergences between reality and the rigid assumptions of such models. The remaining papers did not deal effectively with this objection, and a leading authority on linear programming, Gerchuk, has recently mounted a similar attack over the whole range of applications.[26] There is evidence from some more recent studies that application of the technique within the enterprise is proceeding, though perhaps not at a very rapid pace.[27]

At this level the distinction between purely technological and economic problems is sometimes hard to draw. Time saved or waste reduced has social value, but is a matter of moving on to the production function rather than along it. Or at least so it appears in the model, where the cost of reaching the new point in terms of additional setup time, computing costs, etc., does not show up. Somewhat similar are the studies of appropriate loading of a set of steam or electric power stations. The criterion here may be to supply some given description of demand with minimum expenditure of conventional power or to minimize some function of operating characteristics of the system which relate to the quality and reliability of the service. Even when the relevant decision is simply a two-fold choice between manual and automatic control, the problem is not purely technological, since in practice demand is likely to

26. Gerchuk, 1965.
27. Bagrinovskii, 1963; Bykov, 1963; Bykov and Gavrilets, 1963; Efimov and Maksimov, 1963.

be affected in several ways, some positive and some negative, by such a shift. These models make use of nonlinear programming and are often dynamic.[28]

Interest in agricultural applications of linear programming seems also to have followed this pattern of relatively slow development. Though a good description of illustrative applications to agriculture appeared in the periodical literature in 1961, in 1964 simple expository accounts were still appearing and reports even of experimental calculations seemed relatively scarce.[29] An exposition by Kravchenko in 1963 discusses three types of applications: the choice of a sowing plan which maximizes the production of conventional units of feed subject to constraints on the use of land, labor, machinery, etc.; the choice of a minimum cost livestock diet; and minimum cost assignment of farm machinery of different types to the carrying out of some specified set of tasks.[30] Calculations that may have been experimental were made for problems of these three types in two *sovkhozy* near Leningrad and Moscow respectively. Aganbegian reports some work carried out in Novosibirsk.[31] A calculation for the Soviet Union as a whole divided the country into eighteen regions and developed a sowing plan for seventeen crops, using a heuristic or "multistage" model like that described earlier in this study. An initial solution of the transportation-problem interpretation of the environment gave a highly specialized assignment of crops to regions. This was then modified in successive steps, taking account not only of factors such as yield and cost, which appeared in the first stage, but of additional factors such as transport costs, climatic constraints, etc. The shadow prices of preceding solutions were used (in part) in evaluations at later stages in the solution. Experience with this

28. Krumm, 1963; Krumm and Syrov, 1964; Shakhanov, 1960.
29. Al'tshuler, 1961; Popov, 1961.
30. Kravchenko, 1963.
31. Aganbegian, 1964b.

broad but purely experimental work has led to a serious attempt to construct some practical solutions, ranging in size from a portion of Novosibirsk *oblast* to a grain-sowing plan for the U.S.S.R.[32] But for the most part, even recently reported work makes use of "illustrative" data.[33]

As for applications of linear programming above the level of the firm, only the enterprise location problem seems really to have caught on by the end of 1963. The Laboratory of Mathematical-Economic Research of Novosibirsk University alone solved about twenty such problems during 1963, dealing with everything from the distribution of garages for truck repair in 1965 to the distribution of ferrous metals plants in 1970–80. In these problems, nonlinear unit cost functions were approximated by a small number of points and discrete-valued solutions sought essentially by the method described above.

The perspective distribution plan for ferrous metals constitutes a multibranch problem, though a high degree of aggregation of individual products was certainly necessary. Attempts to step outside the confines of the transportation problem, especially in getting short-run solutions, do not as yet seem to have got off the ground. A paper by Tret'iakova and Batalina uses the format on pages 163–64 above to work out experimental calculations for both perspective and annual fuel balances.[34] Another, by Kuznetsov et al., takes account of substitution possibilities and the existence of different types of consumers, formulating a general linear program which meets given differentiated demand at minimum cost.[35] They estimate that an acceptable solution would have to take account of 30 to 40 different types of fuel, allocating to 10 or 12 different groups of consumers in each of 80 to 100 cities, a problem beyond

32. Ibid., p. 31.
33. See Kardash, 1964.
34. Tret'iakova and Batalina, 1963.
35. Kuznetsov, 1962.

the capacity of, for example, the BESM-2M computer. There is no mention of implementation of the model.

A final type of extra-enterprise problem is worth a brief comment. Nemchinov has discussed in very general terms the application of a criterion of optimality to an input-output model of an economic region, for example by the familiar procedure of maximizing a linear combination of the final demands or minimizing the use of the scarce factor while producing a given bill of final demands.[36] N. Kovalev has made some use of value-based regional input-output tables within an optimizing context.[37] Minimum and maximum values are set for the gross outputs, the former being determined by some previous production level or by capacity limits, the latter by resource constraints or other a priori information. A fixed availability of homogeneous labor is assumed; the same assumption is made for capital. And net exports of each product are also given. Subject to these constraints, one seeks an extreme value of one of the following: gross material costs of production, gross output, net output, or the import of some product into the region. Using a mixture of actual and fictitious data, Kovalev carried out a number of calculations at Gosplan S.S.S.R.'s Computing Center.[38] These indicate considerable similarity in results using different criteria, though Kovalev comes down on the side of net output. However, he also believes that a variety of calculations provides essential information about alternatives in situations where only a portion of the economy is being considered, so that the national social-economic criterion cannot be applied directly.

Several regions have been making calculations along the lines suggested by Kovalev. However, in January 1965 a bat-

36. Nemchinov, 1961c.
37. Kovalev, 1964b.
38. No description of the computing procedure is given. He appears to have calculated at least 35 solutions for a 17-sector model. Possibly the data was taken from the White Russian economic region.

tery of nine well-known economists, including Gol'shtein, Dadaian and Mash, strongly attacked both Kovalev's model and his presentation.[39] They pointed to the danger of using value data in constructing such models, the arbitrariness of the lower and especially the upper bounds to gross outputs, the failure to integrate capital requirements with production levels, and so on. But most of all they criticized the partial context of the calculations and the fact that the interregional problem is assumed solved by the fixing of net imports. The proper approach, they suggested in passing, is the construction of "dynamic interregional models of optimal planning." The Soviets too have their problems with mathematical purists! Though Kovalev's model is indeed crude, the critics seem to have missed the appropriate comparison, which is not with some ideal model that can be practically applied only in the distant future, but with current practice. Regional planners in the Soviet Union do have to solve a problem rather like that posed by Kovalev; they must, at some stage, work out their regional plan constrained by a previously prescribed set of dealings with the rest of the economy. One might speculate that if Kovalev's approach offers any advantage here it is with respect to industries of secondary importance, whose interdependence with other sectors is probably given more careful attention by Kovalev than by current practice.[40]

The constraint of computer inadequacy weighs heavily on most extra-enterprise work. But if the (mythical?) transistorized M250 with its large memory and million or more operations per second makes a swift appearance, the effective constraint on problems at this level—below the na-

39. Volkonskii et al., 1965. Kovalev's reply appeared in the April 1965 issue of the same journal.

40. The bibliography plus this brief description of some of the cited studies should serve to provide a general idea of the state of published work using linear programming approaches in Soviet economic planning.

tional economy as a whole and above the enterprise—
would quickly shift to data collection. No doubt the range
of problems considered would be greatly expanded, for
example, to include short-run branch production and supply models. Indeed the approach of "piecemeal social engineering," of extending the use of linear programming a
step at a time, starting with the areas that promise the best
results given existing circumstances, is advocated by Aganbegian as the most expedient.[41] But as will be seen below,
this view is not universally held.

## CENTRALIZED PLANNING: A GRAND SCHEME

The Soviet work reported to this point reflects attempts
to introduce programming calculations into the economy
piecemeal. Widespread applications have been found for
linear programming at the enterprise and plant levels.
With a handful of exceptions, work at higher and more inclusive organizational levels has produced programming
interpretations of problems rather than practical solutions.
An extrapolation of this trend would indicate that work
has hardly begun at the level of national economic programming.

Such is not the case. The Institute of Cybernetics of the
Ukrainian Academy of Sciences and the Central Economics-
Mathematics Institute (CEMI) of the Academy of Sciences
U.S.S.R. have each assertedly produced national economic
models intended as appropriate bases for a national, mathematically sophisticated planning process.[42] Unfortunately,
I have seen only incomplete verbal descriptions of the models. The first appears to be dynamic throughout its structure and will be ignored here. The second, as recently
described by V. Pugachev, though it uses dated variables,
appears in its short-run version to be based on an essen-

41. Aganbegian, 1964b, p. 35.
42. Glushkov and Fedorenko, 1964.

tially static programming model.[43] For this reason, and because of Pugachev's claim that here at last is a means for solving the "millions of equations" that became famous in the socialist dispute, it will be described here. Rather, to be more precise, I will use his description as a basis for speculation as to the nature of his planning scheme.

No detail is provided about long-run planning. It seems that a highly aggregative, dynamic model will provide some basic characteristics of a series of alternatives and that a time-dependent function of variables representing social consumption will be used in choosing among these. From this result, and presumably also in interaction with previous plans and performance, a quadratic criterion function—in which products or product groups are the arguments—will be derived.

A two-stage description of productive activity is envisioned. The economy will be divided into roughly a thousand branches, the criterion of partitioning being minimization of the number of enterprises producing the products of more than one branch. Within branches, production will be characterized by Leontief activities. That is, it is assumed that in general each product can be produced in several ways, though in every case there are constant returns to the scale of the activity, and each activity produces only one product. Limitation on the level of activity within a branch is provided either by some given level of provision of a composite resource (which could be branch capacity), or by requiring the achievement of some given bill of final demands.

The upper stage of branch interaction is similar in structure. Each branch is now characterized as a bundle of possible Leontiev activities, constrained by some resource limitation generalized for the economy as a whole. In a typical plan there will be a characterization of each branch in this form for each of several (say five) years. The first stage in

43. Pugachev, 1964a.

this "automated" planning scheme then is to find values for the activity levels of product and branch which maximize the value of the criterion.

In solving this problem the first step would be to produce in effect the hyperplanes representing production possibilities in each branch, assuming it is constrained by a likely value for the scarce factor of that branch. Several most probable points on each hyperplane will be selected and, in terms of these, each branch characterized as a small number of alternative activities. These activities then constitute the structure of the larger interbranch problem, which is solved in the same way. The solutions at branch and national levels also contain prices. The national solution is then fed back to the branches. Where capacity constraints on branch operation appear crucial, branch solutions may be recalculated as before with the exception of the new value of the constraint. For other branches, recalculation can be done by minimizing cost (scarce factor use), subject to fulfilling the bill of final demands implied by the national solution. The prices emerging from the national calculation may be used to revalue constraints at lower levels. At the end, each enterprise receives a complete plan of production in physical terms, together with the corresponding input-supply schedule. Finally, via the solution of the appropriate transportation problems, suppliers are assigned to consumers, and production is assigned rationally over space.

Pugachev's model, as reconstructed, is clearly not complete. More or less ad hoc decisions enter at several points (e.g. in aggregating branch activities), and there is no provision for integrating the final supply plan with earlier calculations. Also, the time dimension is apparently handled by simply varying the values of the constraints in different years, using results obtained from the perspective plan and elsewhere. The simplifications were justified in the following way. Pugachev first notes that a complete national

economic plan requires values for some fifty million variables which interact through some five million relations. To
attempt to solve directly a general linear program of such a
size would put an impossible burden on computing facilities. In measuring the computing requirements for various
problems, Pugachev takes as his unit a "standard problem,"
a linear program containing 10,000 unknowns and 1,000
constraints, which he claims a computer capable of a million operations a second could solve in three to five hours.
To solve the big problem directly using the simplex
method would be equivalent to solving $125 \cdot 10^9$ standard
problems. Even taking advantage of the fact (or at any rate
assuming) that most of the coefficient array could be made
block diagonal, so that the decomposition principle could
be used efficiently in solution, it would still require the
equivalent of solving $15 \cdot 10^6$ standard problems. This is
too heavy a demand, so further simplification is essential.

If I have understood him, Pugachev's two chief simplifications consist in aggregation and use of the substitution theorem. It seems highly unlikely that the process of
aggregation and disaggregation he advocates can be associated with any formally optimal result. The second simplification provides an algorithm that produces an optimum choice of activities for each stage in the calculation
seeking bills of activity levels.[44] The structure of the problem is such that the optimum choice of activities can be
made independently of the choice of an optimal bill of
goods.[45] He asserts that these simplifications reduce the
calculation requirements to about $10^4$ standard problems

44. Malinvaud, 1963.

45. Some of Pugachev's ideas may have come from a study of
optimizing within the framework of activity analysis and input-output
by Iudin and Gol'shtein (1961). There is no mention of Malinvaud or
of the substitution theorem in Pugachev's verbal description of the
planning model, but I can think of no other way to account for the
very great simplification of the calculations which he claims.

per iteration. Allowing a month for each iteration, he asserts that the problem would require computer capacity (in terms of the total number of operations per second that could be performed simultaneously by the available computers) somewhat less than that presently existing in the United States.

The Soviets are some years from even this goal of computer capacity, not to mention the problem of assembling the hundreds of billions of binary bits of information that Pugachev requires as initial data. Any attempt at introducing a scheme of this kind in the near future would clearly involve, at the least, a much more extensive aggregation at both stages of the production process. And as it stands the simplifications have already reached heroic proportions. There is no evidence that this scheme and the one proposed by the Institute of Cybernetics have any present purpose beyond that of assaying the Soviet economy's information-processing requirements as a basis for designing the new national computer system. The effort appears so far to have stopped short of an attempt to describe the economy (or even a branch) empirically in terms of the model.

## ORGANIZATIONAL IMPACT

The applied work surveyed here was carried out during 1963 or earlier. It is clear that by 1963 a large volume of work using linear programming was under way over a broad front. It is also clear that few programming studies had actually been substituted for the more traditional planning methods. A great deal of the Soviet writing on the subject has been purely expository. Much of the specific model building is little more than a general exposition of linear programming, with some limited adaptation to the specific problem at hand. Perhaps the most striking feature of this work lies not in the nature of the applications nor the mathematical technique but in the pragmatic approach.

Ideological constraints do not seem to impinge on the interpretation of specific models.

If work in this area has not yet had a substantial impact on planning practice, the question that seems most pertinent is whether or in what form it will have an impact in the future. This is essentially the question of what constraints are effective and at what level of use of programming techniques they become effective. Since the answer seems to vary with the inclusiveness of the model, we will start with the lowest level and work up.

If the impression of rather slow development of enterprise applications is a correct one, it may well be that the key constraint here is cadres. Those with the opportunity and incentive to learn something about programming are likely to have been absorbed by the variety of research institutes at the universities, gosplans, ministries, etc. Many enterprise applications would be of modest dimension, so that computer availability would be relatively less serious as a constraint. The organizational problem would also be relatively less constraining, though inertia, vested interests, and the initial costs of information collection are significant at all levels. Of course there must be a great deal of work done which is not published, but the incentives to report successful experience in an area that is now ideologically fully acceptable would suggest that the emphasis in published work on illustrative examples reflects some real lag in practical work.

Applications such as perspective planning of enterprise distribution are not constrained by computer availability. The ceramic materials study and nearly all others of its type were computed by hand and other studies did not make serious time demands on the relatively small computers on which they were calculated. Also, the information problem assumes a quite different and probably less complex form for problems of this kind. Uncertainties as to the nature of demand ten or fifteen years hence provide ample excuse for aggregation, thus greatly simplifying the assortment planning problem. This particular class of problems seems to provide a welcome solution which can be used rather widely and requires little reorganization of existing practice to introduce. The same transportation problem applied to short-run planning has run into more difficulties. The problem is complicated by quality differences even in relatively homogeneous products, and by the heavy costs associated with taking effective account of substitution possibilities. But computer time cannot be a very serious constraint here either, so long as it remains formally a transportation problem.

More complex problems require much more time-consuming calculation for a comparable number of constraints. There is no doubt that solution of, say, the fuel balance problem, in which substitutions are possible and the assortment of alternative fuels is given realistic treatment, would put a very heavy strain on existing computing facilities and provide only a very incomplete answer to the problem. There is no doubt that computer availability is a limitation of some importance for problems at this level, problems including short-run branch planning as well as sectoral distribution. But setup times and the cost of collecting the appropriate information also increase rapidly with the complexity of the problem. And the organizational problem too becomes more difficult.

The difficulty with working across organizational lines has already been mentioned. Essentially the problem arises because information is prepared for internal use, and incentives to adjust to the needs of external units are weak. The primary information must be extracted from working enterprises whose staffs are already burdened with excessive reporting requirements and who stand to gain little from the results of the new program. Also, for widespread piecemeal application of the new techniques, problems of conflicts would begin to develop in the type of information collected which could substantially increase collection costs. For example, the kind of demand information appropriate for the transportation study (a point estimate) is rather different from that required in a model taking account of substitution. Or alternative models using respectively linear and nonlinear descriptions of a productive activity may be used for different problems. The cost of producing several quite different quantitative descriptions of the same set of activities could easily become substantial.

The organizational problem poses special difficulties because of the different extent to which adjustments are explicitly made under the two systems. To return to the cement transportation problem, the process of filling up the *nariady,* of assigning producers to consumers, contained elements of optimizing not all of which are present in the formal assignment scheme. The assignment of guidelines like the normal directions of traffic flow by the Ministry of Transport has its analog in the minimum cost criterion of the formal problem. But assortment adjustment by the supply-procurement organization has no analog. As will be recalled, this was an adjustment of the bill of demands for grades and types of cement at construction sites. Though Birman undoubtedly has good reason to inveigh against its arbitrary nature, one would imagine that the agency has some awareness of the relative priorities of these projects—the interest of participants is certainly aroused on this point by the system. In effect it is a low-level analog of coefficient forcing, a far from ideal process but nonetheless, broadly speaking, a process aimed at improving outcomes.

The formal scheme cannot adjust demands in this way. The organizational dilemma is reversed when supply assortment is forced. The formal scheme can be used to deal with an adjustment of this kind, but if it is to do so one of two things must happen: either the supply-procurement agency must be given full authority to vary production targets or an explicit criterion limiting the kinds of adjustments to be permitted must be assigned it. The first entails a radical reorganization of planning, while the second, by formalizing a complex administrative routine, would imply an awareness of the precise nature of the current plan-making process which does not seem to exist. Also, it would require formal study to produce and would most likely be all too revealing of the arbitrariness of the procedure.

Before turning briefly to the national planning schemes it is well to note again that the very modest savings implied by the studies reported previously are based on an incomplete assessment of the gains to be achieved from the new planning techniques, even when introduced piecemeal. The speed with which an answer can be produced and the flexibility with which plans may be adjusted—taking account of indirect effects in responding to data changes —may bring about a very substantial gain, but one which does not figure in the numerical estimates of savings. In the case of short-run planning this means that the system targets (and even prices) on which enterprises base their decisionmaking can be made more responsive to current changes of data. In both the long run and the short it also means that variants of the plan are relatively easily produced, a factor which, if American experience is relevant, means an improvement not only in knowledge of alternatives, but also in knowledge of the appropriate criterion, as planners and the leadership are forced to make more sophisticated decisions.

Taken at their face value, schemes like those of Glushkov and Pugachev are truly revolutionary in their organizational implications. Pugachev's scheme (on our interpretation) implies a return to the branch-ministerial hierarchy. Its thoroughgoing centralization, with input and output targets assigned for all goods to every enterprise, would have to be accompanied by a quite different incentive and control system than the existing one. And the demand for a unified national economic information system itself has profound implications for economic organization. But since nothing remotely resembling such a system is feasible over the next two or three years (and probably for much longer), these implications will not be discussed here.

Instead, we may consider the possibility of a more modest, but still systematic, use of programming at the national level. Specifically, the Pugachev (really the Malinvaud) scheme appears to have some possibilities within the framework of the planning scheme as described above on pages 191–92. A case can be made against the use of Leontiev activities on a highly disaggregated scale because the kind of interaction which is taken account of by the scheme is not crucial for a great many industries. Indeed, general tests of the performance of input-output suggest that much simpler approaches that wholly ignore this interdependence perform almost as well.[46] Where it *is* important, particularly in manufacturing industry producing primarily intermediate goods, the Pugachev approach makes it possible to choose a balanced bill of gross outputs for those industries, while at the same time selecting an optimal technology, or presenting a set of alternative feasible technologies. Such a scheme could easily be integrated into the approach to planning referred to above, with coefficient forcing for included industries accomplished by the selection of appropriate alternative activities. The result would be a more systematic use of forcing but, at least for the included industries, would be much more likely to produce a feasible, balanced bill of goods. A problem involving several hundred such activities would not be beyond current Soviet capabilities. Indeed, I imagine a general linear program of this dimension, in which an activity was capable of producing several products and might be subject to a unique (to it) capacity constraint, would be within the realm of possibility. Whatever might be the gains in "cal-

46. Chenery and Clark, 1959, Chap. 6.

culated" savings, the increased speed and flexibility of response of such a scheme would be a strong argument in its favor.

As we have described it so far, the implications of piecemeal social engineering for the Soviet planning system would seem to be determined by the quite limited prospects for gains from improved simulation on the computer (or often simply by routinized hand calculations) of traditional, essentially administrative planning procedures. Having come up against this barrier the Soviets, some three or four years hence, would then face the alternatives of either introducing a revolutionary reorganization of the economy or being content with the probably modest achievements of the piecemeal approach. But this ignores the interaction between organizational change and change in planning routines. The latter generates new information which often points up more clearly than before the inadequacies in existing procedures, thereby creating pressure for change. Also, as noted at the beginning of this paper, new information in one area may turn out to be useful for improving work in other areas. Belkin and Birman have strengthened the case for reorganizing the construction industry as a result of their programming studies at the Institute of Construction Economics.[47] It would be difficult to assert with confidence any properties of the end result of a process of piecemeal reorganization triggered by piecemeal revision of planning routines. If recognized gains (which might be of the overoptimistic type calculated in some of the studies reported above—but in this case the optimism would tend to be self-justifying) are great enough, it too could turn out to be a revolutionary process.

At the present time even this piecemeal approach is seriously threatened by Libermanism. It is ironic that one of the early results of quantitative analysis in Soviet planning has been to help make all too clear the deficiencies of

47. Belkin and Birman, 1964.

the present system of planning and control at the enterprise level. For the gains that the piecemeal social engineers
may yet be able to offer in the form of an improved price
system and much greater flexibility in planning must come
later, perhaps too late. Those who would retain the supply
system and some direct control over enterprise production levels may qualify as right-wing Libermanites, given
the vagueness with which Liberman has formulated his
position. But preservation of the supply system *is* a key
to the piecemeal approach to planning revision; if it goes,
most of the rationale for centralized, highly disaggregated
planning and especially for this kind of short-run planning,
goes with it.

# 4. Soviet Optimizing Models for Multiperiod Planning

*John M. Montias*

If it is true, as one Soviet expert on input-output recently claimed, that "despite a massive expansion of research, in which teams of scientific research institutes are occupied, the method of interindustry balancing has not been introduced into the practical work of planning and economic organs," [1] then what should one say of the gap between dynamic optimizing models and their practical applications? In no field of mathematical economics is the discrepancy between the thought and its execution more flagrant.

While the models constructed in the Soviet Union are by no means devoid of interest, they are so remote from planning practice that there is little to distinguish them from comparable Western work. Soviet mathematical economists cannot be said to form a separate school dealing with special problems or investigating special techniques. They are working the same vineyards as their colleagues in the United States, France, and Japan. Unfortunately much, if not most, of the work published in recent years in the Soviet Union is manifestly derivative and would not deserve mention if it were not for the light these efforts

I am very grateful to Andrea Maneschi and Herbert Scarf for their help on a number of technical points.

1. Cherniak, 1964, p. 190.

may throw on the orientation of Soviet research and on the ideas that animate it.[2]

Since there is relatively little to say about the applicability of most of these mathematical schemes to actual planning situations, I shall concentrate on the technical aspects of the models, which I should have glossed over if I had been surveying one of the fields such as input-output where direct applications are more immediate.

## KANTOROVICH AND NOVOZHILOV

L. V. Kantorovich, in his pioneering contribution of 1939 on "Mathematical Methods for the Organization and Planning of Production"[3] limited himself to static models, although of course the basic tools he used in his later dynamic model were forged in that early work.

The first Soviet writer to construct a model for an optimal long-term plan seems to have been V. V. Novozhilov, notably in a paper published in 1946, which Gregory Grossman brought to the attention of Western economists and carefully analyzed in his article on "Scarce Capital and Soviet Doctrine."[4] In general, I refer the reader to Grossman's account; however, for the sake of establishing a link with subsequent Soviet writings, I should like to single out the following points:

1. Novozhilov's objective function consists in minimizing total labor inputs, which, as Grossman indicated, may not be the essential preoccupation of Soviet planners.

2. End products appear in the model as constraints prescribing a fixed bill of goods at the end of the planned period.

2. This assertion is weakened by the fact that I have not had access to any of the occasional mathematical economic publications of the Novosibirsk section of the Academy of Sciences, which may contain more important contributions than those surveyed in this paper, limited essentially to works published in Moscow and Leningrad.

3. Kantorovich, 1939.

4. Novozhilov, 1946; Grossman, 1953, pp. 327–30.

3. The rate of return on capital is associated with the extra labor cost that would be incurred in a firm if a unit of capital were withdrawn from this use after an optimal allocation had been achieved.

4. Novozhilov's model, even though it involves the allocation of capital, is essentially a single-period scheme in which none of the variables are dated. There is an implicit assumption that the period selected is long enough to encompass the gestation of all investments but that differences in the incidence of investments and outputs through time may be neglected.

The dynamic model sketched out by Kantorovich in 1959, in the first mathematical appendix to his book on *The Economic Calculation of the Optimal Utilization of Resources*,[5] is somewhat more realistic and more satisfactory from a theoretical point of view than Novozhilov's scheme. As in his static model, Kantorovich maximizes a single variable representing the intensity of operation of a vector specifying the proportions in which certain end products are to be delivered.[6] He suggests, for example, that the planners might seek to maximize the number of bundles of production capacities or of consumption goods available in the last period of the plan.[7] In this model, each activity vector comprises the coefficients pertaining to all the time periods considered. When an activity so defined is operated at intensity x, this implies that all the subactivities belonging to the different periods are operated at the same level x. Due to this inflexibility, it is unlikely that a really optimal plan would be generated, as compared to

5. Kantorovich, 1959a.

6. This interpretation of Kantorovich's maximand corresponds to his latest version (1964, p. 328), but it is fully equivalent to that found in his earlier treatments, where the variable to be maximized was defined as the minimum, overall end products, of the ratios of their outputs to the proportional factors $k_j$ $(j = 1, \ldots, n)$.

7. Kantorovich, 1959a, p. 291.

the possibility of varying the activity levels of each period, unless the structure of the model exhibited special properties (as in the original Von Neumann model).

In a 1964 variant of this model, the same rigid feature is preserved.[8] However, there are some new twists worth mentioning on the demand side of the problem. Kantorovich introduces a consumption vector for each period t:

$$(0, \ldots, 0, -C_{n_3+1,t}, \ldots, -C_{n_4,t}, G_{n_4+1,t}) \quad (t = 1, 2, \ldots, T)$$

In this vector the first $n_3$ elements correspond to productive resources (numbered 1 to $n_1$), productive factors ($n_1 + 1, \ldots, n_2$) and intermediate products ($n_2 + 1, \ldots, n_3$). (These elements are all null, since these inputs do not enter final consumptions.) The $C_{it}$ ($i = n_3 + 1, \ldots, n_4$) are the total required quantities of private and social goods consumed. The last component, denoted $G_{n_4+1,t}$, in the above vector is a coefficient equal to unity in each period t. The imposition of a restraint on the equation corresponding to this last component makes it possible to fix the minimum number of "bundles" of consumption comprising the ingredients $-C_{n_3+1}$ to $-C_{n_4}$ that will have to be supplied. If we denote by $x_t$ the level at which the entire consumption vector will be operated at time t, the equation determining this minimum level will read:

$$G_{n_4+1,t}x_t = x_t \geq 1 \quad (t = 1, \ldots, T)$$

At this minimum intensity, exactly the quantities $C_{n_3+1,t}$, $\ldots$, $C_{n_4,t}$ would be made available for consumption in each period.

Then, Kantorovich suggests, one may choose to maximize $\alpha$, the rate of growth of the fixed consumption bundle, such that $x_t \geq (1 + \alpha)^t$ ($t = 1, 2, \ldots, T$) where T is the terminal period.[9] It is important to notice that Kantorovich never compares the utility of bundles of different time periods.

8. Kantorovich, 1964.
9. Ibid., p. 329.

His discount factor arises strictly from the supply side, by way of a comparison of the "objectively determined evaluations" (shadow prices) associated with the outputs and with the availabilities of scarce factors in different periods.[10]

These "evaluations" are of course calculated from the basic principle that the unit operation of any production activity must yield a zero profit. Denoting the evaluations for any product or factor i $(i = 1, \ldots, N)$ at time t $(t = 1, \ldots, T)$ by the symbol $c_{it}$ and the technological coefficients by $a^s_{it}$ where s stands for one of the production processes $(s = 1, \ldots, r)$, we may write:

$$\sum_i \sum_t c_{it} a^s_{it} \leq 0 \qquad (s = 1, \ldots, r)$$

The above expression equals zero when the activity level corresponding to the process is positive.

Kantorovich normalizes the evaluations $c_{it}$ as follows:

$$c'_{it} = \lambda_t c_{it}$$

where the $c'_{it}$ satisfy equations of the following type for a given bundle of n goods:

$$c'_{i_1t} + c'_{i_2t} + \ldots + c'_{i_nt} = 1 \qquad (t = 1, \ldots, T)$$

(Note that n may range from a single good chosen as numeraire all the way to N.) By this means the evaluation of a given set of n products is maintained constant for all time periods.

Kantorovich interprets the coefficients $\lambda_t$ as discount factors. If we compare successive periods, we obtain a measure

10. In the usual linear programming formulations, the relative valuations of the end products are the price weights in the maximand. In Kantorovich's models, only the proportions among end products are given and the rates of transformation between any pair of products emerge from the solution of the problem.

of what Kantorovich calls the "normal effectiveness of investments" in the form of a ratio:[11]

$$\frac{\lambda_t - \lambda_{t+1}}{\lambda_{t+1}}$$

These discount factors, in Kantorovich's opinion, can be used to choose among variants not considered in the initial program. For this to be correct, of course, all inputs and outputs of the variant should be evaluated at the prices of the program.

Unfortunately, the balance equations of Kantorovich's dynamic model are not spelled out. It would have been helpful, for example, if he had shown how he intended to treat the depreciation of existing equipment through wear and tear and, more generally, how the accumulation of endogenously produced capital goods would enter into the capacity balances of subsequent periods.

In the course of his discussion of this same model, Kantorovich remarks that his earlier treatment of the subject (in his 1959 book) attracted less attention than his static model, which, perhaps because it came first in the book, received a more systematic theoretical treatment. This made it difficult for the reader to form a general conception of the problem, although the dynamic model "more fully reflects the real tasks of planning." [12] At a latter point in this recent essay, the Soviet mathematician invokes the following grounds for the superiority of the dynamic approach:

1. Unlike the static model, where technological processes are largely determined by existing capacities, it is possible

11. Note that the $\lambda_t$ will normally be smaller than 1 and will be monotonically decreasing $(\lambda_{t+1} < \lambda_t)$, since the further removed the period the larger must be the discount factor applied to current prices $c'_{1t}$ to reduce them to base-year prices $c_{1t}$.

12. Kantorovich, 1964, p. 324.

to introduce into the dynamic analysis the entire gamut of alternatives opened up by technological progress.

2. The treatment of capital goods as end products in the static model is highly artificial, both methodologically and practically, since, in order to fix targets for these products, one already has to have a development plan for the next period. Yet it is only the choice among the means of production made possible by a dynamic treatment that permits one to realize most of the advantages of an optimized plan.

3. In a model of current planning, the evaluations may be quite unstable: they may undergo brusque changes as a result of "accidental circumstances," and they may fall to zero. In general, they may diverge from "the steady values that are natural for them." In the dynamic model, even if a good is produced in excess quantity, its evaluation will not drop to zero, inasmuch as it can be stored for the use of subsequent periods.

Concerning the choice of the objective function of his model, Kantorovich states that the criterion of optimality is not of decisive importance, since the fairly remote future of the terminal period has relatively little influence on the decisions taken in the first year of the plan, which *are* essential. In view of the "principle of the continuity of the planning process," we should expect that the part of the plan bearing on its last years of operation will in any case be revised in the light of new data and assignments.[13] The notion that the distant future has a negligible impact on present decisions is a characteristic feature of a number of multiperiod models, including certain versions of the turnpike theorem.[14]

In this same essay, Kantorovich suggests that one might try to determine the optimal division of the national product between consumption and investment—or more speci-

13. Ibid., p. 335.
14. Dorfman, Samuelson, and Solow, 1958, p. 330.

fically the upper limit of the sustainable investment ratio—
by studying the relation between real wages and labor
productivity. While the dependence of the latter on the
former was once referred to by Strumilin, this politically
sensitive point has rarely been explored in Soviet economic
literature.[15]

Finally, Kantorovich brushes in broad strokes certain
refinements that might be introduced into his model, including capacity reserves for individual enterprises, gestation periods for construction projects, allowances for working capital, and transportation expenditures for each group
of enterprises associated with uniform or similar technological processes. He claims that the construction of such
an improved program based on branches of production
divided among 200 to 300 enterprises and running for a
period of ten to fifteen years is "fully realizable with the
aid of present-day electronic computers." [16] I am less impressed by this claim than by the apparent lack of any
progress toward building such a program since 1959 when
its main lines were already mapped out.

In the most recent contribution by Kantorovich and
V. L. Makarov, the themes limned by the famous Soviet
mathematician in earlier publications are given more ample
treatment.[17] This work stands out in contemporary Soviet
literature on the subject not so much for its mathematical
reasonings as for the perspicacity and good sense of its observations on the problems arising in modeling the real
world. On the technical side, it does offer a number of
useful hints for computation, based on the utilization of
the structural properties of the matrices associated with
multiperiod programming problems. The transformations
advocated by Kantorovich and Makarov may serve to reduce the number of rows in the matrices, thus making them

15. Strumilin, 1962.
16. Kantorovich, 1964, p. 342.
17. Kantorovich and Makarov, 1964, pp. 50–53.

amenable to inversion in computers with a relatively limited capacity. (While the additional computations made necessary by the concomitant increase in the number of activity columns presumably require additional machine hours, this is not a serious drawback, considering that machine time is usually not a limiting factor in this type of problem.)

Kantorovich and Makarov dwell at some length on problems of aggregation and suboptimalization, particularly on the relation of sectoral plans made up "below" with nationwide plans prepared "above." They consider in detail the methods for constructing an optimal plan for fuels—broken down by types, by regions, and even by production plans—that would dovetail as closely as possible with the more aggregated national economic plan. They suggest various alternative objective functions for the sectoral plan, all of which take as their starting point either price or quantity variables generated in the process of working out the nationwide plan. One alternative is to minimize the discounted sum of current and capital costs necessary to deliver a certain assortment of fuels to the rest of the economy, all costs being expressed in terms of the objective evaluations derived from the national plan. Another starts from Gosplan's tentative sectoral allocation of capital funds for each year and from the corresponding current costs in the Gosplan estimates. The program consists in maximizing the economies in current costs compared to the initial estimates for the given capital expenditures. (In one variant, the current savings are added to the capital funds available to the sector.) The authors casually mention the possibility that tentative capital allocations among sectors might be corrected in the light of sectoral differences in the rate of return on capital, but they unfortunately stop short of any speculation on the complex convergence and stability problems that are likely to arise from these feedbacks. (The only decomposition principle the authors refer to, without elaboration, is that of Dantzig and Wolfe, in which the central coordinating organ issues tentative prices on the basis of which the sectors program their production and communicate tentative vectors of inputs and outputs to the coordinating organ—a procedure the reverse of that just referred to, where allocations were "corrected" by Gosplan on the basis of prices transmitted by the sectors.)[18]

In this article, more explicitly than in Kantorovich's 1964 article, Von Neumann's reproductive model is described in some detail and is given full recognition as a basic contribution to the literature on programming. The authors invoke empirical and theoretical grounds for the lack of sensitivity of optimal solutions for the initial periods of long-term programs to changes in the objective function for terminal period outputs. Without explicit mention of Western literature on turnpike theorems, they cite the existence of a "limiting plan," asymptotically convergent, as time goes to infinity, with a Von Neumann (proportional growth) trajectory. From an ideological standpoint, it is interesting that the authors cite an "economic" (i.e. doctrinal) aspect of this principle, namely, that "any consumption goal selected for sufficiently long-remote period requires, for its optimal fulfillment, the rapid development of the output of means of production." [19] The time may come when the Turnpike Theorem will serve as a rationale for the Soviet Union's industrialization policy in its early years.

Kantorovich and Makarov also amplify on the earlier observations of the senior author on the interdependence

18. Two Hungarian economists, J. Kornai and T. Liptak, have recently developed a decomposition algorithm, which calls for trial allocations of productive factors among sectors and the evaluation of the shadow prices corresponding to each allocation (Kornai and Liptak, 1964). The algorithm terminates when the shadow prices for each factor in all sectors are equalized. Only special game-iterative procedures for determining the reallocations and evaluating the prices guarantee convergence toward price equalization.

19. Kantorovich and Makarov, 1964, p. 50.

of consumption and labor productivity. This time they urge that in constructing future models one should allow for the fact that the size, as well as the productivity, of the labor force depends on the volume of consumption, for "as the production of centrally produced consumption goods decreases, the number of people occupied in private-handicraft production and in household work increases, and the interest in participating in collective production is reduced." [20] (This last point may allude to the lack of interest of *kolkhozniki* in participating in collective work, due among other reasons to low procurement prices for farm produce.) These considerations imply that "variation in the size of the final product, generally speaking, entails changes not only in the vector of constraints but also in the elements of the technology matrix." This argument would seem to weaken the case made out above for the priority development of the means of production, at least in any of its extreme forms.

Kantorovich and Makarov communicate the results of a number of experiments carried out in Novosibirsk with dynamic models based on simple production functions for combining capital and labor inputs according to alternative processes. In their single-product models, there is no technical progress, in the sense in which this word is used in the West; labor productivity, however, grows with time as more capital-intensive processes are introduced pari passu with the accumulation of capital. In all these models, the percentage growth of output was found to decline with time. The conclusions of the authors are consonant with Phelps's Golden Rule:[21] "An economic system, such as the one under examination, with an infinite number of technological processes, that is, capable of increasing labor productivity without limit, and with a labor force increasing at a constant geometric rate cannot function for a

20. Ibid., p. 53.
21. Phelps, 1961, p. 69.

period of any desired duration, as long as consumption per worker increases indefinitely. Furthermore, for any target of final consumption, a finite number of technological processes will be used in the optimal plan, that is, eventually technical progress will cease." [22] From this they infer that increases in labor productivity due to the introduction of ever more capital-intensive processes, where the production function itself remains invariant, do not represent real technical progress and will not, in the long run, solve the problem. One may detect in these other observations of the authors an apprehension, which has become increasingly explicit in the Soviet bloc in recent years, that sustained growth based on a development program relying on "extensive methods" (i.e. on a high rate of investment with little or no technical progress) may be inconsistent with constantly rising levels of living. (It may be speculated that Czechoslovakia's present stagnation, which has been officially blamed on excessive reliance on "extensive methods," may have reached a stage in its development where the above dilemma has become critical.)

The above selection of some of the high points of the Kantorovich-Makarov essay cannot do justice to this contribution, which probably represents the most serious attempt made so far by Soviet scholars to lay the groundwork for the use of long-term programming methods at the national level.

## TRANSITION MODELS: OPTIMIZED INTERINDUSTRY SCHEMES

While Kantorovich's dynamic model could easily be made to encompass interindustry flows, it focuses, as we have seen, on the dual properties of the model rather than on the balances where these flows would appear explicitly. The models in the present section, while generally paral-

22. Kantorovich and Makarov, 1964, p. 69.

leling previous Western work, are perhaps worth surveying for the light they throw on the evolution of Soviet thinking on the subject.

The most elaborate and sophisticated of these models, at least up to the time of its publication in 1962, must surely be the one B. N. Mikhailevskii presented at the Conference on the Application of Mathematical Methods in Economic Research in April 1960.[23] Mikhailevskii discusses both Leontief-type dynamic input-output models and multiperiod linear programming models with objective functions minimizing the expenditure of resources for given perspective demands for end products or, following the lead of Dorfman, Samuelson, and Solow, maximizing an appropriately weighted combination of the final year capital stocks

23. Mikhailevskii, 1962. Even more complicated static and dynamic models based on systems of differential equations drawn from the theory of thermodynamics and chemical reactions have been published by B. I. Pliukhin, alone (Pliukhin, 1962) and with R. N. Nazarova (Pliukhin and Nazarova, 1961). While it is always perilous to hazard even a tentative opinion on the basis of an imperfect understanding, I formed the impression that these contributions, while original, had little insight to offer for the analysis of growth problems, still less for the purpose of practical applications. I decided therefore to omit their detailed consideration.

The conclusions reached by Pliukhin on the basis of his long-run multisector model seem to be either of doubtful character (i.e. the world is made up of Cobb-Douglas production functions) or trivially familiar (tangency at optimal points of a constant costs hyperplane with the convex production surface generated by an aggregate Cobb-Douglas function) (Pliukhin, 1962, p. 96). Pliukhin's theoretical justification for S-shaped growth curves, backed by least-squares fitting of statistical data from capitalist countries, was criticized at the conference by the Soviet mathematician A. N. Kolmogorov as a "strictly formal result" devoid of predictive significance (*Trudy*, 1961–62, p. 254). Kolmogorov also suggests that the analogy of economic processes with chemical reactions is "strictly external": the idea of reducing the problem to a system of linear differential equations is all right in principle, but "its really serious implementation may lead to conclusions having nothing in common with the authors' conclusions." (Ibid.)

and desired inventories in the various branches of the national economy.[24] With the exception of an instructive— if laborious—exercise in matrix algebra required to bring gestation periods into this multisector, multiperiod model, the bulk of the article relies on results obtained by "Western" scholars, including the Japanese mathematical economists M. Morishima and S. Ichimura, as well as G. Debreu, W. Jorgenson, and W. Leontief. (This was one of the first papers on an economic theme published in the Soviet Union since the 1920s to cite and utilize the work of scholars outside the communist sphere without subjecting them to ideological criticism or apologizing for their intrusion.)

While Mikhailevskii's formal treatment of the problem is not particularly original, his overall conception of programming models and of their potential contribution to the planning of the economy struck new (and dissonant) notes in Soviet economic thought. Mikhailevskii considers that the "greatest problem" to be solved in multiperiod, optimized models is the "choice between a greater speed of disproportional growth on the basis of autarky and the loss due to the rupture of ties with the world market and to internal disproportion[s]." [25] At another juncture, he claims that it should be possible to introduce demand and supply functions for different consumer goods into his long-term planning model and to find "a closed set of fixed points, characterizing the relations among quantities and prices, which would be optimal from the viewpoint of the entire government program, as well as of the individual enterprises and consumers." [26] The conjecture that this problem can be solved at the present time seems unduly optimistic: so far efforts by mathematical economists in the West to program a general equilibrium model of the type

24. Dorfman, Samuelson and Solow, 1958, p. 338.
25. Mikhailevskii, 1962, p. 190.
26. Ibid., p. 191.

Mikhailevskii describes have been fruitless.[27] The proof of the existence of a set of fixed points is by no means equivalent to the discovery of a method for finding them. And it may well be that a totally different approach from the one followed in pursuing the existence proofs will have to be adopted to arrive at operational results.

However that may be, Mikhailevskii restricts his concrete proposals regarding the objective functions of the linear programming models he constructs to the introduction of parametric programming techniques. He argues that the behavior of the system should be studied where the weights $k_j(t)$ assigned to the capital stocks and inventories in the objective function[28] are free to vary between the limits $\delta$ and $\psi$:

$$\delta \leq [k'_1(t), \ldots, k'_n(t)] \leq \psi$$

Generalizing this approach, Mikhailevskii suggests that one might wish to assign probabilities to the different $k'_j(t)$ (where only the terminal stocks are positively valued), reflecting the fact that the marginal rates of substitution among the different end period stocks cannot be known precisely ahead of time. Insofar as these ratios $\left(\text{e.g. } \dfrac{k'_i(t)}{k'_j(t)}\right)$ may not be independent of each other, the distribution of the probabilities attached to them will not necessarily be normal. But if the sectoral nomenclature is fine enough

27. Herbert Scarf has pointed out to me that results have been obtained where certain sweeping simplifications have been made in the utility functions (e.g. where all goods are assumed to be gross substitutes). This particular assumption is made by L. V. Girsanov (1963, p. 64) in his suggestions for an algorithm, which, however, was still far removed from concrete results.

28. In the Dorfman, Samuelson, Solow model, all but the terminal-year stocks are assigned zero weights. Mikhailevskii argues that if the defense potential of the country depends on the presence of basic and working capital funds, then each year's funds should be inserted into the objective function with positive weights. Mikhailevskii, 1962.

(n ≅ 200–50), the probabilities attached to any pair of goods i and i + 1 will be more or less independent of those for any other pair j and j + 1, where the sectors have been numbered and arranged in such a way that |i − j| is large. If this property holds, then the above parametric function, rewritten in terms of probabilities, may be interpreted as a linear stochastic function. "Consequently," he writes, "the task of maximizing accumulation may be represented by a stochastic linear programming problem, which may be converted into an ordinary parametric programming problem." [29]

Among the other Soviet multiperiod, interindustry models with optimizing features, those published by the distinguished veteran economist A. A. Konius should be mentioned. His 1961 model is even more comprehensive in the range of its variables than Mikhailevskii's.[30] It includes not only the choice of technological processes but the possibility of starting investment projects at various times to obtain additional capacities in a given year; it allows for the option of not fully utilizing productive capacities and considers the possibility of meeting the external balance of payments in a variety of ways. Konius also incorporates additional restraints in the foreign trade sector to take into account the limited demand for individual exports.

The chief instrument variable in Konius' model is the proportion of national income invested in each period, where national income is expressed in fixed prices. These prices are evidently not endogenous, and one may wonder how they relate to the efficiency prices derived from the solution of the model. Given the level of desired national consumption in each period (also expressed in terms of fixed prices), his objective function may consist, alternatively, in minimizing the expenditure of human labor in

29. Ibid., p. 204.
30. Konius, 1961.

the final period, or in "maximizing national income" (presumably also in the terminal period).[31] Konius makes no attempt to compare the benefits yielded by the plan in different periods.

Konius is mindful of the computing problem posed by the great number of variables and restraints introduced in his model. To get around this difficulty, he proposes that all the required coefficients should be computed by careful aggregation of sectors in the base period from current statistics and from projected capital projects in the detailed nomenclature.[32] He does not estimate the number of sectors and periods that could be accommodated into his model, given the limited capacity of Soviet computers (whether in operation or perceivable on the horizon).

In a more recent paper, Konius abandons altogether the notion, presumably impractical at the present time, of optimizing a program encompassing all the variables he considers essential in every period.[33] By postulating a constant rate of growth of all capital goods during each period, he finds it possible to limit his analysis to the examination of the initial and the final period of the plan. He elaborates all his balances in terms of the outputs and coefficients of the terminal period, all expressed as percentage relatives of the magnitudes of the base period. Granted the internal consistency of his scheme, it may still be asked whether the gain in computability warrants the loss of realism due to the constant-rate-of-growth assumptions. The gains and losses, or trade-offs, open to the programmers from varying the number of sectors and periods considered and from introducing simplifying assumptions about interperiod relations, can probably be ascertained only by simulating realistic planning situations. The for-

31. Ibid., p. 75.
32. Ibid., p. 77.
33. Konius, 1964.

mal exploration of reduced models, unless it brings out
new principles or rules of action, contributes relatively
little to our understanding of the issues involved.

## AGGREGATIVE MODELS

In this section, I confine myself to an examination of
one- and two-sector growth models whose behavior is
governed by explicit objective functions. This excludes a
long string of models, from Fel'dman's to Gor'kov's,
in which the expansion rate is set as soon as certain proportions are specified (e.g. the ratio of investment to national income or the apportionment of the investment
fund between the producer goods and consumer goods
sectors), and the only optimization possible consists in
exploring alternative paths by varying the initial proportions and eventually in choosing the most desirable
among them.[34]

S. G. Strumilin published an elementary model with
optimization properties in *Planovoe khoziaistvo* for June
1962, which was later formalized by Nemchinov.[35] Strumilin's model was meant to show how one should divide up
the national product each year between investment and
consumption in such a way as to maximize the sum of the
consumption funds generated in each year over a fixed
period of time (forty years in Strumilin's model). The
model is open to the evident objection that it does not take
into account the preferences of society, or of the planners
themselves, for consumption today over that of forty years
hence. Depending on the structural coefficients of the
model, it might seem advantageous to accumulate capital
at a fast rate in the first thirty-five years and then, in the
last five years, let consumption rise rapidly, starting from
a relatively low base. This pattern of consumption, viewed

34. See Domar, 1957, pp. 222–61; Gor'kov, 1962.
35. Nemchinov, 1962, pp. 242–48.

ex ante, might not be acceptable politically, even if one were to disregard individuals' preferences.[36]

But how can planners' intertemporal preferences be built into a growth model? This is the chief problem examined by V. F. Pugachev of the Laboratory of Economic-Mathematical Methods in his paper on "Criteria of Optimality for the Economy" published in July 1963.[37] This paper, one of the more audacious contributions made by Soviet scholars in this field, merits detailed treatment.[38]

We may start the discussion by writing down Pugachev's objective function:

$$\max U = \int_0^\infty Q(t)u[x(t)]\, dt$$

where $x(t)$ is a vector of consumpttion goods, including leisure, available at time $t$, $u[x(t)]$ is the utility index attached to that bundle, and $Q(t)$ is a "weighting function" (or discount factor), which is given the value of one at the start of the planning period and decreases monotonically thereafter.

The reasons Pugachev adduces for the introduction of his weighting function $Q(t)$, as well as the factors he claims should influence its actual magnitude at every point of time, illustrate the relative freedom from ideological restraints that Soviet mathematical economists may now afford in discussing this type of problem:

1. $Q(t)$ should "first of all" reflect the actual time preferences of the population: "for a majority of people, the

36. As Kantorovich, among others, has pointed out (see above, p. 211) a low level of consumption may have a negative effect on labor productivity and thus undermine the model's assumption of the constant productivity of new investments.

37. Pugachev, 1963b.

38. Pugachev's contribution cannot be isolated from other contemporary work by Soviet mathematical economists on demand theory in static models. See in particular: Dudkin, 1963; Girsanov, 1963; and Konius, 1959. On the model of Pugachev and on related papers in Soviet demand theory, see Zauberman, 1965.

present acquisition of a good is more desirable than its future acquisition."

2. These time preferences of the population have an objective, as well as a subjective basis, since, for every person living at time $t = 0$, the probability of remaining alive at time t is smaller than one and declines with t.

3. The weighting function $Q(t)$ should take into account "a certain degree of indefiniteness" in the perspective plans. The discovery of new production processes may render nugatory the efforts undertaken in an earlier period. The benefits derived from the consumption bundles delivered at a given time may turn out smaller than expected.

Pugachev asserts that in order to deal appropriately with the problem of uncertainty one should also adopt the technique of "sliding plans," that is, one should revise perspective plans periodically in the light of new, unanticipated circumstances. One might then ask, he goes on, whether it makes any difference at what level the discount factor is set, "since errors resulting from the irrational choice of $Q(t)$ would be corrected, along with other errors, in subsequent revisions of the plan." [39] But this, he argues, would be most undesirable, inasmuch as "the introduction into a system of economic management (*upravlenie*) of additional errors, not determined by the actual absence of exact information, is equivalent to a conscious deterioration in the quality of the system." [40] An incorrect selection of $Q(t)$ will affect mainly the continuity of planning decisions: commands made at different times may be contradictory; capital investments launched at an earlier point of time may seem inferior at a later point. The function $Q(t)$ must therefore be selected in such a way that the plan should require the fewest possible corrections in future periods.

This is how Pugachev envisages the "practical realiza-

39. Pugachev, 1963b, p. 68.
40. Ibid., p. 69.

tion" of the above principle. Before preparing each optimal perspective plan, one should make a preliminary examination of several plan versions of smaller dimensions, based on aggregated data, for a number of reasonable values of Q(t). The entire set of these draft plans should give a "clear representation of the production possibilities open to society in the period considered." In the framework of these alternatives, "some competent organ or other" will choose the concrete variant of future economic development. Simultaneously it will chose Q(t) corresponding to this alternative, which will be used to prepare the fully deployed (disaggregated) version of the plan.

Passing over Pugachev's discussion of implicit prices in such a model, which I did not find particularly illuminating, I enter directly into his simplified model. Since there are some fairly obvious flaws in the argument, which will not be brought out until the model has been fully deployed, the reader is invited to follow the logical sequence with care.

Pugachev posits only two goods, a consumption good whose output is denoted x(t) at time t and a capital good whose available stock[41] is written y(t) and which is produced in quantity $\frac{dy(t)}{dt}$. This capital good may be used either to reproduce itself or in the production of x. The stock y(t) is always kept fully employed. It takes one unit of y to produce one unit of x and 10 units of y to produce a new unit of y. The production equations are:

(1)
$$x(t) = k(t)y(t)$$
$$\frac{dy(t)}{dt} = \frac{[1 - k(t)]y(t)}{10}$$

41. According to an editor's note the "depreciation of capital funds is offset as a result of the expenditure of inputs not taken into account in the model, so that the funds may be supposed to have an unlimited service life."

where k(t) is the share of the capital stock alloted to consumption. The maximand written above applies to this simplified model, where x(t) now represents a single-component vector (a scalar).

From equation (1), one may eliminate k(t) and express x(t) as a function of y(t):

(2) $$x(t) = y(t) - 10\,\frac{dy(t)}{dt}$$

When this expression for x(t) is introduced into the maximand, the resulting integral may be seen to belong to the general form:

$$\int_0^\infty F\left(t, y(t), \frac{dy(t)}{dt}\right) dt$$

According to the classical Euler-Lagrange theorem of the calculus of variations, the maximum of this integral occurs where:

$$\frac{\partial F}{\partial y} - \frac{d}{dt}\left(\frac{\partial F}{\partial\left(\frac{dy}{dt}\right)}\right) = 0$$

Substituting the actual values obtained in (2) and integrating, we obtain:

$$Q(t)\,\frac{du[x(t)]}{dx(t)} = Ce^{-.1t}$$

where C is a constant of integration.

From this may be derived the optimal consumption path $\mathring{x}(t)$:

(3) $$\mathring{x}(t) = v^*[v(x(0))Q^{-1}(t)e^{-.1t}]$$

where $v = \dfrac{du}{dx}$ and $v^*$ is the inverse function relative to v(x).

Suppose that the planners' utility function is concave and assumes the simple form:

$$v(x) = 2\sqrt{x}$$

Then:

$$v(x) = \frac{du}{dx} = \frac{1}{\sqrt{x}}; \qquad v^* = \frac{1}{v^2}$$

Hence:

(4) $$\mathring{x}(t) = x(o)Q^2(t)e^{.2t}$$

and

(5) $$\mathring{y}(t) = y(o)e^{.1t} - .1x(o)e^{.1t}\int_0^t Q^2(t)e^{.1t}\,dt$$

where $\mathring{y}(t)$ is the optimal path of the capital stock.

Let the weighting function $Q(t)$ assume the form of the convex, monotonically decreasing function $e^{-at}$.

In that case the following results may be calculated from (4) and (5):

(6) $$\mathring{x}(t) = x(o)e^{(.2-2a)\,t}$$

and

(7) $$\mathring{y}(t) = y(o)e^{.1t}\left[1 - \frac{.1}{2a - .1}\frac{x(o)}{y(o)}\left(1 - e^{-(2a-.1)t}\right)\right]$$

The optimal growth rate $\alpha(t)$ for the consumer good will be:

(8) $$\alpha(t) = .2 - 2a$$

It is recalled that a is the constant in the expression $e^{-at}$ for the weighting function.

To find the growth rate of the capital stock y, Pugachev argues that one must first choose an initial ratio of consumption to the capital stock $\dfrac{x(0)}{y(0)}$. Setting this initial ratio at .5, he calculates the growth rate $\beta(t)$ to be:

(9)
$$\beta(t) = \frac{.1 - .05e^{-(2a-.1)t}}{1 - \dfrac{.05}{2a - .1}\left(1 - e^{-(2a-.1)t}\right)}$$

If it is posited that consumption may not decline and the capital stock can never fall below zero, then certain restrictions can be imposed on the magnitude of the parameter a of the discount function. In particular: $a \leq .1$ and $2a - .1 > 0$. Therefore, $.05 < a \leq .1$. Moreover, from (7) one may deduce that the following equation must hold if the capital stock is not to become negative as $t \longrightarrow \infty$.

$$a \geq .05\left(1 + \frac{x(0)}{y(0)}\right)$$

Thus for an initial $\dfrac{x(0)}{y(0)} = .5$, the constant a must lie between the limits $.075 \leq a \leq .1$.

By this method, Pugachev claims to have succeeded in showing, at least for the parameters he has selected, that the range of choice of a and hence the profile of $Q(t)$ must lie within fairly narrow limits, lest consumption decline or the capital stock fall to zero over an infinite time horizon. A serious defect in Pugachev's argument is that the capital stock in his model cannot decline at all, let alone fall to zero, since it is supposed to be everlasting.[42]

It should also be noted that at least one of the limits on the exponential constant a of the discount function can be reasoned from economic considerations alone, without

42. The assumption that has been violated by the fall of the capital stock is that $k(t)$, the proportion of the stock employed in making $x(t)$ cannot be less than one. This proportion equals $\dfrac{x(t)}{y(t)}$. If $2a - .1$ in equation (7) should be smaller than zero, then $k(t)$ would be negative at $t = 0$.

resort to any optimizing procedure: If a should be larger than $b_1$, the output-to-capital ratio for reproducing y (.1 in Pugachev's model), then it would never pay to accumulate capital at all. For investment will not appear desirable at $t = 0$, unless the discounted utility of the extra consumption that will be made possible by this investment should exceed at some subsequent time T the utility of the consumption initially foregone. If future utility is discounted at the constant rate $e^{-at}$, we must have:

$$e^{-aT}U(\Delta X_T) > U(\Delta X_0)$$

where $\Delta X_T$ is the extra consumption corresponding to the opportunity loss of $\Delta X_0$.

Now the maximum increment of future consumption that can be obtained by saving $\Delta X_0$ and continuously reinvesting the proceeds until time T equals $\Delta X_0 e^{b_1 T}$, where $b_1$ is the output-to-capital ratio in reproducing capital (.1 in Pugachev's model).[43] If we assume that the utility function is strictly concave (exhibiting strictly diminishing marginal utility), then we can see that:

$$e^{-aT}U(\Delta X_0 e^{b_1 T}) < e^{-aT}e^{b_1 T}U(\Delta X_0)$$
$$= e^{(b_1-a)T}U(\Delta X_0) < U(\Delta X_0)$$

if $a > b_1$.

Thus our condition for successful investment will never be fulfilled.

My other comments on the Pugachev model call for some preliminary remarks on related Western research (which,

43. Note that $b_2$, the output-to-ratio in producing x, has no influence on this result. For the capital economized by not producing an increment of consumption—or $\dfrac{\Delta X}{b_2}$—will grow at a maximum rate of $b_1$ and eventually yield $\dfrac{\Delta X_0 e^{b_1 T}}{b_2}$ units of new capital. These in turn will be capable of generating $\Delta X_0 e^{b_1 T}$ units of consumption, which magnitude does not depend on $b_2$.

incidentally, is nowhere referred to by the Soviet author). The model bears close formal resemblance to the Fel'dman-Domar scheme. One might also mention the famous article by F. Ramsey, where the calculus of variations was first used to maximize utility over an infinite time horizon. An even closer kinship emerges from a comparison with the models of Koopmans and S. Chakravarty, especially with the latter's articles published in 1962 in the *International Economic Review* and in *Econometrica*.[44]

It so happens also—by coincidence rather than omission —that Andrea Maneschi recently reached results, starting from Chakravarty's model, that were in part identical with, though in some respects more general than, Pugachev's.[45] However, the results of these two independent investigations diverged for reasons which I will presently explain.

A curious feature of Pugachev's article, as the reader may have observed, is that he never considers the impact of different output-to-capital ratios in producing the two goods of his model on the growth paths of his variables. As it turns out, $b_2$, the output-to-capital ratio for $x(t)$, has no influence on $\overset{\circ}{x}(t)$, but it does influence $\overset{\circ}{y}(t)$.[46] The other ratio, which we have already denoted by the letter $b_1$, affects both consumption and capital accumulation. We recall that Pugachev set $b_1$ at .1 (see (1) above).

From Maneschi's model we can derive the following equations for the growth paths (making the same assumptions as Pugachev):

$$(10) \qquad\qquad x(t) = x(0)e^{[(b_1-a)/\gamma]t}$$

44. See Domar, 1957, pp. 248–54; Ramsey, 1928; Koopmans, 1963; and Chakravarty, 1962a, 1962b.

45. Maneschi, 1966.

46. This invariance of the rate of growth of consumption to the output-to-capital ratio in the production of the consumer goods was already noted by Chakravarty.

and

$$(11) \quad \mathring{y}(t) = \left( y(o) - \frac{x(o)}{b_2 \left( 1 - \frac{(b_1 - a)}{b_1 \gamma} \right)} \right) e^{b_1 t}$$

$$+ \frac{x(o)}{b_2 \left( 1 - \frac{(b_1 - a)}{b_1 \gamma} \right)} e^{[(b_1 - a)/\gamma]t}$$

The only new symbol is $\gamma$, which stems from Maneschi's marginal utility function:

$$\frac{du}{dx} = x^{-\gamma}$$

In Pugachev's utility function ($u = 2\sqrt{x}$), we see that $\gamma = \frac{1}{2}$.[47]

From the above expressions for $\mathring{x}(t)$ and $\mathring{y}(t)$, Maneschi infers that:

$$b_1(1 - \gamma) < a < b_1$$

which, for $b_1 = .1$ and $\gamma = \frac{1}{2}$, yields Pugachev's first set of limits for a "reasonable" a (.05 to .1).

The choice of $b_1$, the output-to-capital ratio in producing capital goods, is crucial. If $b_1$ were equal to .5, a more realistic value than Pugachev's .1, then the constant a would have to lie between .25 and .5. When these limits are substituted in the weighting function $Q(t) = e^{-at}$, they imply that a unit of consumption ten years hence would be worth from .6 to 8 percent of a unit today (versus 35 to 60 percent for the values chosen by Pugachev).

We now come to a serious oversight in Pugachev's paper.

47. Pugachev, at a later point in his paper (1963b, p. 86) introduces the same utility function as Maneschi and examines the effect of $\gamma$ on $Q(t)$. But he retains unique values for $b_1$ and $b_2$ throughout his paper.

Reverting to equation (7), we note first that if k(t) is not to exceed unity then:[48]

$$y(o) - \frac{.1 \; x(o)}{2a - .1} \geq o$$

and hence

$$x(o) \leq \frac{(2a - .1)}{.1} y(o)$$

But from (6), we know that $x(o)$ must be as large as possible (that is, as large as $y(o)$ permits) to maximize total utility. Therefore, as Maneschi points out for his more general model, the equality sign must hold in the above expression. After making the proper substitution in (6) and (7), we find that both $x(t)$ and $y(t)$ must grow at the identical rate $(.2 - 2a)$, or at the rate $\dfrac{b_1 - a}{\gamma}$ in the more general model. If this reasoning is correct, Pugachev's arbitrary choice of an initial ratio $\dfrac{x(o)}{y(o)}$ does not lead to an optimal solution, and the paths he computes for the capital stock, insofar as they diverge from the consumption paths for various admissible values of the constant a (e.g. for $a = .07, .08, .09$ and $.1$), are inefficient.

To summarize the main part of his paper, Pugachev attempts to calculate discount rates appropriate for use in economy-wide planning from the structural properties of a two-sector model. These rates, he argues, must fall within certain limits, lest the stock of capital or consumption decline. A technical flaw in the argument is that capital, by

48. From (10) and (11) it is evident that if the conditions below were not met then we should have:

$$\overset{\circ}{y}(t) = -Ae^{b_1 t} + \frac{\overset{\circ}{x}(t)}{B} \text{ or } \overset{\circ}{x}(t) = By(t) + \frac{B}{A} e^{b_1 t}$$

where A and B are positive constants. Consumption would then be a monotonically increasing proportion of the capital stock and would eventually exceed the latter.

assumption, is everlasting and therefore may not be allowed to run down. Moreover, it is easily shown that the discount rate cannot be larger than the output-to-capital ratio in producing capital goods if capital accumulation is going to yield a positive product after discounting. The arbitrary selection of a low output-to-capital ratio makes it artificially appear that the discount rate is confined to lie below a limit—ten percent per year in the model—which the planners might wish to transgress in practice. The choice of a more realistic ratio, however, would raise the maximum discount rate above the realm of plausible alternatives (say, to 50 percent per year). Finally, Pugachev's model is overdetermined inasmuch as he arbitrarily selects an initial ratio of consumption to the capital stock, which ratio should be endogenously determined.

In the second part of his article, Pugachev introduces a Cobb-Douglas function in the production of the consumer good. The inputs consist in a reproducible factor—capital —and a factor in fixed supply—which may be identified with labor.[49] Capital is produced exclusively with labor, according to the fixed ratio of h units of capital to one unit of labor. For the sake of simplifying the mathematics of the problem, the utility function is reduced to its simplest expression: $u = x$. Availing himself of essentially the same calculus-of-variations technique as in his more elementary model, Pugachev calculates the optimal growth paths of capital and consumption. The resulting expressions are quite complicated. Unfortunately, the author does not attempt to find the range of admissible values of a (for the same discount function $Q(t) = e^{-at}$). From his diagrams it would appear that where a exceeds .075, the rate of growth of consumption falls toward zero (consumption begins to decrease after thirty years if a is as high as .09). Where a is exactly equal to .075, the rates of growth of consumption and capital are the same at all times (falling off

49. Pugachev, 1963b, p. 88.

from an initial 7 percent at t = 0 to less than 1 percent at t = 40); but it is not clear in this case whether the growth rates must be identical for both consumption and capital to keep on growing.

For both models Pugachev derives the implicit efficiency prices corresponding to optimal paths and shows how these prices evolve with time. He also computes a "norm of effectiveness," or internal rate of return, which, barring changes in the price level for consumer goods over time, turns out to be equal to $b_1$ (the output-to-capital ratio in the production of capital) in the first model and to a, the parameter of the discount function in the second. The result, as he recognizes, hinges on the identity of the utility function with the volume of production of the consumer good $x(t)$.

In his concluding section, Pugachev makes some suggestions for the linearization of utility functions for models involving many commodities. In particular he proposes that one should treat the most satisfactory version of the perspective plan elaborated by the usual (i.e. nonmathematical) methods as the starting point for the optimization process. Denoting the consumption set in this plan by the $\overline{x}(t)$ we may write:

$$u(x(t)) = u(\overline{x}) + \nabla u(\overline{x}(t))(x(t) - \overline{x}(t))$$

where $x(t)$ is the optimal plan in the neighborhood of $x(t)$ and $\nabla u(\overline{x}(t))$ is the gradient of the maximand (the vector of partial derivatives of the utility function with respect to each of its arguments at the point $\overline{x}(t)$).

Therefore, the objective function, but for a scale constant, may be rewritten:

$$\int_0^\infty Q(t) \, \nabla u(\overline{x}(t)) x(t) \, dt$$

According to Pugachev, this expression for total discounted utility over an infinite horizon should be linear.

This is by no means evident, for the vector $\nabla u(\bar{x}(t))$, which represents the undiscounted weights attached to the outputs $x(t)$ in the objective function, need not be constant at any time t. This will only be the case if the utility function is quadratic, an implicit assumption that is not brought out in this paper.[50]

This concludes my discussion of Pugachev's article. The reader may wonder whether this occasional paper deserved such elaborate treatment. It is not entirely original; some of its arguments are debatable; it does not even have much bearing on planning practice. But it is a competent and, in some respects, imaginative effort by a Soviet scholar to construct a sophisticated model with an important practical aim—the determination of reasonable discount functions.[51]

## Dynamic Programming Models

The only Soviet contribution to dynamic programming that can make a serious claim to originality consists in the "maximum principle" of mathematicians L. S. Pontryagin, V. G. Boltyanskii, and R. V. Gamkrelidze, which was apparently discovered in connection with the study of the optimal control of physical processes. Original as the method may be, it is not certain whether "Pontryagin's principle" leads to methods superior to those elaborated in recent years by Richard Bellman and other American mathematicians.

50. In another paper by Pugachev, published in mimeographed form by the Higher Economic School of Bratislava (p. 123), he specifies that the utility function in the neighborhood of x may be approximated by the first two terms of a Taylor series expansion:

$$u(x) = u(\bar{x}) + \nabla u(\bar{x})(x - \bar{x}) + \frac{1}{2} \sum_{i,j} \frac{\sigma^2 U \, (x_i - x_i^0)(x_j - x_j^0)}{\sigma x_i x_j}$$

51. For an interesting attempt to calculate discount rates from aggregated Soviet data, see Mikhailevskii, 1965.

Pontryagin's work has excited more interest on the part of American mathematical economists than on the part of their Soviet confreres.[52] Although basic articles by Boltyanskii, Gamkrelidze, and Pontryagin had started coming out in 1956, not a single mention was made of this work in the two papers on dynamic programming presented at the 1960 conference on mathematical economics.[53] In their surveys of the subject, V. Trigubenko and I. V. Romanovskii essentially summarized the findings of Richard Bellman (whose contributions, incidentally, date back at least to 1954).[54]

Rather than follow through the logic of Pontryagin's principle, I will illustrate by an elementary example taken from the *Mathematical Theory of Optimal Processes*, by Pontryagin, Boltyanskii, Gamkrelidze, and Mishchenko and then show how this same problem would be treated by Bellman.[55]

Consider a variable x and a control u. The "law of motion" of x may be expressed in the general case by the differential equation:

$$\frac{dx}{dt} = f(x, u)$$

In this problem, we have given that the acceleration $\left(\dfrac{d^2x}{dt^2}\right)$ of the variable x is equal to u. It is also posited that u is

52. See, for example, Mordecai Kurz's constructive use of Pontryagin's principle in his article on optimal paths of capital accumulation, where he chooses as the objective of his growth problem the minimization of the time taken to reach economic maturity (Kurz, 1966). Kenneth Arrow and David Cass have also applied Pontryagin's principle to trace out the optimal paths of growth models (these models were not published at the time these lines were written).

53. Romanovskii, 1962; Trigubenko, 1962.

54. Bellman, 1954.

55. Pontryagin, Boltyanskii, Gamkrelidze, and Mishchenko, 1962. This comparison was suggested and worked through by Herbert Scarf.

constrained to lie within the limits $-1$ and $+1$ (i.e. $|u| \leq 1$).

In order to reduce the differential equations generated by the system to the first degree, the problem is rewritten in the phase coordinates $x_1 = x$ and $x_2 = \dfrac{dx}{dt}$. (Each point of the space has two coordinates, the first representing $x$ itself, the second its velocity.) It follows immediately that:

$$(1) \qquad \frac{dx_1}{dt} = x_2; \qquad \frac{dx_2}{dt} = u$$

The "time-optimal" problem consists in finding the path that will minimize the time $(t_1 - t_0)$ necessary to move from any initial state $x_0$ to the origin $(0,0)$.

In general, the device used by Pontryagin and his associates to solve this type of problem is to introduce auxiliary variables $\psi_\alpha$ ($\alpha = 1, \ldots, n$) and to construct equations in the form:

$$(2) \qquad H(\psi, x, u) = \sum_{\alpha=1}^{n} \psi_\alpha f^\alpha(x, u)$$

where $n$ is the number of variables in phase space, $f^\alpha(x, u)$ is equal to $\dfrac{dx_\alpha}{dt}$, the derivative with respect to time of the $\alpha'$th variable. The auxiliary variables are such that:

$$(3) \qquad \frac{d\psi_i}{dt} = -\sum_{\alpha=1}^{n} \frac{\partial f^\alpha(x, u)}{\partial x_i} \psi_\alpha \qquad (i = 1, \ldots, n)$$

For the above problem we have:

$$(4) \qquad H = \psi_1 \frac{dx_1}{dt} + \psi_2 \frac{dx_2}{dt} = \psi_1 x_2 + \psi_2 u$$

From (2) and (3), it follows that:

$$(5) \qquad \frac{d\psi_i}{dt} = -\frac{\partial H}{\partial x_i} \qquad (i = 1, \ldots, n)$$

Differentiating (4) with respect to $x_1$, and $x_2$, and using (5), we obtain:

(6) $$\frac{d\psi_1}{dt} = 0, \qquad \frac{d\psi_2}{dt} = -\psi_1$$

After integration of these results, we find that:

$$\psi_1 = c_1 \quad \text{and} \quad \psi_2 = c_2 - c_1 t$$

where $c_1$ and $c_2$ are constants of integration. Substituting these expressions for the auxiliary variables in (4):

(7) $$H = (c_2 - c_1 t)u + c_1 x_2$$

*The maximum principle states that, for* $u(T)$ *and* $x(T)$ *to be time optimal, the function* $H(\psi(t), x(t), u)$ *must attain its maximum at the point* $u = u(T)$. *Moreover, the maximum value of the function at* $T$ *must be non-negative.*

It can readily be seen that $H$ reaches its maximum when $u$ equals $+1$ or $-1$, depending on the signs of the constants of integration.

When u equals $+1$, we have from (1):

(8) $$x_2 = t + s_2$$
$$x_1 = \frac{t^2}{2} + s_2 t + s_1 = \frac{1}{2}(x_2)^2 + s$$

where $s_1$ and $s_2$ are constants of integration and

$$s = s_1 - \frac{1}{2}(s_2)^2$$

Similarly, when $u$ equals $-1$, we have:

(9) $$x_2 = -t + s_2'$$
$$x_1 = -\frac{1}{2}(x_2)^2 + s'$$

where

$$s' = s_1' + \frac{1}{2}(s_2')^2$$

From (8) and (9), it follows that the relation between $x_1$ and $x_2$ may be represented by a system of parabolas whose foci lie on the abscissa. When $u = +1$, the parabolas open out to the right; when $u = -1$, they open out to the left. Whatever the starting point $x_0$, the optimal strategy consists in following the parabola on which $x_0$ is to be found and stay on its course (i.e. maintain u at $+1$ or at $-1$, depending on $x_0$) until one reaches either the origin itself, if $x_0$ happens to lie on such a line, or a parabolic line going through the origin. In the latter case, upon reaching this new line one should reverse course (e.g. change the sign of u) and follow through to (o, o).[56] The nature of the auxiliary variables $\psi_i$, which Pontryagin and his colleagues leave obscure, emerges more clearly when we follow Bellman's approach to the problem.

Generally speaking, Bellman's device consists in dividing any multiple-period problem into two parts: (1) an initial period and (2) all other periods taken together. Suppose we start at time $t_0$ and consider an increment of time $\Delta t$ as the first period, small enough so that the optimally set control variable may be supposed to remain constant during this interval. The optimal path after $\Delta t$ depends only on the phase coordinates $(x'_1, x'_2)$ at $t_0 + \Delta t$.[57] From (1), it follows that:

$$x'_2 = x_2 + u\,\Delta t$$

$$x'_1 = x_1 + \Delta t x_2 + \frac{u\,\Delta t^2}{2}$$

where $(x_1, x_2)$ are the coordinates at $t_0$.

56. Ibid., pp. 23–27. Unless $x_0$ lies on a parabola going through the origin, the optimal path must cross the abscissa, at which point $x_2$, the acceleration, $\dfrac{dx_2}{dt}\left(=\dfrac{d^2x}{dt^2}\right)$ equals zero. But of course the velocity $\dfrac{dx}{dt}$ will not be zero at this point.

57. According to Bellman's principle of optimality, once the variable x has taken on the new values associated with the increment of time $\Delta t$, the remaining part of the trajectory of x must be optimal with respect to this initial move.

The problem is to find the admissible u, which minimizes the time required to trace out the optimal path. Since this time depends on the initial states $x_1$ and $x_2$ at $t_0$, the minimand may be written:

$$(10) \quad \phi(x_1, x_2)$$

$$= \min_{-1 \leq u \leq 1} \left[ \Delta t + \phi \left( x_1 + \Delta t x_2 + u \frac{\Delta t^2}{2}, x_2 + u \, \Delta t \right) \right]$$

If we subtract $\phi(x_1, x_2)$ from both sides of (10) and divide through by $\Delta t$, we obtain:

$$(11)$$

$$o = \min_{-1 \leq u \leq 1} \left[ 1 + \frac{\phi \left( x_1 + \Delta t x_2 + u \frac{\Delta t^2}{2}, x_2 + u \, \Delta t \right)}{\Delta t} - \frac{\phi(x_1, x_2)}{\Delta t} \right]$$

We now compute the increments to the two variables $x_1$ and $x_2$ from a Taylor's series expansion and let $\Delta t \longrightarrow o$, thus eliminating all higher terms of the Taylor's series. We are left with:

$$(12) \qquad\qquad o = \min_{-1 \leq u \leq 1} [1 + x_2 \phi_1 + u \phi_2]$$

where $\phi_1$ is the partial derivative of $\phi(x_1, x_2)$ with respect to $x_1$ and $\phi_2$ of the same function with respect to $x_2$. Now if this function is to be minimized, u must clearly take the value $+1$ if $\phi_2$ is negative and $-1$ if it is positive. After substituting these values for u, the resulting pair of partial differential equations in x, $\phi_1$ and $\phi_2$ may be solved by familiar methods to arrive at results identical with those of Pontryagin. But we need not solve these equations to see the relation of equation (12) with the Pontryagin system and in particular with equation (4) above. Introducing the additional auxiliary variable $\psi_0$, equal to $f^0(x, u) \equiv 1$ in the time-optimal problem, we may derive the following relations from equation (3) in Pontryagin's system:

$$\Omega(\psi, x, u) = \psi_0 + H(\psi, x, u) = 1 + H(\psi, x, u)$$
$$= 1 + x_2\psi_1 + u\psi_2 = 1 + x_2\phi_1 + u\phi_2$$

where $\Omega(\psi, x, u)$ is the generalized function in the auxiliary variables $\psi_j$ in Pontryagin's system.[58] ($\psi_0$, which is constant in the time-optimal problem, obviously plays no part in the maximizing process.) The auxiliary variables $\psi_1$ and $\psi_2$ and the partial derivatives of the time function are algebraically equal but of opposite signs (since H is maximized and $\phi$ minimized). If the problem were solved with the use of the calculus of variations, it would turn out that $\psi_1$ and $\psi_2$ also coincide with familiar Lagrange multipliers.

Since, as Pontryagin and his associates admit, Bellman's approach is more general than theirs, where is the novelty of their contribution? The Soviet authors allege that their method dispenses with the assumption, essential in their opinion, which requires that Bellman's functions have continuous partial derivatives with respect to all the coordinates of the vector x. This was the implicit assumption behind equation (12), where $\phi_1$ and $\phi_2$ are the partial derivatives of $\phi(x_1, x_2)$ with respect to $x_1$ and $x_2$. However, these partial derivatives are not defined at points along the "switching curve" of the above problem. Since this curve is the locus of points where u in the process of tracing out an optimal path changes sign, and since each optimal path involves at least one such change (unless the initial point happens to lie on a parabola going through the origin), the assumption of differentiability holds on none of the trajectories.[59]

The question remains whether, for practical purposes, this makes any difference, whether in other words Bellman's method cannot cope with any problem solved with the aid of the "maximum principle," if appropriate care is taken

58. Pontryagin, Boltyanskii, Gamkrelidze, and Mishchenko, 1962, p. 20.

59. Ibid., p. 73.

about differentiability conditions and their consequences.

Before concluding this section, a few words should be said about the potential applications of dynamic programming models with control variables constrained within a closed and bounded set, as examined above. Essentially these techniques permit one to deal with problems involving nonconvexity in the constraints (e.g. such as may arise in integer programming or in problems where the production functions exhibit economies of scale). In such cases, significant discontinuities in allocation are apt to occur when certain levels of the variables are attained. Viewed in this light, investment planning *cum* indivisibilities would seem to be a particularly suitable field of application for these techniques.

### Suboptimization: Location of Investment Projects and Selection of Technological Variants

Soviet literature in this field is as abundant as it is (for the most part) tedious. Fortunately, for both the readers and the writer of this survey, little of it qualifies as mathematical. In any case, between Abram Bergson's excellent discussion of the choice of technology in his book *The Economics of Soviet Planning* and the earlier contributions by Grossman and Kaplan, the subject has been adequately covered.[60] Further mathematical refinements of the standard Soviet formulas are, in any event, chiefly of technical interest, inasmuch as irrationalities in the price system would tend to outweigh the second-order benefits that such refinements might produce.[61]

The only significant idea I have come across in the application of mathematical methods to this field has been the use of efficiency formulas as objective functions for

60. Bergson, 1964, pp. 241–65; Grossman, 1953; and Kaplan, 1952.
61. For a sophisticated Soviet discussion of the coefficients of relative efficiency, see Boltov, 1963.

programming problems. I shall briefly sketch out such a scheme, even though it has more in common with static than with multiperiod models *stricto sensu*.

The model was designed for the perspective development of the cement industry in the Kazakh Republic.[62] The programmers were assigned the task of minimizing total unit costs over the variants considered for all cement production projects:

$$(1) \qquad \sum_i C_i' + C_i'' + K_i E + \Pi_i$$

where $C_i'$ is the cost of the raw materials per ton of cement output for variant i, $C_i''$ is its unit costs of processing, $K_i$ the capital investments required, E the normative coefficient of relative efficiency approximate to the project, and $\Pi_i$ the unit cost of transporting the finished cement from each factory to the consuming center.[63] E, the normative coefficient, was set at .15 for new constructions and at .2 for the expansion of existing plants.[64]

There are taken to be n consuming centers, m existing plants, r points where new plants may be constructed or where capacity may be significantly expanded; $A_j(j = 1, \ldots, n)$ is the yearly consumption of the j'th consuming center; $B_i$ is the output of plant i, where $i = 1, \ldots, m$ refers to existing units, and $i = m + 1, \ldots, m + r$ refers to the maximum capacity of new or significantly expanded units; $c_{ij}$ denotes the cost of transporting a ton of cement from production unit i to consuming center; and $x_{ij}$ is the number of tons so transported. The combination costs of production and transportation may be represented as:

62. Nezhintsev and Rakhmanin, 1963. See also Loginov, 1964, for a similar model.

63. Nezhintsev and Rakhmanin, 1963, p. 102.

64. This discrimination against investment in existing plants is widely practiced in this type of calculation. It is perhaps meant to compensate for the higher depreciation costs of old plants scheduled for expansion, which is not otherwise taken into account.

$$F(x, y) = \sum_{i=1}^{m+r} \sum_{j=1}^{n} c_{ij}x_{ij} + \sum_{i=m+1}^{m+r} \phi_i(y_i) - \sum_{i=1}^{m} \phi_i(B_i)$$

where, in addition to the symbols already identified, $\phi_i(y_i)$ stands for the yearly costs of producing $y_i$ tons in one of the new or expanded plants and $\phi_i(B_i)$, the yearly costs of producing output $B_i$ in existing plants. For any investment variant we have:

$$\phi(y) = [C'(y) + C''(y) + .15K(y)]y$$

The total cost functions were statistically observed to be *concave* (owing to increasing returns to scale). They were assumed to be continuous and such that they could be extrapolated backward to the origin ($\phi(0) = 0$).

The constraints of the program are:

$$\sum_{i=1}^{m+r} x_{ij} = A_j \qquad (j = 1, \ldots, n)$$

$$\sum_{j=1}^{n} x_{ij} = y_i \qquad (i = 1, \ldots, m+r)$$

$$x_{ij} \geq 0, y_i \geq 0$$

$$y_i = B_i \qquad (i = 1, \ldots, m)$$

$$y_i \leq B_i \qquad (i = m+1, \ldots, m+r)$$

Presented in this manner,[65] the problem calls for the *minimization* of a *concave* function over a convex set.[66] According to the authors of the model, no algorithms are

65. Note that the substitution of $B_i$, the capacity outputs in each of the m existing plants, has already been made for $y_i$ ($i = 1, \ldots, m$) in the objective function.

66. The sum of the concave functions $\phi_i$ is itself concave, and retains that property upon addition of the linear functional

$$\sum_{i=1}^{m+r} \sum_{j=1}^{n} c_{ij} x_{ij}.$$

available to solve this type of program.[67] To render a solution possible, the objective function must be linearized. This is done, initially, by calculating the average costs of the new production units at capacity output and introducing these numbers into the objective function. The linearized problem yields a set of outputs $\bar{y}_i(i = m + 1, \ldots, m + r)$, which need not necessarily fully employ the capacity of each unit. If we now multiply the derivative of the cost function $F_1(x)$ at $\bar{y}_i$ by the shortfalls $x_{i, n+1}$ from capacity ($x_{i, n+1} = B_i - \bar{y}_i$), and sum the results, we obtain an estimate of the change in production costs associated with a deviation from the initial plan. We may now revise the objective function to read:

$$\min F_2(x) = \sum_{i=1}^{m+r} \sum_{j=1}^{n} c_{ij}x_{ij} - \sum_{i=m+1}^{m+r} \left(\frac{d\phi_i}{dy_i}\right)_{\bar{y}_i} x_{i,n,+1}$$

where $F_2(x)$ represents the incremental cost of deviations from the plan obtained in the first solution. If necessary, one may further reduce costs by constructing a third program where, in the cost function $F_3(x)$ to be minimized, the marginal cost of deviations from capacity output would be determined at the points $\bar{y}_i$ corresponding to the minimization of $F_2(x)$.

So far, in this summary which followed the authors' outline of the model, the time dimension has not been made explicit. At this point we are informed that in order to apply the full-fledged linearized model to the location of cement plants in the Kazakh Republic—14 production points and 16 consumption centers—the planners would have had to cope with 900 variables and 200 constraints.[68] But it is not clear how many periods would have been kept distinct in this count of the variables and constraints of the model, which was apparently designed to fit the

67. Actually, it might be transformed into an integer-programming problem.

68. Nezhintsev and Rakhmanin, 1963, p. 110.

perspective plan for the Kazakh Republic for 1960–80. Further simplifying assumptions were apparently made in the program that was finally constructed. The program was limited to a few benchmark (*kontrol'nye*) years, for which consumption targets were assigned in the plan's directives. The cost functions for the production of cement as well as transportation costs were assumed constant throughout the plan period. The only time-dependent variables were thus the $A_j$—the consumption requirements in each region in the benchmark years. In spite of these and other simplifications, the calculations were said to generate "optimal or nearly optimal plans." In view of the vagueness of the description of these adjustments, we must take this claim at face value.

It is hardly necessary to stress that the model, for all its sophistication, is not free of the basic defect mentioned at the beginning of this section: it is tied to the rest of the economy, the planning of which is *not* optimized, by an irrational price system and by an arbitrary rate of return. The price system intrudes into the model via the calculation of direct production and transportation costs; the rate of return intrudes via the calculation of capital costs. One could readily imagine a situation where the cost of transporting a ton of cement from unit i to center j, based on present accounting costs, might bear only an incidental relation to the opportunity cost that would be incurred in carrying out this operation five, ten, or fifteen years hence.

A few years ago I wrote in a review of the papers presented at the Moscow conference on mathematical economics of 1960 on "expanded reproduction" that Soviet mathematical economists were now abreast of Western work in the field of mathematical economics.[69] I was impressed at that time by the familiarity of Soviet scholars

69. *Trudy*, 1961–62.

in this field with the most recent and advanced Western work, as well as by their willingness to shed doctrinal prejudice and approach problems praxeologically. In retrospect, I now realize I underestimated the gap between the ability to spin variations on recent themes in the professional literature and the ability to spawn new and meaningful ideas. So far I have not seen many of the latter in Soviet work—with the signal exceptions of Kantorovich's great and original contribution of 1939 and of the Pontryagin Maximum Principle—either in the field surveyed in the present paper or in the realm of static linear programming models, or even in input-output work. When new and offbeat ideas crop up, as in the papers of B. I. Pliukhin, they fail to meet minimum criteria of relevance and operationality. These criticisms might also be addressed to some of the current work published in *Econometrica* and the other journals specializing in mathematical economics. But at least there have appeared in the West in recent years a number of insightful simplifying and integrating notions, such as the Golden Rule of Accumulation, the Turnpike Theorem, and Richard Bellman's dynamic programming, that transcend previous work and open new frontiers in the field.[70] While I am not competent to judge the quality of contributions by Western mathematical economists that are limited to the elaboration of ideas already in the public domain, my impression is that this sort of work has been more sophisticated and neater than comparable Soviet efforts. It has also, for the most part, been more explicit about previous contributions.

To recapitulate, there is no longer anything really distinctive about Soviet work in mathematical economics; it belongs to the body of world literature. But this is an arid field where new ideas are hard to come by, and where latecomers, as diligent as they might be, do not have as

70. See Phelps, 1961; Dorfman, Samuelson, and Solow, 1958; and Koopmans, 1964.

good a chance to produce important work as their predecessors in the West, where mathematical economics has flourished without discontinuity for at least a generation.

Until the publication of Kantorovich's most recent articles, it seemed as if Soviet mathematical economists, concerned with immediate applications of mathematical models, were not attracted by sweeping simplifications, such as the Turnpike Theorem or the Golden Rule. But these latest articles suggest that the search for realism—for lengthening the planning horizon, for the disaggregation of sectors and regions—has added so much complexity to the models that simplifying notions are necessary to make order out of chaos, to orient the programmer toward a priori reasonable plans, to guide him away from theoretical dead ends. The programmers need to have deeper knowledge of the "laws of motion" of the Soviet economy before they can map out its future development intelligently.

On the strength of their increasingly complex models and of the experiments they have conducted to widen their understanding of growth processes, the Soviet mathematical economists should eventually have a good deal to offer the pragmatists in the top planning organs, as the best of them will have acquired an excellent command of the logic of planning as well as perceptive insights into the economy's underlying problems. One may wonder whether the practitioners and politicians in the top organs will have any convincing arguments to oppose the adoption of mathematical methods in perspective planning, once the theoreticians have studied the problem thoroughly along the lines blocked out by Kantorovich and other Soviet scientists. Indeed, the usual justifications for the use of empirical methods seem much weaker for long- than for short-term planning. The short-term planners may have an instinct based on long experience for what can or what cannot be done during the course of the year, for the exogenous events that are likely to disturb the course of the plans, or for the shortcomings of the men who will be responsible for carrying them out; this sort of knowledge may be difficult if not impossible to incorporate into mathematical programs. But these imponderables should play a distinctly smaller role in long-term planning, where such factors can probably be treated as so much "noise" in the system and need not bias the solution in any systematic way.

If the direct participation of the mathematical economists in the elaboration of perspective plans is rejected, it will not be on strictly rational grounds. Bureaucratic inertia, personal rivalries, and the fear of introducing outsiders into the arcana of high economic policy are the kinds of obstacles the scientific planners will have to overcome.

*Edward Ames*

"In no field of [Soviet] mathematical economics," says Montias, "is the discrepancy between the thought and its execution more flagrant" than in that of optimizing models for multiperiod planning. I shall argue here that these Soviet models are not used more because they are not very useful. It is odd, on the whole, that Soviet mathematical economics should have developed along "ivory tower" rather than "useful" lines. For the U.S.S.R. has had thirty-five years of planning, during most of which Soviet economists were encouraged to do very applied work and to eschew theory. Now that theory is beginning to revive, the wonder is not that it lacks generality or technique, but rather that it seems to be formulated without reference to whatever experience the profession has acquired over these years.

An optimizing model has two basic parts: a formal statement of the preferences and dislikes of the planners, and a formal statement of the constraints from among which they must choose. Such a model will be useful to planners if the utility function in the model has important points of resemblance to the planners' welfare function and if the constraints have important points of resemblance to the constraints facing the planner. When these conditions are met, the planners can say that the model is an abstract formulation of an important part of their problem, and they can use the logical properties of the model to consider the consequences of the possible courses of action they might pursue. Such a model is relevant to the planners' situation. If the planners choose to ignore it, they do so at their own risk. But if the model is not relevant to the planners' situation, they will not benefit by considering it.

A first problem in analyzing the class of models in question relates to the time horizon. Planning models are frequently formulated with respect to infinite horizons (as Pugachev did), while planners deal with finite horizons. It might appear that if the Soviet economists had actually prepared a relevant model with an infinite horizon, and put it into the computer, then Gosplan might disband, for the computer could then print out, as needed, the instructions for each successive year as the calendar went by. But it is not clear that this is the purpose of the infinite horizon. It may be that plans for relatively short periods of time may be considered as single steps in the direction of the infinite, and that if each step is correctly oriented, the entire path must travel in the correct direction. Problems of this sort are discussed in Western literature on decision theory, and it is surprising to find that the Soviet literature has not considered the question of how far ahead to plan. One would think that both theoretical and practical issues would abound here.

It is said that Von Moltke, on being awakened in 1870 to be told that war had broken out, instructed his orderly to find the orders, and went back to sleep. We have the suspicion that Soviet plans are not as foolproof, and that they must be revised in the light of events. What sort of "disturbance" (to use the econometrician's term) should alter a plan? How sensitive should plans be with respect to changes in planners' tastes or in domestic or foreign constraints? There must be costs involved either in retaining or in altering a plan, and one would think that the Soviet economists, with experience of many years of alterations in plans, would have discussed this sort of question. Apparently, however, the process of preparing and altering directives is considered costless.

While relevance (or its absence) is essentially an empirical attribute of a model, it is possible to discuss relevance in terms of a model of an economy. In what follows, a very simple economy is described. It operates according to rules we shall assume, but under conditions that enable us to consider those parts of the model which might be useful to planners.

Assume an economy which produces a single homogeneous commodity. Sliced and rolled, it provides textiles, food, or building materials. Molded it provides the parts to machinery and may thus (with the aid of labor) be said to reproduce itself. All output is used either for consumption or for investment, so that at any time t,

$$\text{(1)} \qquad \gamma_t = C_t + I_t$$

Production of the commodity requires labor (L) and capital (K) in a Cobb-Douglas production function:

$$\text{(2)} \qquad \gamma_t = gK_t^b L_t^a$$

where a and b are positive numbers. Since Cobb-Douglas functions cannot be aggregated by linear means, it is convenient to assume that the entire output takes place in a single factory.

The labor force, always fully employed, grows by a constant factor $\lambda$, which cannot be influenced by public policy. That is

$$\text{(3)} \qquad L_{t+1} = \lambda L_t$$

so that $L_t = L_0 \lambda^t$ where $L_0$ is the labor force at an arbitrary base period.

To simplify matters, we shall treat income Y as "net" product, so that depreciation is disregarded. $I_t$ is thus net investment, so that

$$\text{(4)} \qquad I_t = K_{t+1} - K_t$$

The foregoing elements, in the West, might be considered the basis for a growth model. In a planned economy, they are the constraints within which plans must be formulated. One purpose of plans is to select values of variables which maximize the values of functions characterizing the planners' tasks. The amount of choice which planners have depends in part upon the objectives they wish to achieve. To illustrate this assertion, we consider a case in which it turns out that the planners have only one admissible course of action. In the economy just described, assume there are two elements of policy.

First, the stock of capital is to grow at a constant rate. That is,

$$K_{t+1} = \chi K_t$$

so that

$$(5) \qquad K_t = K_0 \chi^t$$

where $K_0$ is the stock of capital at the base period.

Second, consumption is to be a constant proportion of income. That is

$$(6) \qquad C_t = c\gamma_t$$

Propositions (1)–(6) now permit conclusions to be drawn about the course of development of this economy over time.

From (4) and (5)

$$I_t = K_0(\chi - 1)\chi^t$$

From (6)

$$I_t = (1 - c)\gamma_t$$

so that

$$(7) \qquad \gamma_t = \frac{1}{1 - c} K_0(\chi - 1)\chi^t$$

From (2), (3), and (6), however,

$$(8) \qquad \gamma_t = gL_0^a K_0^b \lambda^{at} \chi^{bt} = \gamma_0 \lambda^{at} \chi^{bt}$$

so (7) and (8) may be combined:

$$\frac{1}{1 - c} K_0(\chi - 1)\chi^t = \gamma_0 \lambda^{at} \chi^{bt}$$

$$(9) \qquad \frac{\chi - 1}{1 - c} \frac{K_0}{\gamma_0} = \lambda^{at} \chi^{(b-1)\,t}$$

The left side is independent of t. In particular, therefore, set t equal to zero. Then

$$(10) \qquad \frac{K_0}{\gamma_0} = \frac{1 - c}{\chi - 1}$$

The left side of (9) is thus equal to 1. Therefore

$$\chi^{(1-b)\,t} = \lambda^{at}$$

and

$$(11) \qquad a \log \lambda = (1 - b) \log \chi$$

This last expression may be simplified (if $\chi$ and $\lambda$ are close to 1) by the approximation:

$$(12) \qquad \frac{\chi - 1}{\lambda - 1} = \frac{a}{1 - b}$$

Consequently, if a, b, and $\lambda$ are assumed to be data given the planners, c and $\chi$ are uniquely determined. That is

$$(13) \qquad \begin{aligned} \chi &= 1 + \frac{a(\lambda - 1)}{1 - b} \\[2mm] c &= 1 - \frac{K_0}{\gamma_0}\frac{a(\lambda - 1)}{1 - b} \end{aligned}$$

In this case, public policy is completely defined once decisions (5) and (6) have been taken. There is exactly one value of c and one value of $\chi$ which are admissible. Moreover, (11) implies that the stock of capital will grow faster than the labor force $(\chi > \lambda)$ if and only if there are increasing returns to scale $(a + b > 1)$. The standard of living, which varies with $\left(\dfrac{\chi}{\lambda}\right)^t$, will grow if and only if there are increasing returns to scale. The capital-output ratio will be constant, since both vary with $\chi^t$.

It may be suggested that the state would be foolish to make decisions (5) and (6). But surely that is a matter of taste. We have a long tradition in economics of insisting that personal tastes be taken as data, and there is no reason to abandon the principle merely because the chief of state (who makes these decisions) is an important man. It is true that economists might wish to inform the chief of state that if he makes these decisions the consequences described in the preceding paragraph follow, but they can have no professional objections to policies (5) and (6), whether there are increasing or decreasing returns.

The economist is making a useful statement if he tells the planners: there is exactly one value of $\chi$ and one value of c which will enable you to achieve (5) and (6). In order to make the statement, of course, he must be able to formulate all of statements (1)–(6), and especially the last two. I find it interesting that Montias has discussed no paper in which a utility function is used that is recognizably a simplified form of Gosplan's practices.

I turn to the statement of the constraints. These were written as equalities, but actually they are inequalities. Specifically,

1. The production function given in (2) is an inequality:

$$\gamma_t \leq gL_t^a c_t^b$$

If the plant with given inputs can produce $\gamma$, it can easily produce less than $\gamma$ (for instance, by installing a coffee machine). There must be some means of ensuring that the plant produces as much as it can, so that the inequality becomes an equality.

2. The labor force given in (3) is strictly speaking an inequality:

$$L_t \leq L_0 \lambda^t$$

That is, workers would as soon be idle as work, unless they have reason to work. There must be some way of ensuring that enterprise receives the number of workers it needs to keep output at planned levels, that is, to convert the inequality into an equality.

3. The consumption function given in (6) is an inequality:

$$C_t \geq c\gamma_t$$

Consumers would rather have more goods than fewer. Unless consumption is restricted, there will be no way of supplying the enterprise with the capital called for in the plan. This inequality must also be made into an equality.

Furthermore, the values which the economic parameters, c and $\chi$, may assume depend upon the "biological datum" $\lambda$ and the "engineering data" a and b. Only for convenience do economists treat these as data. Planners must find ways of altering them.

Economic institutions in a planned economy have a mathematical characterization. In part, they are designed to replace inequalities, such as those just discussed, by equalities. Planners must devote a great deal of effort to devising rules which ensure that people do what they are supposed to. The analysis so far has said nothing at all about institutions. Let us therefore prescribe a simple Soviet-type set of institutions. Workers are paid an annual wage w, which they must spend in state stores. The enterprise sells its entire output to the state at price p, and the state allocates a part to investment, reselling the rest to the workers at a price $(p + \pi)$. The plant uses the entire proceeds of its sales to pay the workers. Then

$$p\gamma_t = wL_t = pC_t + pI_t$$

(14)
$$(p + \pi)C_t = wL_t$$

$$\pi C_t = pI_t$$

In this case, using (6)

$$I_t = (1 - c)\gamma_t$$

$$pI_t = \pi C_t = \pi c\gamma_t = p(1 - c)\gamma_t$$

so that the various quantities may be expressed in terms of w, a, b, and $\lambda$:

$$(15) \quad \frac{w}{p} = \frac{\gamma_t}{L_t} = \frac{\gamma_0}{L_0}\left(\frac{\chi}{\lambda}\right)^t = \frac{\gamma_0}{L_0}\left[\frac{1}{\lambda}\left(1 + \frac{a(\lambda - 1)}{1 - b}\right)\right]^t$$

$$\frac{p + \pi}{p} = \frac{1}{c} = \left[1 - \frac{K_0}{\gamma_0}\frac{a(\lambda - 1)}{1 - b}\right]^{-1}$$

If it is assumed that workers would rather work than starve, that they get no pay unless they fulfill their norms, and that the plant is able to prevent the workers from eating on the job, then the state is able to enforce (6) by using (15) as a means for fixing the price of goods at the factory (p) and the turnover tax ($\pi$), given any wage rate w.

Formula (14) offers a statement of the national accounts. That is, it summarizes the economic context in which the planning model is imbedded. There are three sectors: labor, enterprise, and the state. The state finances investment by means of a turnover tax on consumer goods; enterprises sell output to the state as a means of paying wages; workers spend their wages on consumer goods. There is thus a set of three identities:

$$(16) \quad \begin{array}{c} wL - (p + \pi)C = 0 \\ p(C + I) - wL = 0 \\ (p + \pi)C - p(C + I) = 0 \end{array}$$

Since the third equation of (16) is the sum of the first two, (16) provides two independent constraints on the system. If there is a production function which relates output (C + I) to labor for each stock of capital, then there is effectively a system of six variables subject to three constraints. This means that if the planners assign values to three of the variables, the remainder, at any moment, are uniquely determined.

In this simple model, therefore, the condition "prices are fixed" means "$\chi$ and c are fixed" for so long as the prices are fixed. Economists will be able to tell planners, providing that the institutional parts of the model are like those of the economy, what the consequences of fixing prices, or of fixing $\chi$ and c may be. They may tell the planners, in particular, what the time path of consumption and capital formation will be. The model will be irrelevant (though perhaps still of interest to economists) if (a) it gives the planners information about variables which do not interest them, or (b) it does not resemble the economy the planners must influence.

Has any Soviet economist formulated a model in which the utility function is one which the Central Committee of the Communist Party (if it knew a little more calculus) would be prepared to call its own? Has any Soviet economist formulated a set of constraints which are in some recognizable sense simplifications of those confronting Gosplan? It would appear from the examples given by Montias that both these questions deserve an emphatic negative answer. We should not be surprised if Gosplan and the economists are not in communication.

I now suggest a partial classification of planning and growth models:

*Socialist* models explicitly formulate a planners' welfare function which is to be maximized. *Bourgeois* models do not.

*Utopian* models specify only a production function, while *scientific* models also specify a set of economic institutions.

*Permanent revolution* models specify conditions under which economic institutions must be altered, because they no longer yield results which satisfy the planners.

*Trotskyite* models assume that world revolution has occurred, so that the welfare function of the state does not include as arguments any events occurring abroad. *Encirclement* models include events abroad as part of the welfare function.

*Dogmatist* models treat prices as fixed numbers. *Revisionist* (or Cosmopolite) models assume that prices vary in response to economic conditions.

The first part of this discussion was utopian, for it specified no economic institutions. It became scientific by the addition of the set of national accounts. Both discussions were Trotskyite, for external events were disregarded. The argument summarized by (15) is revisionist, since prices are determined once values of λ and c have been assigned. It is not permanent revolutionary, however, for there is no consideration of the possibility that the state would consider itself better off by altering the set of national accounts constraints. Moreover, the model is potentially dogmatist, since it is possible to fix prices rather than the variables χ and c.

It is likely, of course, that some interpretations of this model would irritate each faction on the Central Committee. A few would irritate all factions. Soviet economists are therefore probably wise not to consider relevant models in their publications.

Soviet literature, as reported by Montias, is utopian and Trotskyite. It is difficult to decide whether the models reported are dogmatist or permanent revolutionary, because they are generally silent on the subject of prices and economic institutions. It is possible that they assume prices to be arbitrary numbers; but it is also possible that they assume the state will automatically change institutions which it does not like. In the latter case, however, the authors have failed to publish the most interesting parts of their results.

The casual reader of either the Soviet or the American press might suspect that there are occasional differences in the growth processes of private enterprise and socialist economies. Nothing of the sort is to be concluded from the literature under discussion. I cannot but wonder whether the authors cited, or their employers, would agree with this conclusion.

It is surprising to find that the Soviet models are bourgeois rather than socialist. From Lenin's dictum that "Socialism equals Soviet power plus electrification," Soviet leadership at the political level has insisted upon concrete, frequently very simple objectives. It is strange that economists educated on slogans have not expressed welfare functions in terms of the simple slogans they see around them every November 7 and May 1.

Soviet economists could hardly be expected to have emerged from thirty years of silence with interesting and relevant bodies of theory. But it is surprising that, after all these years of having been told to examine assembly lines and not to dabble in theory, the economists should be so backward about generalizing on their experiences. One might have thought that the "first generation" of Soviet economic theory would have started from this background of empiricism, rather than from a sort of abstraction which is popular in the West, where economists have no particular empirical information.

Montias, of course, suggests that to move from utopian to scientific models is to leave the mainstream of economics and to enter operations research. I would certainly concur with this statement as a sociological categorization of what Schumpeter used to call "our unhappy profession." It would have been humiliating if Soviet economists, liberated from the Stalinist yoke, had formulated interesting problems in a relevant way. It is with some relief, therefore, that I observe that they are as reluctant as we are to dirty their hands constructing models which have demonstrable connections with reality.

### Clopper Almon

Let me begin my brief remarks on John Montias' interesting paper with some comments on his discussion of the "maximum principle." First, American economists might have found it less exciting and Soviet economists more exciting had Pontryagin and his associates made it perfectly plain that these multipliers, $\psi$ in Montias' notation (Equation V.2), are always just Lagrangian multipliers, shadow prices, objectively determined values, or whatever one wishes to call this class of things. For in the case of discrete time periods, all of the maximum principle can be read right out of the Kuhn-Tucker theorem. From the point of view of computing with digital computers, which must use discrete time periods, the maximum principle offers us nothing new. It reduces the problem to the same two-point boundary value problem we have always had.[1] The work of Pontryagin, to be sure, assures us that the differential equation cognates of the discrete-time difference equations do, in fact, hold for continuous time. This is a reassuring fact of which the proof may well tax the ingenuity of excellent mathematicians, but it can hardly be called a "powerful" or "revealing" result, as it sometimes has been.

On the other hand, Pontryagin's emphasis on the use of this principle to solve *time-optimal* problems and particularly, as in Montias' example, to determine the *structure* of the solution of many such problems, appears to be new and important. But one may ask whether economic problems really come in the form: "How do I get from A to B as quickly as possible?" I doubt that saving time is often the true objective, but true objectives are often so difficult to state that the short-cut of just saving time may prove quite appealing.

In Pugachev's work discussed by Montias on pages 219–31, the combination of cardinal utility and the constant discount factor in the objective function seems to me (and to others) strong and somewhat curious assumptions. It is interesting, therefore, to find that Koopmans deduced exactly this form of the objective function from seemingly

1. This reduction may, of course, be very useful. See the book by Liang-Tseng Fan, *The Discrete Maximum Principle* (New York, 1964), for a number of real problems solved by the discrete version of the maximum principle—i.e. the Kuhn-Tucker theorem.

innocuous assumptions.[2] Had Pugachev included this reference, I should have been really impressed by how well he had done his homework. (Koopmans prefers slightly weaker assumptions which give a variable discount factor.)

In reading Montias' paper, one can scarcely avoid being struck by the gap between proposals and performance in the Soviet literature on growth models. We are surely all accustomed to a wide disparity between theoretical models (such as the Walrasian system) and empirical models (such as input-output systems). But the purpose of most abstract theoretical schemes in Western journals is to prove a theoretical result, while the Soviet models seem to be advanced as computing schemes, as methods of applying operations research to planning. Compared to them, the Western forecasting or planning models on a national scale which I have seen actually implemented with numbers are modest indeed. Compared, however, to anything the Soviets have tossed into the empirical ring, these dynamic models of Holley, Klein, Stone, the French or the Dutch planning offices (or even my own models) begin to look highly developed indeed. One gathers that at least some Soviet writers look forward to a "great leap" from tiny numerical examples to enormous, comprehensive models with no halfway stations at realistic (but modest) models of, say, twenty to two hundred sectors.

Though Montias' paper is limited to dynamic models with optimization, the general impression would be much the same had it included the few studies I know on dynamic input-output without optimization. In none of these does a Soviet author come to grips with the principal mathematical problem of such studies, namely, how to determine the course of investment from the course of final demands. While the solution used by those who have calculated numerical solutions of input-output models are

2. See his article "Stationary Ordinal Utility and Impatience," *Econometrica* (1960), p. 307.

simple enough, they are perhaps not altogether trivial, for all the discussion over the stability of dynamic input-output systems stems from taking a misleading approach to this problem. Because the Soviets have not calculated with modest but realistic models, they seem not to have discovered that the problem exists.[3]

While one may speculate on the possibility of leaping over the modest model to the super system, it is perhaps more interesting to ask why modest models, with or without optimization, have not been developed. Lack of a use for such models appears unlikely, for it seems fairly clear that planners could employ their results as "orienting calculations" to help them in the use of their present planning methods. Such an approach would encounter few bureaucratic obstacles. Nor does there seem to be any reticence on the part of Soviet economists to deal with macro-economic policy matters, for several two-sector models have appeared that deal in a bold fashion with the question of capital versus consumer goods in growth programs. The immediate reason for the absence of the modest model is much simpler: the Soviet national accounts are completely inadequate for its construction. One can set up a static input-output system on one year's data, but a dynamic model requires the study of investment, consumption, and employment over several years in order to estimate its parameters. It is no accident that "econometric" models have followed closely the pattern of the national accounts or that integrating input-output with the national accounts has been a necessary step in building dynamic input-output systems. In fact, in view of the lack of adequate national accounts, construction of a modest model in the Soviet Union is no longer a modest task for a small group; rather it would first require a large invest-

3. It has been reported that one recent visitor to Moscow was shown such a modest model and that its makers were indeed having trouble with its "stability."

ment in some rather mundane accounting. Soviet mathematical economists can hardly be blamed for this situation; but there is a curious irony in the fact that, having discovered that Leontief is Russian, they are now being held up by, so to speak, not having discovered that Kuznets is Russian also.

# Appendix

## CHARACTERISTICS OF SOME CONTEMPORARY SOVIET COMPUTERS

The first Soviet digital computer, the MESM, was developed in 1950 by a group of specialists from the Academy of Sciences, Ukrainian S.S.R., under the leadership of S. A. Lebedev.[1] In 1953, work was completed on the first large-scale computer, the BESM.[2] Throughout the 1950s, a number of other "first generation" Soviet computers made their appearance. These included the Strela, Ural-1, Setun, SESM, Pogoda, Kristall, M-2, M-3, Minsk-1, Kiev, and a few others. These were all tube-type machines designed for mathematical, scientific, and engineering uses.[3] In the late 1950s and early 1960s, designs were completed on a number of transitional and "second generation" computers. The transitional group included the Ural-2, Ural-4, Minsk-11, Minsk-14, Minsk-2, Minsk-22, BESM-2, Strela-2, and others. The "second generation" group includes the Razdan-2, Aragats, Erevan, ERA, and M-20. The second generation group differs from the transitional group in that it

Prepared by Richard Judy.

1. Sources for this brief history of the development of Soviet computer technology are Golyshev, 1963, p. 10; Kitov and Krinitskii, 1961, pp. 23–24; and Bazilevich and Son, 1964, pp. 5–7. The acronym MESM stands for Malaia Elektronniia Schetnaia Mashina (Small Electronic Computing Machine).

2. BESM stands for Bol'shaia Elektronniia Schetnaia Mashina (Large Electronic Computing Machine). This machine was also developed by Lebedev's group at the Institute of Precise Mechanics in Moscow.

3. Many details of these earlier Soviet computers are given in Ware et al., 1960. This source is the report of a group of American computer experts who visited the Soviet Union in 1959.

## Table A-1

## SOME RECENT SOVIET DIGITAL COMPUTERS

### ARITHMETIC CHARACTERISTICS

| Machine | Operational date | Add time | Multiply time | Divide time | Word length | Number representation | Number range | Serial/ Parallel | Fixed/ Floating point | Operations per second |
|---|---|---|---|---|---|---|---|---|---|---|
| RAZDAN-2 | 1961? | | | | 36 bits | Binary | $\pm 1 \cdot 10^{\pm 19}$ | | Both | 5,000 |
| URAL-4 | 1962 | 80+ μs or 130+ μs | 330+ μs or 470+ μs | 530+ μs or 810+ μs | 40 bits | Binary | $\pm 1 \cdot 10^{\pm 19}$ | Parallel | Both | 5,000 to 6,000 |
| ERA | 1962 | | | | 6 or 12 decimal digits | Binary-coded decimal | $\pm 1 \cdot 10^{\pm 12}$ | | Fixed | 40,000 |
| MINSK-22 | 1965 (scheduled) | 156 μs | 272 μs | 696 μs | 37 bits | Binary | $\pm 1 \cdot 10^{\pm 19}$ | | Both | 5,000 to 6,000 |
| ATE-80 | 1963 (scheduled) | | | | 12 decimal digits | Binary-coded decimal | $\pm 1 \cdot 10^{\pm 12}$ | | Fixed | 500 |
| PROMIN | 1962? | 1 ms | | | | | | | | 1,000 (additions) |
| PEVR-80 | 1963 (scheduled) | | | | | | | | | |

Sources: Riazankin, 1963; Kovalev, 1964; Rapoport, 1964; Golyshev, 1963; Dymarskii et al., 1963; Gavrilenko et al., 1962; Anisimov and Chetvernikov, 1962; and Datamation (November 1963).

## Table A-1 (continued)

| | CONTROL CHARACTERISTICS | | | STORAGE CHARACTERISTICS | | | | | | | |
|---|---|---|---|---|---|---|---|---|---|---|---|
| | | | | Core storage | | Magnetic drum | | | Magnetic tape | | |
| Machine | Instruction format | Number of instructions | Clock rate | Size (words) | Cycle time | Number of units | Words per unit | Average access time | Number of units | Words per unit | Transfer rate (words/ sec.) |
| RAZDAN-2 | 2 address | 22 | | 2048 | | None | | | | 120K | 2000 |
| URAL-4 | 1 address | 51 | Asyn. | 4096 | 12 µs | 8 max. | 16,384 | | 20 max. | 262K | 3000 |
| ERA | 1 address | 36 | | 2048 | | None | | | | 240K | 1000 |
| MINSK-22 | 2 address | 101 | | 8192 | | None | | | 5 max. | 1500K (total) | 2500 |
| ATE-80 | 2 address | 14 | | None | | 1 | 1,024 | 10 ms | None | | |
| PROMIN | | | | 100 | | | | | | | |
| PEVR-80 | | | | | | | | | | | |

## Table A-1 (continued)

| | | INPUT-OUTPUT CHARACTERISTICS | | | | | | | | OTHER CHARACTERISTICS | | | | |
|---|---|---|---|---|---|---|---|---|---|---|---|---|---|---|
| | | Perforated tape | | Card reader speed (cards/min.) | Card punch speed (cards/min.) | Printer | | | Power (KW) | Kind of components | Size (sq. meters) | Price in rubles (thousands) | Mean time between failures | Recommended technical staff |
| Machine | Number form | Punch speed (words/min.) | Read speed (words/sec.) | | | Num. of cols. | Num. of characters | Speed (lines/min.) | | | | | | |
| RAZDAN-2 | Decimal octal | 20–25 | 35 | None | None | None | | | 3 | Solid state | 30 | 150 | | |
| URAL-4 | Decimal octal BCD | 60–120 | 50 | 250 | 100 | 128 | 64 | 300 | 50 | Tubes | 200–250 | 220 | 8 hrs. | 18 engineers and technicians |
| ERA | Decimal octal BCD | | | 300 | 100 | 96 | 46 | 300 | 50 | Tubes | 100 | | | |
| MINSK-22 | Decimal octal BCD | 120 | 60 | 250 | 100 | 128 | 64 | 300 | 6 | Solid state | 100–200 | 250 | | 1 elec. eng 1 elec. mec 1 operator |
| ATE-80 | BCD | None | None | 120–300 | 120–240 | 96 | 48 | 300 | 8 | "ferro-transistors" | 50–60 | | | |
| PROMIN PEVR-80 | Input-output only from console keyboard. | | | | | "Printer contemplated" | | | | Solid state | Desk size | | | |

comprises new machines, not modified or transistorized versions of first generation computers.

Since 1962 a number of small digital computers have been developed for general computational work and for special tasks such as process and other on-line control. These machines include the ATE-80, PROMIN, PEVR-80, UMShIN, UM-1-NKh, VNIIEM-1, UM-1, Stal'-2, and Zenit-3.

Table A-1 provides some details on Soviet computers of the transitional or "second generation" type that have been described by Soviet writers as suitable for economic and "business" data processing. It will be seen immediately that all of these machines are inferior to contemporary American computers for large-scale data processing.

# References Cited

## GENERAL BIBLIOGRAPHIES

Bazhanova, E. V., *Voprosy sovershenstvovaniia rukovodstva narodnym khoziaistvom i planirovaniia—primenenie matematicheskikh metodov v planirovanii i ekonomicheskikh raschetakh,* Ukazatel' literatury, 1959–62 (Moscow, Nauka, 1964), 183 pp., 1783 titles.

*Ekonomika i organizatsiia promyshlennogo proizvodstva,* Bibliografiia rabot uchenykh Sibiri i Dal'nogo Vostoka (Za 1961–63 gg.), Sib. Ot. AN, SSSR (Novosibirsk, 1963), 114 pp., 776 titles.

*Matematiko-ekonomisheskie metody i modeli,* Bibliograficheskii ukazatel' (Primenenie matematicheskikh metodov i elektronnykh vychislitel'nykh mashin v tekhniko-ekonomicheskikh voprosakh) (Moscow-Leningrad, Nauka, 1964), 170 pp., 1905 titles.

United Nations, *Input-Output Bibliography, 1955–1960,* compiled by Charlotte E. Taskier; input-output in the U.S.S.R. compiled by Herbert Levine, Statistical Papers, No. 7, New York, 1961.

———, *Input-Output Bibliography, 1960–1963,* compiled by Charlotte E. Taskier, Statistical Papers, Series M, No. 39, New York, 1964.

United States, 88th Congress, Joint Economic Committee, "Selected Soviet Bibliography on Input-Output," compiled by Vladimir G. Treml, in *Annual Economic Indicators,* Washington, D.C., Government Printing Office, 1964.

---

Abramov and Batrakov, 1964: Abramov, S. A., and Batrakov, V. A., *Elektronnye tsifrovye mashiny i snabzhenie voisk,* Moscow, 1964.

Aganbegian, 1962: Aganbegian, A. G., ed., *Osnovy razrabotki mezhotraslevogo balansa,* Moscow, Ekonomizdat, 1962.

Aganbegian, 1964a: Aganbegian, A. G., "K sozdaniiu optimal'noi

sistemy planirovaniia i upravleniia narodnym khoziaistvom,"
*Vestnik Akademii Nauk SSSR,* 1964:6, 65–68.

Aganbegian, 1964b: Aganbegian, A. G., "Ekonomiko-matemati-
cheskoe modelirovanie i reshenie otraslevykh zadach," in
*Primenenie,* 1964b, 5–38.

Aganbegian and Belkin, 1961: Aganbegian, A. G., and Belkin,
V. D., eds., *Primenenie matematiki i elektronnoi tekhniki v
planirovanii,* Moscow, Ekonomizdat, 1961.

Akademiia nauk, 1964: Akademiia nauk SSSR, otdelenie ekonomicheskikh nauk, *Planirovanie i ekonomiko-matematicheskie
metody,* Moscow, Nauka, 1964.

Alekseev, 1965: Alekseev, N., "Uluchshat' planirovanie material'-
no-tekhnicheskogo snabzheniia," *Planovoe khoziaistvo,* 1965:4,
64–72.

Al'ter et al., 1962: Al'ter, L., Krylov, P., and Miroshnichenko, B.,
"Nazrevshie voprosy metodologii planirovaniia," *Kommunist,*
1962:16, 64–76.

Al'tshuler, 1961: Al'tshuler, L. M., "Lineinoe programmirovanie
v metodike optimal'nogo planirovaniia," *Vestnik sel'khoz.
nauki,* 1961:3, 101–07.

Anisimov and Chetvernikov, 1962: Anisimov, B. V., and Chetvernikov, V. N., *Osnovy teorii i proektirovaniia tsifrovykh
vychislitel'nykh mashin,* Moscow, 1962.

Arzumanian, 1964: Arzumanian, A., "Aktual'nye problemy razvitiia nashei ekonomiki," *Pravda* (February 24, 1964), 3–4.

Askerov, 1963: Askerov, T. M., "Nekotorye voprosy primeneniia
EVM dlia resheniia zadach material'no-tekhnicheskogo snab-
zheniia v sisteme sovnarkhoze," *Tr. Vychisl. Tsentra, AN Azerb.
SSR,* 1963, *Referativnyi zhurnal, Matematika* (1964), 7B474.

Bagrinovskii, 1963: Bagrinovskii, K. A., and Bykov, E. E., "The
Electronic Computer in the Automation of Production Control," *Russian Engineering Journal, 43,* 1963:10, 51.

Bauman and Tolkushin, 1965: Bauman, L., and Tolkushin, V.,
"Ob uchete territorial'nykh razlichii gosudarstvennykh roznich-
nykh tsen," *Vestnik statistiki,* 1965:4, 31–39.

Bazilevich and Son, 1964: Bazilevich, V. L., and Bazilevich, I. V.,
*Sistema komand i programmirovanie dlia BESM-2,* Leningrad,
1964.

Bechin, 1964: Bechin, A., "Kategorii vosproizvodstva i metodologiia ekonomicheskogo analiza," *Voprosy ekonomiki*, 1964:2, 109–22.

Bechin, 1965: Bechin, A., "O teoreticheskikh osnovakh planirovaniia proportsy," *Voprosy ekonomiki*, 1965:1, 41–52.

Becker, 1963: Becker, Abraham S., *Input-Output and Soviet Planning: A Survey of Recent Developments*, RM-3532-PR, Santa Monica, Calif., The RAND Corporation, March 1963.

Belkin, 1959: Belkin, V. D., "Ekonomicheskie raschety s pomoshch'iu elektronnykh vychislitel'nykh mashin," *Voprosy ekonomiki*, 1959:10, 142–44.

Belkin, 1961a: Belkin, V. D., "Kibernetika i ekonomika," in A. I. Berg, ed., *Kibernetika na sluzhbu kommunizmu, 1* (Moscow, 1961), 185–203.

Belkin, 1961b: Belkin, V. D., "O plane koordinatsii rabot po primeneniiu matematicheskikh metodov i elektronnykh vychislitel'nykh mashin v ekonomicheskikh raschetakh," in *Trudy, 1961–62, 1,* 129–49.

Belkin, 1963: Belkin, V. D., *Tseny edinogo urovnia i ekonomicheskie izmeneniia na ikh osnove*, Moscow, Ekonomizdat, 1963.

Belkin and Birman, 1964: Belkin, V. D., and Birman, I. Ia., "Samostoiatel'nost' predpriiatiia i ekonomicheskie stimuly," *Izvestiia* (December 4, 1964), 5. Translated in *Current Digest of the Soviet Press*, 16:50, 14–15.

Bellman, 1954: Bellman, R., "The Theory of Dynamic Programming," *Bulletin of the American Mathematical Society, 60* (1954), 503–16.

Belostotskii et al., 1964: Belostotskii, A. A., Val'denberg, Iu. S., and Merkur'ev, L. I., *Primenenie vychislitel'nykh mashin dlia avtomatizatsii proizvodstvennykh protsessov*, Moscow-Leningrad, 1964.

Belousov, 1963: Belousov, R. A., "Razrabotka metodov korrektirovki denezhnogo vyrazheniia narodnokhoziaistvennykh velichin," in D'iachenko, 1963.

Belousov, Komina, and Komarov, 1965: Belousov, R. A., Komina, E., and Komarov, D., "Opredelenie i ispol'zovanie pokazatelei polnykh trudovykh zatrat v planirovanii," *Planovoe khoziaistvo*, 1965:5, 27–33.

Berg, 1962: Berg, A. I., "V. I. Lenin i nauchnaia organizatsiia truda," *Pravda* (October 24, 1962), 2.

Berg, Kitov, and Liapunov, 1961: Berg, A. I., Kitov, A. I., and Liapunov, A. A., "O vozmozhnostiakh avtomatizatsii upravleniia narodnym khoziaistvom," *Problemy kibernetiki*, Vyp. 6 (1961), 83–100.

Bergson, 1964: Bergson, Abram, *The Economics of Soviet Planning*, New Haven, Yale University Press, 1964.

Berri and Efimov, 1960: Berri, L. Ia., and Efimov, A. N., "Metody postroeniia mezhotraslevogo balansa," *Planovoe khoziaistvo*, 1960:5, 27–39.

Berri, Klotsvog, and Shatalin, 1962a: Berri, L. Ia., Klotsvog, F., Shatalin, S., "Mezhotraslevoi balans i ego ispol'zovanie v planirovanii," *Planovoe khoziaistvo*, 1962:2, 51–62.

Berri, Klotsvog, and Shatalin, 1962b: Berri, L. Ia., Klotsvog, F., and Shatalin, S., "Opyt rascheta eksperimental'nogo planovogo balansa za 1962 god," *Planovoe khoziaistvo*, 1962:9, 34–43.

Berri and Shvyrkov, 1963: Berri, L. Ia., and Shvyrkov, Iu. M., "O strukture proizvodstva SSSR i zarubezhnykh stran," *Voprosy ekonomiki*, 1963:1, 133–44.

Bezrukov and Venikov, 1965: Bezrukov, V., and Venikov, G., "Nekotorye voprosy vnedreniia vychislitel'noi tekhniki v narodnoe khoziaistvo," *Voprosy ekonomiki*, 1965:3, 95–102.

Birkgan and Voskresenskii, 1962: Birkgan, A. Iu., and Voskresenskii, B. P., *Programmirovanie dlia tsifrovoi vychislitel'noi mashiny: "URAL-2,"* Moscow, 1962.

Birman, 1962: Birman, I. Ia., *Transportnaia zadacha lineinogo programmirovaniia*, Moscow, 1962.

Birman, 1963a: Birman, A., "Sto millionov gaek," *Ekonomicheskaia gazeta*, 1963:13, 7.

Birman, 1963b: Birman, I. Ia., "Reshenie zadachi o razmeshchenii proizvodstvua kolichestvennymi metodami," in Birman and Mints, 1963, 1–23.

Birman, 1964: Birman, I. Ia., "Dreif v tikhoi zavodi," *Literaturnaia gazeta* (June 18, 1964), 2.

Birman and Mints, 1963: Birman, I. Ia., and Mints, L. E., eds., *Matematicheskie metody i problemy razmeshcheniia proizvodstva*, Moscow, 1963.

Boiarskii and Dzhaparidze, 1963: Boiarskii, A., and Dzhaparidze, V., "Zadachi nauchno issledovatel'skoi raboty po primeneniiu matematicheskikh metodov i elektronnykh vychislitel'nykh mashin," *Vestnik statistiki,* 1963:10, 3–15.

Boiarskii and Dzhaparidze, 1965: Boiarskii, A., and Dzhaparidze, V., "Edinaia sistema vychislitel'nykh tsentrov," *Ekonomicheskaia gazeta,* 1965:7, 13–14.

Bolotov, 1963: Bolotov, V. V., "Primenenie matematicheskoi modeli razvitiia sotsialisticheskoi ekonomiki dlia obosnovaniia normy effektivnosti kapitalovlozheniia," in *Primenenie,* 1963.

Bor, 1960: Bor, M. Z., *Voprosy metodologii planovogo balansa narodnogo khoziaistva SSSR,* Moscow, Akademiia Nauk SSSR, 1960.

Bor, 1963: Bor, M. Z., "O povyshenii nauchnogo urovnia planirovaniia narodnogo khoziaistva," *Voprosy ekonomiki,* 1963:3, 3–14.

Bor, 1964a: Bor, M. Z., *Ocherki po metodologii i metodike planirovaniia,* Moscow, Ekonomika, 1964.

Bor, 1964b: Bor, M. Z., "Planirovanie narodnogo khoziaistva," *Ekonomicheskaia entsiklopediia, Promyshlennost' i stroitel'stvo,* 2 (Moscow, 1964), 403–14.

Bornstein, 1964: Bornstein, Morris, "The Soviet Price Reform Discussion," *Quarterly Journal of Economics* (February 1964), 15–48.

Breev, 1963: Breev, M. V., ed., *Planirovanie narodnogo khoziaistva SSSR,* Moscow, Ekonomizdat, 1963.

Bruk, 1957a: Bruk, I. S., ed., *Bystrodeistvuiushchaia vychislitel'naia mashina M-2,* Moscow, 1957.

Bruk, 1957b: Bruk, I. S., "Elektronnye vychislitel'nye mashiny na sluzhbu narodnomu khoziaistvu," in *Kommunist,* 1957:7, 124–27.

Bruk, 1960: Bruk, I. S., "Perspektivy primeneniia elektronnykh tsifrovykh mashin v upravlenii ekonomikoi SSSR" in *Trudy,* 1961–62, *1.*

Buzunov, 1964: Buzunov, R., "Indeksnyi metod v analize vliianiia razlichnykh faktorov na uroven' koeffitsientov priamykh zatrat," *Vestnik statistiki,* 1964:3, 26–38.

Bykov, 1963: Bykov, E., "Formirovanie proizvodstvennykh programm v seriinom proizvodstve na EVM, *"Planovoe khoziaistvo,* 1963:1, 63–70.

Bykov and Gavrilets, 1963: Bykov, E. and Gavrilets, Iu., "Reshenie nekotorykh zadach vnutrizavodskogo planirovaniia," *Voprosy ekonomiki,* 1963:1, 84–93.

Campbell, 1958a: Campbell, Robert W., "Accounting for Cost Control in the Soviet Union," *Review of Economics and Statistics* (February 1958), 59–67.

Campbell, 1958b: Campbell, Robert W., "The Mechanization of Accounting in the Soviet Union," *American Slavic and East European Review* (February 1958), 59–80.

Campbell, 1963: Campbell, Robert W., *Accounting in Soviet Planning and Management,* Cambridge, Harvard University Press, 1963.

Chakravarty, 1962a: Chakravarty, S., "The Existence of an Optimum Savings Program," *Econometrica,* January 1962.

Chakravarty, 1962b: Chakravarty, S., "Optimal Savings with Finite Planning Horizon," *International Economic Review,* September 1962.

Chenery and Clark, 1959: Chenery, H. B., and Clark, P. G., *Interindustry Economics,* New York, 1959.

Cherniak, 1961: Cherniak, Iu. I., "Ekonomicheskaia kibernetika na sluzhbe planirovaniia," *Voprosy ekonomiki,* 1961:11, 124–32.

Cherniak, 1962: Cherniak, Iu. I., "Osnovnye cherty mezhotraslevogo balansa ekonomicheskogo raiona," in *Trudy,* 1961–62, *3,* 118–66.

Cherniak, 1963: Cherniak, Iu. I., "Sovnarkhozam—avtomatizirovannuiu sistemu informatsii," *Planovoe khoziaistvo,* 1963:8, 52–56.

Cherniak, 1964: Cherniak, Iu. I., "Metod mezhotraslevogo balansaemnovoe ponimanie, neogranichennye perspektivy," in Fedorenko, 1964.

Cherniavskii, 1963: Cherniavskii, V., "Voprosy optimizatsii planirovaniia," *Voprosy ekonomiki,* 1963:11, 115–22.

Cherniavskii, 1965: Cherniavskii, V., "Kriterii optimal'nosti," *Ekonomicheskaia gazeta,* 1965:11, 9.

Cohn, 1962: Cohn, Stanley, *"Soviet Inter-Industry Tables," ASTE Bulletin, 4* (1962), 3–19.

Cukor, 1962: Cukor, Gy., "Use of Input-Output Tables in Long-Term Planning," in Lukacs, 1962.

Dashevskii et al., 1964: Dashevskii, L. N., Pogrebinskii, S. B., and Shkurba, V. V., *Vychislitel'naia mashina "Kiev,"* Kiev, 1964.

Davydov, 1964: Davydov, Iu., "Kibernetika i planirovanie," *Planovoe khoziaistvo,* 1964:5, 90–94.

Denisov and Popov, 1963: Denisov, A., and Popov, G., "Kak proektiruetsia vychislitel'nyi tsentr," *Ekonomicheskaia gazeta* (April 20, 1963), 26–29.

D'iachenko, 1963: D'iachenko, V. P., ed., *Obshchestvenno neobkhodimye zatraty truda, sebestoimost' i rentabel'nost',* Moscow, Akademiia Nauk SSSR, 1963.

Domar, 1957: Domar, E., *Essays in the Theory of Economic Growth,* New York, 1957.

Dorfman, Samuelson, and Solow, 1958: Dorfman, R., Samuelson, P., and Solow, R., *Linear Programming and Economic Analysis,* New York, Toronto, and London, 1958.

Drogichinskii, 1964: Drogichinskii, N., "Informatsiia, plan, statistika," *Planovoe khoziaistvo,* 1964:10, 19–24.

Dudkin, 1963: Dudkin, L. M., "Matematiko-ekonomicheskaia skhema material'nogo balansa sotsialisticheskogo narodnogo khoziaistva," in *Problemy,* 1963.

Dudkin and Ershov, 1965: Dudkin, L., and Ershov, E., "Mezhotraslevoi balans i material'nye balansy otdel'nykh produktov," *Planovoe khoziaistvo,* 1965:5, 59–64.

Dudorin, 1961: Dudorin, V. I., *Planirovanie i lineinoe programmirovanie v material'no-tekhnicheskom snabzhenii,* Moscow, 1961.

Dymarskii et al., 1963: Dymarskii, Ia. S., Lozinskii, N. N., Makushin, A. T., Rozenberg, V. Ia., and Erglis, V. P., *Spravochnik programista, 1,* Leningrad, 1963.

Efimov, 1963: Efimov, A., "Teoreticheskie i prakticheskie voprosy vnedreniia mezhotraslevogo balansa v planirovanie narodnogo khoziaistva," *Planovoe khoziaistvo,* 1963:5, 11–19.

Efimov, 1964: Efimov, A., "Problemy strukturnykh sdvigov i povysheniia effektivnosti obshchestvennogo proizvodstva," *Planovoe khoziaistvo,* 1964:5, 13–23.

Efimov and Maksimov, 1963: Efimov, P. E., and Maksimov, Iu. P., "Ten-Day Schedules for Component Production and Dispatch Compiled by Computer," *Russian Engineering Journal,* 1963:8, 61-63.

Eidel'man, 1960: Eidel'man, M. R., "K voprosu o postroenii otchetnogo mezhotraslevogo balansa proizvodstva i raspredeleniia produktsii v narodnom khoziaistve SSSR," *Vestnik statistiki,* 1960:1, 55–69.

Eidel'man, 1961a: Eidel'man, M. R., "Opyt sostavleniia otchetnogo mezhotraslevogo balansa proizvodstva i raspredeleniia produktsii v narodnom khoziaistve SSSR," *Vestnik statistiki,* 1961:7, 9–29.

Eidel'man, 1961b: Eidel'man, M. R., "Mezhotraslevoi balans obshchestvennogo produkta i ego ekonomicheskoe soderzhanie," *Voprosy ekonomiki,* 1961:10, 61–74.

Eidel'man, 1962a: Eidel'man, M. R., "Pervyi mezhotraslevoi balans zatrat truda v narodnom khoziaistve SSSR," *Vestnik statistiki,* 1962:10, 3–17.

Eidel'man, 1962b: Eidel'man, M. R., "The Input-Output Table in the Soviet Union," in Lukacs, 1962.

Eidel'man, 1963a: Eidel'man, M. R., "Mezhotraslevoi balans zatrat truda i ego ekonomicheskoe znachenie," *Sotsialisticheskii trud,* 1963:2, 12–23.

Eidel'man, 1963b: Eidel'man, M. R., "Metodologicheskie problemy otchetnogo mezhotraslevogo balansa," *Vestnik statistiki,* 1963:5, 15–26.

Eidel'man, 1963c: Eidel'man, M. R., "Mezhotraslevoi balans truda i ego znachenie dlia opredeleniia obshchestvenno neobkhodimykh zatrat truda," in D'iachenko, 1963.

Eidel'man, 1964: Eidel'man, M. R., "K voprosu ob otsenke produktsii v mezhotraslevom balanse," *Vestnik statistiki,* 1964:9, 10–17.

*Ekonomiko-matematicheskie metody,* 1963: *See* Vainshtein, 1963.

"Ekonomisty i matematiki," 1964: "Ekonomisty i matematiki za kruglym stolom," *Voprosy ekonomiki,* 1964:9, 63–110.

Ellis and Fellner, 1943: Ellis, Howard S., and Fellner, William, "External Economies and Diseconomies," *American Economic Review* (September 1943), 493–511.

*Entsiklopediia,* 1962: *Ekonomicheskaia entsiklopediia, Promyshlennost' i stroitel'stvo,* Moscow, Sovetskaia entsiklopediia, *1* (1962), 2 (1964).

Ershov, 1959: Ershov, A. P., *Programming Programme for the BESM Computer,* trans. M. Nadler, New York, 1959.

Ershov, 1961: Ershov, A. P., "Osnovnye printsipy postroeniia programmiruiushchei programmy instituta matematiki sibirskogo otdeleniia akademii nauk SSSR," *Sibirskii matematicheskii zhurnal*, 1961:6, 835–52.

Ershov et al., 1961: Ershov, A. P., Kozhukhin, G. I., and Boloshin, Iu. M., *Vokhodnoi iazyk sistemy avtomaticheskogo programmirovaniia*, Moscow, 1961.

Evenko, 1965: Evenko, I., "Gluboko analizirovat' obstanovku," *Ekonomicheskaia gazeta* (January 27, 1965), 12.

Ezhov, 1960: Ezhov, A. I., *Istoriia sovetskoi gosudarstvennoi statistiki*, Moscow, Gosstatizdat, 1960.

Fedorenko, 1964a: Fedorenko, N. P., "Otdelenie ekonomiki," *Vestnik Akademii Nauk SSSR*, 1964:4, 63–66.

Fedorenko, 1964b: Fedorenko, N. P., "O rabote tsentral'nogo ekonomiko-matematicheskogo instituta," *Vestnik Akademii Nauk SSSR*, 1964:10, 1–10.

Fedorenko, 1964c: Fedorenko, N. P., ed., *Planirovanie i ekonomiko-matematicheskie metody. K 70-letiiu so dnia rozhdeniia akademika V. S. Nemchinova*, Moscow, Nauka, 1964.

Fedorenko, 1965: Fedorenko, N. P., "Vazhnaia ekonomicheskaia problema," *Pravda* (January 17, 1965), 2–3.

Forms and Instructions, 1959: *Forms and Instructions for 1959 Input-Output USSR*, U.S. Dept. of Commerce, Joint Publication Research Service, 14132, Washington, D.C., 1962.

Forrester, 1961: Forrester, Jay W., *Industrial Dynamics*, Cambridge, 1961.

Gatovskii, 1965: Gatovskii, L. M., "Absurdnye vymysly zhurnala 'Taim'," *Izvestiia* (April 2, 1965), 2.

Gatovskii and Kovalev, 1962: Gatovskii, L. M., and Kovalev, N. L., "Matematika i planirovanie," *Vestnik Akademii Nauk SSSR*, 1962:11, 42–57.

Gavrilenko et al., 1962: Gavrilenko, E. T., Konoplia, N. M., Korobov, B. V., and Livshin, G. L., *Programmirovanie dlia elektronnoi vychislitel'noi mashiny "URAL-1,"* Moscow, 1962.

Gerchuk, 1965: Gerchuk, Ia. P., *Granitsy primeneniia lineinogo programmirovaniia*, Moscow, 1965.

Girsanov, 1963: Girsanov, I. V., "Razreshimost' uravnenii odnoi matematicheskoi skhemy material'nogo balansa sotsialisticheskogo narodnogo khoziaistva," in *Problemy*, 1963.

Glushkov, 1963: Glushkov, V., "Ekonomika i kibernetika," *Vestnik Akademii Nauk SSSR,* 1963:10, 11–14.

Glushkov and Fedorenko, 1964: Glushkov, V., and Fedorenko, N., "Problemy shirokogo vnedreniia vychislitel'noi tekhniki v narodnoe khoziaistvo," *Voprosy ekonomiki,* 1964:7, 87–92.

Glushkov and Iushchenko, 1962: Glushkov, V., and Iushchenko, E. L., *Vychislitel'naia mashina "Kiev,"* Kiev, 1962.

Gokhman, 1963: Gokhman, V. I., "Zatraty na perevozki v pokazateliakh kriteriia optimal'nosti transportnoi zadachi," in Birman and Mints, 1963, 97–148.

Goldmann, 1964: Goldmann, J., "Fluctuations and Trend in the Rate of Economic Growth in Some Socialist Countries," *Economics of Planning,* 4:2 (1964), 88–98.

Golyshev, 1963: Golyshev, L. K., *Elektronnye vychislitel'nye mashiny,* Kiev, 1963.

Gor'kov, 1962: Gor'kov, L. I., "Odnoproduktovaia ekonomicheskaia model': analiz ekonomicheskoi effektivnosti kapital'nykh vlozhenii," in *Trudy,* 1961–62, 2.

Grebtsov and Karpov, 1960: Grebtsov, G. L., and Karpov, P. P., eds., *Material'nye balansy v narodnokhoziaistvennom plane,* Moscow, Gosplanizdat, 1960.

Gromov, 1964: Gromov, E., "Pokazatel' konechnogo obshchestvennogo produkta v planirovanii narodnogo khoziaistva," *Kommunist,* 1964:14, 64–74.

Grossman, 1953: Grossman, G., "Scarce Capital and Soviet Doctrine," *Quarterly Journal of Economics,* 57 (August 1953), 311–43.

Grossman, 1955: Grossman, G., "In the Land of Paper Pyramids," *Problems of Communism* (July–August 1955), 18–26.

Grossman, 1960: Grossman, G., *Soviet Statistics of Physical Output of Industrial Commodities,* National Bureau of Economic Research, No. 69, General Series, Princeton, 1960.

Grossman, 1963: Grossman, G., "Notes for a Theory of the Command Economy," *Soviet Studies, 15* (October 1963), 101–23.

Grundfest and Isakov, 1963: Grundfest, I. A., and Isakov, V. I., *Schetnye mashiny i ikh ispol'zovanie v uchete,* Moscow, 1963.

Gusev, 1964: Gusev, V., "O mezhotraslevom balanse v natural'nom vyrazhenii," *Voprosy ekonomiki,* 1964:6, 100–08.

Hardt, 1959: Hardt, John P., "Industrial Investment in the

USSR," in Joint Economic Committee, *Comparison of the United States and Soviet Economies* (Washington, D.C., 1959), 121–42.

Hardt, 1962: Hardt, John P., "Strategic Alternatives in Soviet Resources Allocation Policy," in Joint Economic Committee, *Dimensions of Soviet Economic Power* (Washington, D.C., 1962), 1–31.

Henderson, 1958: Henderson, James, *The Efficiency of the Coal Industry*, Cambridge, 1958.

Hitch and McKean, 1960: Hitch, Charles J., and McKean, R. N., *The Economics of Defense in the Nuclear Age*, Cambridge, 1960.

Horvath, 1963: Horvath, Robert, "Development and Present Status of Input-Output Methods in Hungary," *Economics of Planning*, *3* (December 1963), 207–20.

Iaremenko, 1963: Iaremenko, Iu., "Izuchenie i planirovanie narodnokhoziaistvennykh proportsii metodom mezhotraslevogo balansa," *Planovoe khoziaistvo*, 1963:4, 34–41.

Il'iushin and Rutenberg, 1965: Il'iushin, S., and Rutenberg, A., "Za bolee effektivnye formy khoziaistvovaniia," *Planovoe khoziaistvo*, 1965:1, 51–59.

Iudin and Gol'shtein, 1961: Iudin, D. B., Gol'shtein, E. G., "Ob odnom metode kolichestvennogo analiza uproshchennykh ekonomicheskikh modelei," in Nemchinov, 1959, 136–99.

Iudin and Gol'shtein, 1964: Iudin, D. B., and Gol'shtein, E. G., *Zadachi i metody lineinogo programmirovaniia*, 2d ed. Sov. radio, 1964.

Iushchenko, 1963: Iushchenko, E. L., *Adresnoe programmirovanie*, Kiev, 1963.

Iushchenko and Grinchenko, 1964: Iushchenko, E. L., and Grinchenko, T. A., *Programmiruiushchaia programma s vkhodnym adresnym iazykom dlia mashiny URAL-1*, spravochnik programmista, Kiev, 1964.

Kantorovich, 1939: Kantorovich, L. V., *Matematicheskie metody organizatsii i planirovaniia proizvodstva*, Leningrad, Leningrad University, 1939.

Kantorovich, 1959a: Kantorovich, L. V., *Ekonomicheskii raschet nailushchego ispol'zovania resursov*, Moscow, 1959.

Kantorovich, 1959b: Kantorovich, L. V., "Dal'neishee razvitie

matematicheskikh metodov i perspektivy ikh primeneniia v
planirovannii i ekonomike," in Nemchinov, 1959.

Kantorovich, 1964: Kantorovich, L. V., "Dinamicheskaia model'
optimal'nogo planirovaniia," in Fedorenko, 1964c.

Kantorovich and Makarov, 1964: Kantorovich, L. V., and
Makarov, V. L., "Optimal'nye modeli perspektivnogo planirovaniia," in Nemchinov, 1964c.

Kaplan, 1952: Kaplan, N., "Investment Alternatives in Soviet
Economic Theory," *Journal of Political Economy, 60* (April
1952), 133–44.

Kardash, 1964: Kardash, V. A., "O matematicheskom modeli-
rovanii struktury posevnykh ploshchadei v khoziaistve," in
*Primenenie,* 1964a, 94–108.

Kaser, 1962: Kaser, M. C., "A Fourth List of Soviet Statistical
Abstracts," *Soviet Studies, 13* (April 1962), 453–57.

"Kibernetika," 1964: "Kibernetika, planirovanie, i sotsialnyi progress. Za kruglym stolom ekonomisty, matematiki, filosofy,
inzhenery," *Ekonomicheskaia gazeta* (June 20, 1964), 7–17. A
more detailed account is presented in "Ekonomisty i matematiki," 1964.

Kitov, 1961a: Kitov, A. I., "Kibernetika v upravlenii khoziaistvom," *Ekonomicheskaia gazeta* (August 26, 1961), 9–11.

Kitov, 1961b: Kitov, A. I., "Kibernetika i upravlenie narodnym
khoziaistvom," in Berg, A. I., ed., *Kibernetika na sluzhbu
kommunizmu, 1* (Moscow, 1961), 203–18.

Kitov and Cherniak, 1962: Kitov, A. I., and Cherniak, Iu. I.,
"Avtomatizatsiia upravlencheskikh rabot," *Avtomatizatsiia
proizvodstva i promyshlennaia elektronika, 1* (Moscow, 1962),
26–32.

Kitov and Krinitskii, 1961: Kitov, A. I., and Krinitskii, N. A.,
*Elektronnye tsifrovye mashiny i programmirovanie,* Moscow,
1961.

Klinskii, 1964: Klinskii, A., "Metodologicheskie problemy razrabotki piatiletnego plana," *Planovoe khoziaistvo,* 1964:7, 90–93.

Koldomasov, 1961: Koldomasov, Iu. I., *Planirovanie material'no-
tekhnicheskogo snabzheniia narodnogo khoziaistva v SSSR,*
Moscow 1961.

Kolganov, 1964: Kolganov, M., "Politicheskaia ekonomiia i matematika," *Voprosy ekonomiki,* 1964:12, 111–25.

Komin, 1964: Komin, A., "Primenenie matematiki v planirovanii tsen," *Planovoe khoziaistvo*, 1964:6, 29–38.

"Konferentsiia," 1963: "Konferentsiia po primeneniiu matematicheskikh metodov i EVM v planirovanii," *Voprosy ekonomiki*, 1963:3, 80–98.

"Konferentsiia," 1964: "Konferentsiia po primeneniiu matematiki v ekonomike," *Voprosy ekonomiki*, 1964:9, 63–110.

Konius, 1959: Konius, A. A., "Skhematicheskii analiz vliianiia izmenenii tsen na uroven' potrebleniia trudiashchikhsia," in Pisarev, 1959, 188–97.

Konius, 1961: Konius, A. A., "Rasshirenie sistemy uravnenii mezhootraslevykh sviazei dlia tselei perspektivnogo planirovaniia," in Nemchinov, 1961b.

Konius, 1964: Konius, A. A., "Perspektivnoe planirovanie pri predpolozhenii ravnomernogo rosta kapitalovlozhenii," in Fedorenko, 1964c.

Koopmans, 1963: Koopmans, T. C., "On the Concept of Optimal Economic Growth," Cowles Foundation Discussion Paper No. 163, December 6, 1963.

Koopmans, 1964: Koopmans, T. C., "Economic Growth at a Maximal Rate," *Quarterly Journal of Economics, 78* (August 1964), 355–94.

"Koordinatsionnoe soveshchanie," 1962: "Koordinatsionnoe soveshchanie po voprosam ispol'zovaniia matematiki i vychistitel'noi tekhniki v ekonomike," *Voprosy ekonomiki*, 1962:4, 66–85.

"Koordinatsionnoe soveshchanie," 1963: "Koordinatsionnoe soveshchanie po voprosam primeneniia matematicheskikh metodov i EVM v ekonomicheskikh issledovaniiakh i planirovanii," *Voprosy ekonomiki*, 1963:6, 108–13.

Kornai and Liptak, 1964: Kornai, J., and Liptak, T., "Planirovanie na dvukh urovniakh," in Nemchinov, 1964c.

Kossov, 1964: Kossov, V. V., ed., *Mezhotraslevoi balans proizvodstva i raspredeleniia produktsii ekonomicheskogo raiona*, Moscow, Nauka, 1964.

Kossov and Mints, 1964: Kossov, V. V., and Mints, L., "Nekotorye itogi razrabotki mezhotraslevykh balansov po pribaltiiskomu ekonomicheskomu raionu," *Vestnik statistiki*, 1964:6, 16–25.

Kosygin, 1965: Kosygin, A., "Povyshenie nauchnoi obosnovannosti planov—vazhneishaia zadacha planovykh organov," *Ekonomicheskaia gazeta* (April 21, 1965), 3–4, and *Planovoe khoziaistvo*, 1965:4, 3–10.

Kovalev, 1961a: Kovalev, N. I., "Vnedrenie matematicheskikh metodov i vychisitel'noi tekhniki v praktiku planirovaniia," *Planovoe khoziaistvo*, 1961:8, 15–25.

Kovalev, 1961b: Kovalev, N. I., "Problemy vnedreniia matematiki i elektronnykh vychislitel'nykh mashin v planirovanie," *Voprosy ekonomiki*, 1961:12, 118–27.

Kovalev, 1963: Kovalev, N. I., "Nekotorye problemy postroeniia mezhotraslevykh balansov v natural'nom vyrazhenii," *Voprosy ekonomiki*, 1963:5, 76–87.

Kovalev, 1964a: Kovalev, N. I., *Vychislitel'naia tekhnika v planirovanii*, Moscow, Ekonomika, 1964.

Kovalev, 1964b: Kovalev, N. I., "Ekonomiko-matematicheskaia model' planirovaniia ratsional'noi struktury proizvodstva ekonomicheskogo raiona," *Voprosy ekonomiki*, 1964:2, 97–108.

Kozlov, 1962: Kozlov, O. V., ed., *Primenenie matematicheskikh metodov i noveishei vychislitel'noi tekhniki v planirovanii mashinostroitel'nogo proizvodstva*, Moscow, Mashgiz, 1962.

Kozlova et al., 1964: Kozlova, O., Brodskii, G., Dydorin, V., Mitin, S., Nikonova, L., and Salamatin, N., *Primenenie elektronno-vychislitel'nykh mashin v upravlenii proizvodstvom*, Moscow, 1964.

Kravchenko, 1963: Kravchenko, R., *Ekonomika i elektronika (iz opyta primeneniia matematicheskikh metodov i elektronno-vychislitel'noi tekhniki v planirovanii sel'skogo khoziaistva)*, Sel'khozisdat, 1963.

Krinitskii et al., 1963: Krinitskii, N. A., Mironov, G. A., and Frolov, G. D., *Programmirovanie*, Moscow, 1963.

Kronrod, 1965: Kronrod, Ia., "Sovokupnyi obshchestvennyi produkt kak kategoriia sotsialisticheskogo vosproizvodstva," *Vestnik statistiki*, 1965:3, 3–15.

Krumm, 1963: Krumm, L. A., "Gradientnyi metod optimizatsii rezhima ob'edinennykh energosistem," *Elektrichestvo*, 1963:5.

Krumm and Syrov, 1964: Krumm, L. A., and Syrov, Iu. P., "Optimizatsiia gradientnym metodom rezhimov ob'edinennykh energosistem, imeiushchikh v svoem sostave gidroelektrostantsii," *Elektrichestvo*, 1964:4, 20–26.

Kurz, 1966: Kurz, M., "Optimal Paths of Capital Accumulation under the Minimum Time Objective," *Econometrica*, *33*, No. 1 (1966).

Kuznetsov, 1962: Kuznetsov, Iu. A., et al., "Opredelenie optimal'-noi struktury perspektivnogo energicheskogo balansa s ispol'zo-vaniem EVM," *Teploenergetika*, 1962:5, 3–9.

Lalaianets, 1963: Lalaianets, A., "Problemy vnedreniia vychisli-tel'noi tekhniki v planirovanie narodnogo khoziaistva," *Voprosy ekonomiki*, 1963:11, 103–11.

Lange, 1959: Lange, Oskar, "Nekotorye soobrazheniia po analizu balansa zatrat i vypuska produktsii," in Nemchinov, 1959, 214–50.

Leibkind, 1963a: Leibkind, Iu. R., "Primenenie blochnykh matrits dlia priblizhennykh planovykh raschetov," in Vainshtein, 1963, 162–79.

Leibkind, 1963b: Leibkind, Iu. R., "Modelirovanie ekonomiche-skikh sistem," *Vestnik Akademii Nauk SSSR*, 1963:10, 15–17.

Leifman, 1963: Leifman, L. Ia., "Matematicheskoe issledovanie zavisimosti potrebleniia otdel'nykh tovarov ot dokhoda," in Vainshtein, 1963, 292–310.

Leontief, 1960: Leontief, Wassily, W., "The Decline and Rise of Soviet Economic Science," *Foreign Affairs* (January 1960), 261–72.

Leont'ev, Mukosian, and Kanygin, 1964: Leont'ev, A., Mukasian, S., and Kanygin, Iu., "Balansy i proportsii," *Vestnik Moskovskogo universiteta*, seriia, ekonomiki, filosofii, 1964:5, 20–25.

Levine, 1959: Levine, Herbert S., "The Centralized Planning of Supply in Soviet Industry," in Joint Economic Committee, *Comparisons of the United States and Soviet Economies*, (Washington, D.C., 1959), 151–76.

Levine, 1961: Levine, Herbert S., "A Study in Economic Planning: The Soviet Industrial Supply System," Ph.D. dissertation, Harvard University, 1961.

Levine, 1962a: Levine, Herbert S., "Input-Output Analysis and Soviet Planning," *American Economic Review*, *52* (May 1962), 127–37.

Levine, 1962b: Levine, Herbert S., "Recent Development in Soviet Planning," in Joint Economic Committee, *Dimensions of Soviet Economic Power* (Washington, D.C., 1962), 47–66.

Liapunov and Kitov, 1961: Liapunov, A. A., and Kitov, A. I., "Kibernetika v tekhnike i ekonomike," *Voprosy filosofii*, 1961:9, 79–88.

Lichtenberg, 1960: Lichtenberg, R. M., *One Tenth of a Nation*, Cambridge, Harvard University Press, 1960.

Liebkind, 1963: Liebkind, Iu. P., "Modelirovanie ekonomicheskikh sistem," *Vestnik Akademii Nauk SSSR*, 1963:10, 15–17.

Linkun and Sokolovskii, 1963: Linkun, N., and Sokolovskii, A., "Koordinatsiia nauchnykh ekonomicheskikh issledovanii," *Voprosy ekonomiki*, 1963:4, 152–56.

Liubchenko and Sergienko, 1963: Liubchenko, G. G., Sergienko, I. B., *Matematicheskie mashiny i programmirovanie*, Kiev, 1963.

Loginov, 1964: Loginov, Z. I., "Razmeshchenie tsementnoi promyshlennosti SSSR (Opyt primeneniia lineinogo programmirovaniia)," in Fedorenko, 1964c.

Loginov and Mints, 1964: Loginov, Z. I., and Mints, L. E., "Razrabotka skhemy optimal'nogo razmeshcheniia tsementnoi promyshlennosti SSSR na 1970 god metodami lineinogo programmirovaniia," in *Primenenie*, 1964b, 86–117.

Loginova, 1963: Loginova, A. M., "Raschet optimal'nykh skhem perevozok tsementa po Ukraine," in Birman and Mints, 1963, 149–61.

Lukacs, 1962: Lukacs, O., ed., *Input-Output Tables* (Budapest, Akademiai Kiado, 1962), 49.

Maizenberg, 1961: Maizenberg, L., "Peresmotr optovykh tsen v tiazheloi promyshlennosti i nekotorye problemy tsenoobrazovaniia v SSSR," *Voprosy ekonomiki*, 1961:11, 42–56.

Malinovskii, 1963: Malinovskii, B. N., *Tsifrovye upravliaiushchie mashiny i avtomatizatsiia proizvodstva*, Moscow, 1963.

Malinvaud, 1963: Malinvaud, E., "Decentralized Procedures for Planning," Technical Report No. 15, Center for Research in Management Science, University of California, Berkeley, November 1963.

Malyi, 1963: Malyi, I. G., ed., *Teoriia statistiki*, Moscow, Gosstatizdat, 1963.

Maneschi, 1966: Maneschi, A., "Optimal Savings with Finite Planning Horizon," *International Economic Review* (January 1966).

Maslov, 1964: Maslov, P., "Statistika i predvidenie," *Ekonomicheskaia gazeta* (December 16, 1964), 11.

McKean, 1958: McKean, Roland N., *Efficiency in Government Through Systems Analysis*, New York, 1958.

Mikhailevskii, 1962: Mikhailevskii, B. N., "Osnovnye puti opredeleniia optimuma fondov novykh kapital'nykh vlozhenii v obshchei dinamicheskoi modeli," in *Trudy*, 1961–62, 2.

Mikhailevskii, 1965: Mikhailevskii, B. N., "Odonosektornaia dinamicheskaia model' otsenki normy effektivnosti kapitalovlozhenii," *Ekonomika i matematicheskie metody*, 1:2 (1965).

Modin, 1964: Modin, A., "Mezhotraslevoi balans i sistema matrichnykh modelei," *Voprosy ekonomiki*, 1964:1, 112–23.

Montias, 1959: Montias, J. M., "Planning with Material Balances in Soviet-Type Economies," *American Economic Review, 49* (December 1959), 963–85.

Montias, 1962: Montias, J. M., "On the Consistency and Efficiency of Central Plans," *Review of Economic Studies, 29*:4, No. 81 (October 1962), 280–90.

Montias, 1964: Montias, J. M., Review of *"Problemy optimal'nogo planirovaniia, proektirovaniia i upravleniia proizvodstvom,"* *American Economic Review, 54* (March 1964), 171-75.

*Nar. khoz.*, 1960: *Narodnoe khoziaistvo SSSR v 1960 godu*, Moscow, Gosstatizdat, 1961.

*Nar. khoz.*, 1961: *Narodnoe khoziaistvo SSSR v 1961 godu*, Moscow, Gosstatizdat, 1962.

*Nar. khoz.*, 1962: *Narodnoe khoziaistvo SSSR v 1962 godu*, Moscow, Gosstatizdat, 1963.

Nemchinov, 1959: Nemchinov, V. S., ed., *Primenenie matematiki v ekonomicheskikh issledovaniiakh, 1*, Moscow, 1959.

Nemchinov, 1961a: Nemchinov, V. S., "Matematiku i elektroniku —na sluzhbu planirovaniiu," *Planovoe khoziaistvo*, 1961:3, 30–40.

Nemchinov, 1961b: Nemchinov, V. S., ed., *Primenenie matematiki v ekonomicheskikh issledovaniiakh, 2*, Moscow, 1961.

Nemchinov, 1961c: Nemchinov, V. S., "A Model of an Economic Region," *Mathematical Studies in Economics and Statistics in the USSR and Eastern Europe*, 1:1 (1964), 3–25. Translated from Nemchinov, 1961b.

Nemchinov, 1962a: Nemchinov, V. S., *Ekonomiko-matematiche-skie metody i modeli,* Moscow, Sotsekgiz, 1962.

Nemchinov, 1962b: Nemchinov, V. S., "Teoreticheskie voprosy mezhotraslevogo i mezhregional'nogo balansa proizvodstva i raspredeleniia produktsii," in *Trudy,* 1961–62, *3,* 3–36.

Nemchinov, 1963a: Nemchinov, V. S., "Razvitie mezhotraslevogo balansa v model' narodnokhoziaistvennogo plana," *Planovoe khoziaistvo,* 1963:6, 1–9.

Nemchinov, 1963b: Nemchinov, V. S., "The Use of Statistical and Mathematical Methods in Soviet Planning," in Barna, Tibor, ed., *Structural Interdependence and Economic Development* (New York, 1963), 171–88.

Nemchinov, 1964a: Nemchinov, V. S., "Nuzhen ekvivalentnyi obmen," *Ekonomicheskaia gazeta,* No. 26 (June 27, 1964), 9.

Nemchinov, 1964b: Nemchinov, V. S., "Modeli narodnokhoziai-stvennogo planirovaniia," *Voprosy ekonomiki,* 1964:7, 75–86.

Nemchinov, 1964c: Nemchinov, V. S., ed., *Primenenie matematiki v ekonomicheskikh issledovaniiakh, 3,* Moscow, 1964.

Nemchinov, 1964d: Nemchinov, V. S., "Ekonomika, matematika, kibernetika," *Pravda* (September 13, 1964).

Nemchinov, 1964e: Nemchinov, V. S., "Sotsialisticheskoe khoziai-stvovanie i planirovanie proizvodstva," *Kommunist,* 1964:5, 74–87. Reprinted in Nemchinov, 1965, 49–73.

Nemchinov, 1965: Nemchinov, V. S., *O dal'neishem sovershe-nstvovanii planirovaniia i upravleniia narodnym khoziaistvom,* 2d ed., Moscow, Ekonomika, 1965.

Nerlove, 1959: Nerlove, Marc, "On the Efficiency of the Coal Industry," *Journal of Business* (1959), 271–78.

"Ne uprazdniat'," 1964: "Ne uprazdniat', a sovershenstvovat'!," *Ekonomicheskaia gazeta* (September 19, 1964), 7–8.

Nezhintsev and Rakhmanin, 1963: Nezhintsev, G. E., and Rakhmanin, G. D., "Raschet optimal'nogo plana i razme-shchenie tsementnoi promyshlennosti," in *Primenenie, 1963.*

Nove, 1958: Nove, Alec, "The Problem of 'Success Indicators' in Soviet Industry," *Economica* (February 1958).

Novozhilov, 1946: Novozhilov, V. V., "Metody nakhozhdeniia minimuma zatrat v sotsialisticheskom khoziaistve," *Trudy Len-ingradskogo politicheskogo instituta imeni M. I. Kalinina,* 1946:1.

Novozhilov, 1959: Novozhilov, V. V., "Izmerenie zatrat i ikh rezul'tatov v sotsialisticheskom khoziaistve," in Nemchinov, 1959.

Novozhilov, 1963: Novozhilov, V. V., "Spornye voprosy primeneniia metoda vspomogatel'nykh mnozhitelei v sotsialisticheskoi ekonomike," in Vainshtein, 1963, 107–44.

"Obshchee sobranie," 1964: "Obshchee sobranie Akademii Nauk," *Vestnik Akademii Nauk SSSR*, 1964:4, 72–79.

"O rabote instituta," 1964: "O rabote Tsentral'nogo ekonomiko-matematicheskogo instituta," *Vestnik Akademii Nauk SSSR*, 1964:10, 3–14.

"Ot redaktsii," 1964: "Ot redaktsii," *Planovoe khoziaistvo*, 1964:6, 95.

Panfilov et al., 1962: Panfilov, M., Shershen', L., and Timofeevskii, T., "Elektronnye mashiny i upravlenie proizvodstvom," *Pravda* (December 6, 1962).

Phelps, 1961: Phelps, E. S., "The Golden Rule of Accumulation: A Fable for Growthmen," *American Economic Review* (September 1961), 638–43.

Pisarev, 1959: Pisarev, I. Iu., ed., *Metodologicheskie voprosy izucheniia urovnia zhizni trudiashchikhsia*, Moscow, 1959.

"Plenum nauchnogo soveta," 1964: "Plenum nauchnogo soveta po primeneniiu matematiki i vychislitel'noi tekhniki v ekonomicheskikh issledovaniiakh i planirovanii," *Voprosy ekonomiki*, 1964:3, 150–53.

*Plenum Tsentral'nogo Komiteta*, 1961: *Plenum Tsentral'nogo Komiteta Kommunisticheskoi Partii Sovetskogo Soiuza, 13–16 iiulia 1960 goda*, Moscow, 1961.

Pliukhin and Nazarova, 1961: Pliukhin, B. I., and Nazarova, R. N., "Upravliaemaia tsepnaia reaktsiia rasshirennogo vosproizvodstva v odnosektornoi i dvusektornoi modeliakh," in Nemchinov, 1961b.

Pliukhin, 1962: Pliukhin, B. I., "K tsepnoi modeli rasshirennogo vosproizvodstva," in *Trudy*, 1961–62, 2.

Polonskii and Ippa, 1963: Polonskii, M., and Ippa, M., "V vychislitel'nom tsentre Belorusskogo ekonomicheskogo raiona," *Planovoe khoziaistvo*, 1963:5.

Pontryagin, Boltyanskii, Gamkrelidze, and Mishchenko, 1962: Pontryagin, L. S., Boltyanskii, V. G., Gamkrelidze, R. V., and

Mishchenko, E. F., *The Mathematical Theory of Optimal Processes,* New York, 1962.

Popov, 1961: Popov, G., *Lineinoe programmirovanie v ekonomicheskikh raschetakh po sel'skomu khoziaistvu,* Moscow, izd. Instituta narodnogo khoziaistva im. Plekhanova, 1961.

Popov, 1963: Popov, G., *Elektronnye mashiny i upravlenie ekonomikoi,* Moscow, 1963.

*Primenenie,* 1962: *Primenenie tsifrovykh vychislitel'nykh mashin v ekonomike, Transportnaiia zadacha lineinogo programmirovaniia,* Akademiia Nauk SSSR, Moscow, 1962.

*Primenenie,* 1963: *Primenenie matematiki v ekonomike,* Leningrad State University, Kafedra i laboratoriia ekonomiko-matematicheskikh metodov, *1,* Leningrad, 1963.

*Primenenie,* 1964a: *Primenenie matematiki v ekonomike,* Leningrad State University, Kafedra i laboratoriia ekonomiko-matematicheskikh metodov, *2,* Leningrad, 1964.

*Primenenie,* 1964b: *Primenenie matematiki pri razmeshchenii proizvoditel'nykh sil,* Akademiia Nauk SSSR, Moscow, 1964.

*Problemy,* 1963: *Problemy optimal'nogo planirovaniia i upravleniia proizvodstvom: Trudy teoreticheskoi konferentsii sostaiavsheisia na ekonomicheskom fakultete M. G. U. v marte 1962,* Moscow, 1963.

*Prom.,* 1964: *Promyshlennost' SSSR,* Moscow, 1964.

Pugachev, 1963a: Pugachev, V. F., "Model' mnogostupenchatoi sistemy optimal'nogo planirovaniia," Ekonomiko-matematicheskie tetradi, Vpsk. 5, 1963. Cited in Pugachev, 1964a, 98.

Pugachev, 1963b: Pugachev, V. F., "O kriterii optimal'nosti ekonomiki," in Vainshtein, 1963, 63–106.

Pugachev, 1964a: Pugachev, V. F., "Voprosy optimal'nogo planirovaniia narodnogo khoziaistva s pomoshch'iu edinoi gosudarstvennoi seti vychislitel'nykh tsentrov," *Voprosy ekonomiki,* 1964:7, 93–103.

Pugachev, 1964b: Pugachev, V. F., *Metody ekonomikostatisticheskogo analiza protsessov material'no-tekhnicheskogo snabzheniia,* Moscow, 1964.

Pugachev, 1964c: Pugachev, V. F., "Model mnohostupnoveho systemu optimalneho planirovania," Slovak translation of Pugachev, 1963a, in *Pokroky operacnej analizy,* ed. A. A. Lasciak, Bratislava, 1964.

Ramsey, 1928: Ramsey, F., "A Mathematical Theory of Saving," *Economic Journal* (December 1928).

Rappoport, 1964: Rappoport, M. G., "Osnovnye napravleniia ekonomiki-matematicheskikh issledovanii," *Vestnik Akademii Nauk SSSR*, 1964:7, 118–19.

Riabushkin, 1957: Riabushkin, T. V., *Statisticheskie metody izucheniia narodnogo khoziaistva*, Moscow, Gosstatizdat, 1957.

Riabushkin, 1959: Riabushkin, T. V., *Problemy ekonomicheskoi statistiki*, Moscow, Akademiia Nauk SSSR, 1959.

Riauzov and Titel'baum, 1961: Riauzov, N. N., and Titel'baum, N. P., *Statistika torgovli*, Moscow, Gosstatizdat, 1961.

Riazankin, 1963: Riazankin, V., "Znakomites': novye mashiny," *Ekonomicheskaia gazeta* (August 17, 1963), 23–26.

Romanovskii, 1962: Romanovskii, I. V., "O dinamicheskom programmirovanii i ego ispol'zovanii v ekonomike," in *Trudy*, 1961–62, 2.

Rozin, 1961: Rozin, B. B., *Matematicheskie metody i schetnaia tekhnika na metallurgicheskom predpriiatii*, Metallurgizdat, 1961.

Serck-Hanssen, 1962: Serck-Hanssen, J., "Input-Output Tables in the U.S.S.R. and Eastern Europe," *Ost-Okonomi* (July 1962), 65–72.

Shakhanov, 1960: Shakhanov, V. S., "Metod i algoritm vychisleniia ekonomicheskogo raspredeleniia nagruzok v slozhnykh gidro-teplovykh energosistemakh na elektronnykh tsifrovykh mashinakh," *Izvestiia Akademii Nauk SSSR*, OTN, Energetika i avtomatika, 1960:1, 12–26.

Shatalin, 1964: Shatalin, S. S., "O mezhotraslevom balanse i ego ispolzovanii v planirovanii ekonomicheskogo razvitiia," paper reported in *Voprosy ekonomiki*, 1964:10, 155.

Shatalin, 1965: Shatalin, S. S., "Tempy i proportsii ekonomicheskogo razvitiia i effektivnost' obshchestvennogo proizvodstva," *Voprosy ekonomiki*, 1965:1, 14–26.

Shchedrin, 1962: Shchedrin, N. I., "Voprosy mekhanizatsii statisticheskogo ucheta v systeme TsSU," *Voprosy statistiki i ucheta*, Vpsk. 6 (Moscow, 1962), 183–204.

Sheviakov, 1964: Sheviakov, F., "V nauchno-issledovatel'skom institute gosplana SSSR," *Planovoe khoziaistvo*, 1964:3, 92–93.

Shura-Bura, 1958: Shura-Bura, M. P., ed., *Sistema standartnykh podprogramm MGU,* Moscow, 1958.

Shura-Bura and Liubimskii, 1964: Shura-Bura, M. P., and Liubimskii, E. Z., "Transliator ALGOL-60." Cited in *Referativyni zhurnal, Matematika,* 1964:9, 9B35.1.

Shvyrkov, 1962: Shvyrkov, Iu. M., "Nekotorye voprosy klassifikatsii ostraslei i produktov v mezhotraslevom balanse," in Oznobin, N. M., ed., *Ocherki po sovremennoi sovetskoi i zarubezhnoi ekonomike, 3* (Moscow, Ekonomizdat, 1962), 20–37.

Shvyrkov, 1965: Shvyrkov, Iu. M., "Klassifikatsiia otraslei i narodno-khoziaistvennoe planirovanie," *Planovoe khoziaistvo,* 1965:5, 13–18.

Sik, 1965: Shik, O., "Poisk naibol'shego effekta," *Izvestiia* (February 7, 1965), 4.

Simon, 1960: Simon, Herbert A., *The New Science of Management Decision,* New York, 1960.

Smirnov, 1962: Smirnov, G. B., "Arifmeticheskoe ustroistvo," in *Avtomatizatsiia proizvodstva i promyshlennaia elektronika* (Moscow, 1962), 95–97.

Smirnov, 1964: Smirnov, A. D., *Dinamicheskaia model' mezhotraslevogo balansa,* Moscow, 1964.

Smol'nikov, 1961: Smol'nikov, N. I., *Osnovy programmirovaniia dlia tsifrovoi mashiny "URAL,"* Moscow, 1961.

"Snabzhat'," 1964: "Snabzhat' ili torgovat'?," *Ekonomicheskaia gazeta* (June 27, 1964), 9–11.

Sobolevskii, 1965: Sobolevskii, T., "Upravlenie i informatsiia," *Planovoe khoziaistvo,* 1965:5, 57–59.

Solov'ev, 1964: Solov'ev, N., "Otsenka produktsii v mezhotraslevom balanse," *Planovoe khoziaistvo,* 1964:6, 22–28.

Sorokin, 1961: Sorokin, G. M., *Planirovanie narodnogo khoziaistva SSSR: Voprosy teorii i organizatsii,* Moscow, Sotsekgiz, 1961.

"Soveshchanie," 1962: "Soveshchanie po voprosam primeneniia matematicheskikh metodov v ekonomike," *Voprosy ekonomiki,* 1962:1, 115–21.

Stalin: 1951: Stalin, I., *Voprosy Leninisma,* 11th ed. Moscow, Gospolitizdat, 1951.

Strelkova, 1961: Strelkova, N. N., *Opisanie sistemy komand elektronnoi vychislitel'noi mashiny "STRELA-3,"* Moscow, 1961.

"Stroitel'stvo Kommunisma," 1962: "Stroitel'stvo kommunisma i planirovanie," *Planovoe khoziaistvo,* 1962:10, 1–15.

Strumilin, 1962: Strumilin, S. G., "K probleme optimal'nykh proportsii," *Planovoe khoziaistvo,* 1962:6.

Trapeznikov, 1964: Trapeznikov, V., "Za gibkoe ekonomicheskoe upravlenie predpriiatiiami," *Pravda* (August 17, 1964), 3–4.

Treml, 1963: Treml, Vladimir G., "The 1959 Soviet Intersectoral Flow Table," Ph.D. dissertation, University of North Carolina, 1963, *Dissertation Abstracts,* 24:8 (Ann Arbor, Mich., 1964), 3123–24.

Treml, 1964a: Treml, Vladimir G., "Economic Interrelations in the Soviet Union," Joint Economic Committee, *Annual Economic Indicators for the U.S.S.R.* (Washington, D.C., 1964), 183–213.

Treml, 1964b: Treml, Vladimir G., *The 1959 Soviet Intersectoral Flow Table, 1* and *2,* Research Analysis Corp., TP-137, Washington, D.C., 1964.

Tret'iakova, 1962: Tret'iakova, A. F., "Raschety optimal'noi skhemy perevozok energeticheskogo uglia" in *Primenenie,* 1962, 45–64.

Tret'iakova and Batalina, 1963: Tret'iakova, A. F., and Batalina, G. I., "Optimal'nyi toplivno-energeticheskii balans" in Birman and Mints, 1963, 47–75.

Trigubenko, 1962: Trigubenko, V. V., "O primenenii dinamicheskogo programmirovaniia v ekonomicheskoi oblasti," in *Trudy,* 1961–62, 2.

*Trudy,* 1961–62: *Trudy nauchnogo soveshchaniia o primenenii matematicheskikh metodov v ekonomicheskikh issledovaniiakh i planirovanii (4–8 aprelia 1960 goda),* Moscow, 1961–62.

Usatov, 1964: Usatov, I., "Neotlozhnye problemy ucheta," *Ekonomicheskaia gazeta,* No 38 (September 19, 1964), 6.

Vainshtein, 1963: Vainshtein, A. L., ed., *Narodnokhoziaistvennye modeli, Teoreticheskie voprosy potrebleniia,* Moscow, Akademiia Nauk SSSR, 1963.

Vairadian, 1964: Vairadian, E. L., "K istorii razvitiia metodologii izucheniia mezhotraslevykh sviazei v SSSR," in Malyi, I. G., ed., *Voprosy statisticheskoi metodologii* (Moscow, Statistika, 1964), 193–240.

Volkonskii, 1963: Volkonskii, V. A., "Ob ob'ektivnoi matematicheskoi kharakteristike narodnogo potrebleniia," in Vainshtein, 1963, 201–40.

Volkonskii, 1964: Volkonskii, V. A., "Skhema optimal'nogo perspektivnogo planirovaniia i otsenki resursov," in Nemchinov, 1964c.

Volkonskii et al., 1965: Volkonskii, V. A., Gol'shtein, E., Dadaian, V., Kossov, V., Mas, V., Fridman, A., Khrytskii, E., Iusupov, M., and Iakovlev, E., "Po povody stat'i N. Kovaleva," *Voprosy ekonomiki*, 1965:1, 153–55.

Volodarskii, 1961: Volodarskii, L. M., "Tempy, proportsii, garmoniia," *Ekonomicheskaia gazeta*, No. 9 (October 2, 1961), 5–6

Ware et al., 1960: Ware, William H., et al., "Soviet Computer Technology—1959," *IRE Transactions on Electronic Computers*, Vol. EC-9, No. 1 (March 1960), 72–120.

Wiener, 1948: Wiener, Norbert, *Cybernetics*, New York, 1948.

Wiles, 1962: Wiles, P. J. D., *The Political Economy of Communism*, Oxford, 1962.

"Za i protiv," 1965: "Za i protiv," *Ekonomicheskaia gazeta*, No. 10 (March 10, 1965), 9–10.

Zauberman, 1962: Zauberman, Alfred, "A Few Remarks on a Discovery in Soviet Economics," *Bulletin of the Oxford University Institute of Statistics*, 24:4 (1962), 437–45.

Zauberman, 1963: Zauberman, Alfred, "A Note on the Soviet Inter-Industry Labour Input Balance," *Soviet Studies*, 15:1 (July 1963), 53–58.

Zauberman, 1965: Zauberman, Alfred, "On the Objective Function for the Soviet Economy," *Economica*, 32:127 (August 1965).

Ziborov, 1962: Ziborov, A., "Razrabotat' skhemu balansa narodnogo khoziaistva soiuznykh respublik," *Ekonomicheskaia gazeta*, No. 33 (August 11, 1962), 16.

Zimin, 1962: Zimin, V. A., *Elektronnye vychislitel'nye mashiny*, Moscow, 1962.

# Contributors

CLOPPER ALMON
 Department of Economics
 University of Maryland

EDWARD AMES
 Department of Economics
 Purdue University

ABRAHAM S. BECKER
 Economics Department
 The RAND Corporation

ROBERT W. CAMPBELL
 Department of Economics
 Indiana University

MICHIO HATANAKA
 Institute of Social and Eco-
 nomic Research
 Osaka University

RICHARD W. JUDY
 Department of Political
 Economy
 University of Toronto

HERBERT S. LEVINE
 Department of Economics
 University of Pennsylvania

JOHN M. MONTIAS
 Department of Economics
 Yale University

ROBERT SUMMERS
 Department of Economics
 University of Pennsylvania

VLADIMIR G. TREML
 Department of Economics
 Duke University

BENJAMIN WARD
 Department of Economics
 University of California at
 Berkeley

# Index